# BEHIND THE SPUTNIKS

## A Survey of Soviet Space Science

F. J. KRIEGER

THE RAND CORPORATION

Public Affairs Press, Washington, D. C.

«Земля колыбель разума, но нельзя вечно
жить в колыбели».
—К. Э. Циолковский


*"The earth is the cradle of the mind, but
one cannot live forever in a cradle."*
—K. E. Tsiolkovskii

Published by the Public Affairs Press
419 New Jersey Ave., S.E., Washington 3, D.C.

# PREFACE

This work, as its title indicates, is a survey of Soviet astronautics based entirely on the open literature. It is by no means an exhaustive effort, for that would be an almost impossible task. Rather, it is a preliminary attempt at uncovering evidence of increasing Soviet concern with the challenging problems of space flight. What the Russians have written on the subject of astronautics provides important insights into their intent and aspirations in the conquest of outer space. Their technical literature clearly shows that their interest is not merely academic or superficial. It is as serious and purposeful as interest can be in a science that is sponsored to the hilt by a ruthless totalitarian regime.

The Introduction to the survey delineates, briefly, the history of the development of astronautics in Russia from the turn of the century up to the launching of the first artificial earth satellite. It is intended to provide the reader with a background of the events that presaged Sputnik I and to acquaint him with some of the personnel entrusted with the exposition of the problems of space flight.

The articles and papers that form the main portion of the survey are, for the most part, translations from the Russian. They were written by various authorities on Soviet astronautics and have been selected from a wide variety of publications. Adherence to chronology within the specific subject categories has been deliberate in order to show not only the singleness of purpose in the Soviet space flight program but also the Russian technique in developing the subject in the open literature.

The Bibliography, which contains more than 339 items, has been divided into two parts in order to increase its value to the general reader as well as to the scholar. Part I lists books and monographs dealing with the historical, scientific, and technical aspects of rocketry and astronautics. Part II contains references drawn from various Russian newspapers, popular magazines, and serious technical journals.

Most of the articles and papers in this book appeared in RAND Research Memoranda RM-1760 and RM-1922, which formed Parts I and II of a series entitled "A Casebook on Soviet Astronautics," dated June 21, 1956, and June 21, 1957, respectively. The material from these studies has been collated and supplemented with new material in order to round out, and integrate the story behind the Sputniks.

F. J. KRIEGER

124121

# ACKNOWLEDGMENTS

The preparation of a work of this kind, by its very nature, involves the participation of a large number of people in one capacity or another. I want to express my sincere appreciation to all the members of The RAND Corporation staff whose contributions have made this report a reality.

I am particularly grateful to Anne Jonas of The RAND Washington staff for her continuing interest in the subject of this study and for her singular efforts not only in bringing new material to my attention but also in locating certain original Russian items and making them available to me.

On the editorial side I wish to thank Dorothy Stewart and Ann Greene for the use of their talents in helping to remove the deep Russian "accent" from the translations that make up the major portion of this survey.

I am indebted to F. C. Durant, III, for the information concerning the composition and functions of the Soviet Interdepartmental Commission on Interplanetary Communications.

This study was prepared as part of the research program undertaken for the United States Air Force by The RAND Corporation.

F. J. K.

*Santa Monica, California*

# CONTENTS

v

# INTRODUCTION

*F. J. Krieger*

Russia has a rich historical background in astronautics that began at the end of the nineteenth century with the works of I. V. Meshcherskii on the dynamics of bodies of variable mass and the publications of K. E. Tsiolkovskii on the principles of rocket flight. Early Russian rocket enthusiasts made many original and fundamental contributions to this new technology.

Of the early pioneers, Tsiolkovskii, the father of (and to the Soviets, the patron saint of) the science of astronautics, has been fairly well represented by rocket historians in the Western literature. Not so, however, his contemporaries—F. A. Tsander, who developed the idea of utilizing as fuel the metallic structural rocket-ship components which were no longer necessary and who in 1932 built and successfully tested a rocket motor operating on kerosene and liquid oxygen; Yu. V. Kondratyuk, who proposed the use of ozone as an oxidant and developed the idea of aerodynamically braking a rocket returning from a voyage in space; N. A. Rynin, who during the period 1928-1932 published a monumental nine-volume treatise on interplanetary communications; Ya. I. Perel'man, the great popularizer of astronautics; and I. P. Fortikov, the organizer.

In 1929 Perel'man, Fortikov, and other disciples of Tsiolkovskii founded a competent scientific organization for investigating and systematically developing new rocket devices. It was called GIRD, after the initials of the Russian words for "Group for the Study of Reactive Motion." The Moscow branch, founded by Fortikov, and the Leningrad branch, founded by N. A. Rynin and Ya. I. Perel'man, were known as *Mosgird* and *Lengird*, respectively. GIRD was essentially a part of a larger organization known as OSOAVIAKHIM (Society for the Promotion of Defense and Aero-Chemical Development). The papers written by various members of this enthusiastic organization contain a wealth of evidence of native competence in the various aspects of rocketry and space flight and clearly indicate that

1

the Russians possessed a relatively high degree of technical sophistication more than two decades ago.[1]

The GIRD publications included contributions by I. A. Merkulov, Yu. A. Pobedonostsev, and M. K. Tikhonravov, who are still very active in the field of rocket propulsion and space flight.

Quick to realize the enormous military potential of the rocket, the Soviet Government had organized, by 1934, a Government-sponsored rocket-research program—only five years after Germany had embarked on its rocket program but eight years before similar systematic Army-sponsored research began in the United States.  Stalin's personal interest in the development of long-range, rocket-propelled guided missiles is discussed in the book *Stalin Means War* by Colonel G. A. Tokaev, formerly chief of the aerodynamics laboratory of the Moscow Military Air Academy, who defected from the Soviet zone of Germany to Great Britain in 1948.

The Soviets have pursued an aggressive rocket policy since 1945. In addition to appropriating most of the German rocket factories and test stations, they have induced several hundred German rocket experts to work for them behind the Iron Curtain.  The Russians have built a large number (probably several thousands) of German V-2 missiles, presumably for fundamental rocket and upper-atmosphere research, for gaining experience in mass-producing large rocket missiles, and for training rocket-launching crews.  They have not only improved on the V-2 rocket engine—increasing its thrust from 25 to 35 metric tons by increasing the propellant flow rate [2]—but have also developed a super-rocket (Model 103) with a fantastic thrust of 120 metric tons at a chamber pressure of 60 atmospheres.  These developments indicate that the Russian effort has been more than an extension of previous German work; to all indications it is based on independent thinking and research.  This is not surprising, since Russia has its share of exceptionally capable technical men such as Semenov (the recent Nobel Prize winner in chemistry) and Zel'dovich, Khristianovich and

---

[1] For example, *The Proceedings of the All-Union Conference on the Study of the Stratosphere, March 31-April 6, 1934* was published by the USSR Academy of Sciences in 1935, and the collections of papers entitled *Raketnaya Tekhnika* (Rocket Technology) and *Reaktivnoe Dvizhenie* (Jet Propulsion) were published by the Union of Scientific Technical Publishing Houses in 1935 and 1936. Unfortunately, few, if any, of the later items found their way to the United States. The Library of Congress, for instance, has only Russian All-Union Book Chamber file cards for three of these volumes. Copies of these publications were probably not released for export for obvious reasons.

[2] This is essentially what Rocketdyne, a division of North American Aviation, did in this country in developing the Redstone 75,000-pound thrust rocket engine.

Sedov — to mention but a few in the fields of combustion theory and fluid dynamics.

Because of high security restrictions, very little factual information on Russian missile developments has ever been released. However, in his address to the World Peace Council in Vienna on November 27, 1953, Academician A. N. Nesmeyanov, speaking on the problems of international cooperation among scientists, made the following significant statement: "Science has reached a state when it is feasible to send a stratoplane to the moon, to create an artificial satellite of the earth. . . ." [3] This statement is particularly interesting in view of the events that have transpired since it was made. In his official capacity as president of the USSR Academy of Sciences, Nesmeyanov was, of course, familiar with all aspects of Soviet scientific progress; his statement clearly implied that Russian progress in rocket propulsion as of 1953 had made feasible such feats as launching an earth satellite and flying to the moon.

To all indications, Nesmeyanov's statement as to the feasibility of sending a stratoplane to the moon and of creating an artificial earth satellite became the keynote for a flood of articles on the problems of space flight that began to appear early in 1954 in almost every type of Russian newspaper and periodical.

There is considerable evidence of early acceptance of the science of space flight by the Soviet hierarchy. It is not without significance that Volume 27 of *Bol'shaya Sovetskaya Entsiklopediya* (Large Soviet Encyclopedia), published in June, 1954, contained an article entitled "Interplanetary Communications" by M. K. Tikhonravov.[4] (See Chapter 2.) There is as yet no corresponding entry in any of the Western encyclopedias. Interestingly, the *New York Times* began to index articles on space ships and space flight under the term "Astronautics" only after the White House announced on July 29, 1955, that the United States intended to launch an earth satellite.

Soviet interest in space flight was further revealed by the fact that on September 24, 1954, the Presidium of the USSR Academy of Sciences established the K. E. Tsiolkovskii Gold Medal for outstanding work in the field of interplanetary communications, to be awarded every three years beginning with 1957. (See Appendices A and E.) At about the same time, the Presidium established the permanent Interdepartmental Commission on Interplanetary Communications to "co-

---

[3] *Pravda,* November 28, 1953.

[4] In Russian the term "interplanetary communications" is a synonymous with "astronautics" and "space flight."

ordinate and direct all work concerned with solving the problem of mastering cosmic space." (See Appendix B.) Academician L. I. Sedov, a topnotch hydrodynamicist, was appointed chairman, and M. K. Tikhonravov — who designed and successfully launched liquid-propellant atmospheric research rockets in 1934 — was appointed vice chairman.

In addition to the ICIC, an Astronautics Section was organized early in 1954 in Moscow at the V. P. Chkalov Central Aeroclub of the USSR. (See Chapter 3.) Its goal was "to facilitate the realization of cosmic flights for peaceful purposes." Its charter members included Chairman N. A. Varvarov, Professor V. V. Dobronravov, Design Engineer I. A. Merkulov, Stalin Prize Laureate A. D. Seryapin, Professor K. P. Stanyukovich, Yu. S. Khlebtsevich, and International Astronautics Prize Winner A. A. Shternfel'd.

Although the White House announcement of July 29, 1955—that the United States intended to launch an earth satellite sometime during the International Geophysical Year (1957-1958)—led to considerable speculation concerning the Soviet position and capability in this field of technology, the imperturable Russians, as usual, did not commit themselves. Possibly they were only too well aware of the United States Earth Satellite Vehicle Program, the existence of which was first publicly announced by Secretary of Defense Forrestal in December, 1948.

A notable event occurred in the week following the White House announcement. The Sixth International Astronautical Congress sponsored by the International Astronautical Federation convened in Copenhagen, Denmark. It was notable because, unlike previous meetings, it was attended by two Soviet scientists, Academician L. I. Sedov, Chairman of the USSR Academy of Sciences Interdepartmental Commission on Interplanetary Communications, and Professor K. F. Ogorodnikov of the department of astronomy at Leningrad State University, who was an exchange professor at Harvard in 1937.

The Russians were observers at the Congress and did not participate in any formal discussion of the papers. Sedov, however, did hold a press conference on August 2 at the Soviet Legation in Copenhagen, but unfortunately some of the statements attributed to him were garbled in the Western press. Three days later, on August 5, *Pravda* published an official version of the press conference (Appendix C) in which Sedov indicated that "recently in the USSR much consideration has been given to research problems connected with the realization of interplanetary communications, particularly the problems of creating an artificial earth satellite. . . . In my opinion, it will be possible to launch an artificial earth satellite within the next two years, and there is a technological possibility of creating artificial satellites of various sizes and weights. From a technical point of view, it is possible to create a satellite of larger dimensions than that reported in the newspapers which we had the opportunity of scanning today. The realization of the Soviet project can be expected in the comparatively near future. I won't take it upon myself to name the data more precisely." It is interesting to compare this obviously edited official Soviet version of the press conference with the unedited version published in the Western press two days earlier. Later, after his return to Moscow, Sedov's impressions of the Astronautical Congress appeared in the Soviet press. (See Chapter 9.)

Six months later, in February, 1956, the Russians held a conference at Leningrad State University to discuss problems of the physics of the moon and the planets. More than fifty scientists participated. The two principal topics for discussion were (1) the questions of planetology connected with the problems of astronautics and, primarily, the question of the state of the moon's surface, and (2) the exchange of opinions and plans for observations of the coming great opposition of Mars in September, 1956. Professor N. P. Barabashev, conference chairman and director of the Khar'kov University Observatory, pointed out that the importance of planetology was growing substantially in connection with the demands of cosmonautics and that, at the same time, the responsibility of planetary, and especially lunar, investigators was increasing. M. K. Tikhonravov, vice chairman of the Commission on Interplanetary Communications, enumerated the basic questions to which astronauts expect answers from the science of planetology.

At the Conference on Rockets and Satellites, held on September 11, 1956, during the fourth general meeting of the Comité Spécial de l'Année Geophysique Internationale (CSAGI) in Barcelona, Spain, there occurred a prime example of official Soviet reticence to make factual pronouncements concerning rocketry and space flight. In presenting the general description of the Soviet Union's rocket and satellite program to an audience that was eagerly awaiting the Russian announcement, Academician I. P. Bardin, chairman of the USSR IGY National Committee and a vice president of the USSR Academy of Sciences, read the following statement in Russian:[5]

---

[5] Dr. V. A. Troitskaya, scientific secretary of the Soviet National Committee, read the accompanying English version immediately after Bardin's original statement.

"At the request of the General Secretary of the CSAGI, Dr. M. Nicolet, inquiring as to the possibility of the Soviet Union's participation in the Rocket-Satellite program, the Soviet National Committee announces that:

"(1) In addition to the USSR program already presented to the Barcelona meeting the Rocket-Satellite program will be presented at a later time.

"(2) The USSR intends to launch a satellite by means of which measurements of atmospheric pressure and temperature, as well as observations of cosmic rays, micro-meteorites, the geomagnetic field and solar radiation will be conducted. The preparations for launching the satellite are presently being made.

"(3) Meteorological observations at high altitudes will be conducted by means of rockets.

"(4) Since the question of USSR participation in the IGY Rocket-Satellite observations was decided quite recently the detailed program of these investigations is not yet elaborated.

"This program will be presented as soon as possible to the General Secretary of the CSAGI."

Needless to say, this unexpected and vapid statement left the assembled throng with a sense of complete frustration. No mention of it appeared in the Soviet press for more than two weeks. Finally, on September 26, a Tass report, captioned "Preparation for the International Geophysical Year" and bearing no dateline, appeared on page 4 of *Krasnaya Zvezda* (Red Star). The report quoted Academician Bardin as saying that "The Soviet delegation's statement that work is being conducted in the USSR, just as in the USA, on preparations for upper atmosphere research by means of rockets and artificial satellites evoked great interest among the participants of the session. These satellites will revolve around the Earth, making a complete revolution in less than one hour and a half. They will be relatively small, approximately the size of a [soccer] football. They will weigh about nine kilograms. Now scientists are making more precise a number of conditions for successfully launching the satellites. . . ."

The Bardin item is in keeping with the generalized nature of Soviet reports and articles concerning their satellite plans and specifications. Stereotyped statements and reports are apparently a matter of policy. This was admirably summarized by an American IGY scientist, who (according to an Associated Press dispatch datelined Washington, October 2, 1957) said that Russian delegates had told him repeatedly that they consider it "bad taste to make announcements in advance.

Our policy is not to release any details until we have experimental results."

By 1956 the USSR Academy of Sciences felt the need to apply for membership in the International Astronautical Federation. The application was voted on favorably during the Seventh International Astronautical Congress in Rome in September of that year. Moreover, the Soviet Union's lone observer-delegate to that Congress— L. I. Sedov—was elected a vice president of the Federation.

More than a year passed, however, before the Soviet Union complied with the by-laws of the International Astronautical Federation and submitted, through Sedov, a description (that is, an equivalent of a constitution) of the Academy's Interdepartmental Commission on Interplanetary Communications (Appendix G) and a list of its members (Appendix H).

The main purpose of the Commission, it seems, is to assist in every way possible the development of Soviet scientific-theoretical and practical work concerning the study of cosmic space and the achievement of space flight. Its specific duties and functions are manifold and involve the initiation, organization, coordination, and popularization of the problems of space flight, as well as the propagandization of the successes achieved.

The list of twenty-seven members of the Commission is a very impressive one. It includes eight academicians, some of Russia's— and the world's—top scientists. There is no question of the stature in world science of such men as P. L. Kapitsa, the famed physicist, N. N. Bogolyubov, the mathematical genius who is said to be the Russian counterpart of the late John von Neumann, V. A. Ambartsumyan, the noted Armenian astrophysicist, and others. Although most of the members of the Commission are pedagogues, that is, connected with some institute of higher learning, a number of them wear several hats, including military hats. Academician A. A. Blagonravov, for example, is a Lieutenant General of Artillery and is a specialist in automatic weapons. G. I. Pokrovskii is a Major General of Technical Services and an explosives expert. V. F. Bolkhovitinov, who designed rocket-powered aircraft in the early 1940's, holds the rank of Major General and is a professor of aeronautical engineering at the Military Air Academy. Yu. A. Pobedonostsev is a Colonel, a professor of aerodynamics at Moscow State University and a specialist in gas dynamics. It is quite evident that the military is well represented in the Interdepartmental Commission on Interplanetary Communications.

Because of the Soviets' extreme reticence to reveal their activities in the field of astronautics, the myriad articles on the problems of space flight that appeared in the popular press prior to the end of 1956 presented, for the most part, well-known information from the Western press with only occasional broad hints as to developments in the Soviet Union. Soviet technical journals, however, continued—as they had in the past—to present articles of considerable interest and merit, especially in the fields of flight mechanics and hydrodynamics.

Soviet uncommunicativeness ended in December, 1956, when a delegation of thirteen scientists, headed by Academician A. A. Blagonravov, an armaments specialist and a member of the Presidium of the Academy of Sciences, attended the First International Congress on Rockets and Guided Missiles in Paris. There the Russians presented two papers which revealed the prodigality of their rocket-test program: In the Soviet experimental technique, the measuring instruments are not carried in the rocket itself but in automatically jettisoned containers, the results being recorded on film and the containers recovered by parachute. The papers were entitled "Study of the Upper Atmosphere by Means of Rockets at the USSR Academy of Sciences," by S. M. Poloskov and B. A. Mirtov, and "Study of the Vital Activity of Animals during Rocket Flights into the Upper Atmosphere," by A. V. Pokrovskii, director of the USSR Institute of Experimental Aeromedicine. (See Chapters 10 and 14.)

The paper by Poloskov and Mirtov describes an instrument container, 2 meters long and 0.4 meter in diameter, used for upper-atmosphere research. It is essentially a metal cylinder divided into three sections. The lower section is hermetically sealed and contains power supplies, ammeters, camera, and the program mechanism which controls the operation of all the instruments in the container. The center section—which is open to the atmosphere—contains evacuated glass sampling flasks, thermal and ionization gauges, etc. The upper section contains a parachute and is also hermetically sealed. A set of spikes in the bottom of the container ensures a vertical landing. The container, which weighs about 250 kilograms, is jettisoned automatically in the descending phase of the trajectory at a height of 10 to 12 kilometers above the earth's surface.

Pokrovskii's paper describes a catapultable chassis used in studying the behavior of dogs during round-trip flights to altitudes of 110 kilometers. The dog is secured in a hermetically sealed space suit with a removable plastic helmet and is provided with a two-hour supply of oxygen. The chassis is equipped with radio transmitter, oscillograph, thermometers, sphygmometer, camera, and parachute. Two such chassis are fitted in the rocket nose section, which separates from the body of the rocket at the apex of the trajectory. One chassis separates from the nose section at a height of 80 to 90 kilometers and parachutes to the ground from a height of 75 to 85 kilometers. The other chassis separates at a height of 45 to 50 kilometers and falls freely to a height of 3 to 4 kilometers before parachuting to the ground.

As one might expect, the subject matter of these two papers received extremely wide publicity in the Soviet press. Probably the most comprehensive review was given by Academician Blagonravov himself in an article entitled "Investigation of the Upper Layers of the Atmosphere by Means of High-Altitude Rockets," which appeared in *Vestnik Akademii Nauk SSSR* in June, 1957. Besides mentioning by name the key personnel in the program, Blagonravov stated that cosmic-ray investigations by means of rockets were initiated in the Soviet Union in 1947, that atmospheric composition studies to altitudes of 100 kilometers began in 1949, and that systematic studies of the atmosphere—including the use of dogs—were conducted from 1951 to 1956.

By way of interlude, a Tass dispatch datelined Moscow, June 18, 1957, reads as follows:

"At a press conference held by the State Committee for Cultural Relations with Foreign Countries on June 18, the correspondents were shown living travelers into extraterrestrial space—three dogs who were sent up in rockets to a height of 100 kilometers and more. Two of them have made two flights each and are in good health. All the flights were filmed. It was found that the animals behaved normally when flying to this height at a speed of 1170 meters per second. Alexei Pokrovskii, a member of the Soviet Committee for the International Geophysical Year, said, 'I would like the British correspondents to inform the British Society of Happy Dogs about this because the Society has protested to the Soviet Union against such experiments.'"

In June, 1957, Academician I. P. Bardin submitted by letter to CSAGI at Brussels the official USSR Rocket and Earth Satellite Program for the IGY. (See Chapter 34.) This program, which was merely an outline, indicated, among other things, that the Russians would fire 125 meteorlogical research rockets from three different geographical zones and would establish an unspecified number of artificial earth satellites.

Of the numerous statements made by various Soviet scientists in the press and on the radio concerning the imminent launching of the first Soviet satellite those by Academician A. N. Nesmeyanov were probably the most pertinent.   On June 1, 1957, *Pravda* quoted Nesmeyanov as follows: "As a result of many years of work by Soviet scientists and engineers to the present time, rockets and all the necessary equipment and apparatus have been created by means of which the problem of an artificial earth satellite for scientific research purposes can be solved." (See Chapter 33.)   A week later, Nesmeyanov said that "soon, literally within the next months, out planet earth will acquire another satellite. . . . The technical difficulties that stood in the way of the solution of this grandiose task have been overcome by our scientists.   The apparatus by means of which this extremely bold experiment can be realized has already been created." [6]

In addition to these guarded statements by Nesmeyanov, and those of other Soviet scientists, the scientific literature contains several specific indications of the forthcoming launching of the first Soviet satellite.   For example, a one-page announcement entitled "On the Observation of the Artificial Satellite," by A. A. Mikhailov, chairman of the Astronomical Council of the USSR Academy of Sciences, appeared on page one in the astronomical journals *Astronomicheskii Tsirkulyar,* May 18, 1957, and *Astronomicheskii Zhurnal,* May-June, 1957.   (See Chapter 35.)   After a brief description of what observers were to expect as the satellite passed overhead,[7] the announcement concluded with the following statements:

"The Astronomical Council of the USSR Academy of Sciences requests all astronomical organizations, all astronomers of the Soviet Union, and all members of the All-Union Astronomical and Geodetic Society to participate actively in preparations for the visual observations of artificial satellites.

"Instructions and special apparatus for observation can be obtained through the Astronomical Council." [8]

---

[6] *Komsomolskaya Pravda,* June 9, 1957.

[7] Readers will find a striking similarity between this description and that of the Moonwatch program of the Smithsonian Astrophysical Observatory at Cambridge, Massachusetts, the various aspects of which are described in the observatory's *Bulletin for Visual Observers of Satellites* which began publication in July, 1956. This bulletin, issued at irregular intervals, may be found as a center insert in the monthly journal *Sky and Telescope.*

[8] The telescopes used by members of Russian Moonwatch teams, as shown in photographs in *Pravda* and other Russian newspapers, after the launching of Sputnik I, are suspiciously similar in outward appearance to the design described in the *Bulletin for Visual Observers of Satellites.*

Two articles in the June, 1957, issue of the Russian amateur-radio magazine *Radio* [9] provide further evidence of the imminent establishment of Sputnik I. The articles, entitled "Artificial Earth Satellites — Information for Radio Amateurs," by V. Vakhnin (Chapter 36), and "Observations of the Radio Signals from the Artificial Earth Satellite and Their Scientific Importance," by A. Kazantsev (Chapter 37), gave a fairly comprehensive description not only of a satellite's orbit and how the subsequent appearances of a satellite can be predicted, but also of the satellite's radio transmitters, how the 20- and 40-megacycle frequency signals are to be used, and what information about the upper atmosphere can be derived from them.

The July and August issues of *Radio* carried articles on how to build a recommended short-wave-radio receiver and a direction-finding attachment for tracking the Soviet Sputniks. Moreover, to inform the Russian radio amateurs about developments in the United States, the July issue of the magazine carried an article based on material taken from the American amateur-radio magazine *QST* describing the Minitrack II system which would permit radio amateurs to track American satellites with comparatively inexpensive equipment. This item was followed immediately by a notice in boldface type (Appendix F) to Soviet radio amateurs to make preparations for tracking the Russian scientific earth satellites and contained detailed instructions on how to submit data on the signals received and recorded to *Moskva — Sputnik* for reduction and analysis by the Institute of Radio Engineering and Electronics of the USSR Academy of Sciences.

That the Soviets were in earnest about their missile capabilities and space-flight intentions became indubitably clear on August 27, 1957, when a TASS report (Chapter 27) in *Pravda* stated that "successful tests of an intercontinental ballistic rocket and also explosions of nuclear and thermonuclear weapons have been carried out in conformity with the plan of scientific research work in the USSR."

There was considerable prognostication that the Soviets would launch a satellite on September 17, 1957, the 100th anniversary of the birth of K. E. Tsiolkovskii, the founder of the science of astronautics. Needless to say, this day was the occasion for speeches by many leading scientists, both at the Hall of Columns in Moscow and at Peace Square in Kaluga, a small town about 160 kilometers southwest of Moscow,

---

[9] *Radio* is an organ of the USSR Ministry of Communication and of DOSAAF (The All-Union Volunteer Society for the Promotion of the Army, Aviation and Navy) and corresponds to the American amateur-radio magazine *QST* published by the American Radio Relay League.

where Tsiolkovskii had spent the greater part of his life.  At Kaluga
the Soviets will erect a monument depicting Tsiolkovskii in flowing
cape, looking into the sky, and standing on a pedestal in front of a
long slender rocket poised in a vertical takeoff position.

The climax to this chronicle occurred, of course, on October 4, 1957,
when Sputnik I was established in its orbit.  (See Chapters **38 and
39.**)  Appropriately enough, even on this occasion the far-sighted
Soviets had scientific delegations strategically placed in foreign cap-
itals.  Washington played host to IGY delegates A. A. Blagonravov,
V. V. Belousov, A. M. Kasatkin, and S. M. Poloskov, who were, needless to say, overjoyed on hearing that the satellite had been launched
successfully.  In Barcelona, where the Eighth International Astronautical Congress was convening, a Soviet delegation of four, headed
by L. I. Sedov, made the most of the occasion by presenting two papers, one by L. V. Kurnosova on the investigation of cosmic radiation
by means of an artificial earth satellite and the other by A. G. Masevich
on the preparation for visual observation of artificial satellites — a
Soviet version of the Moonwatch program.  Sedov also distributed a
limited number of copies of the special 284-page September, 1957,
issue of *Uspekhi Fizicheskikh Nauk,* which contains seventeen papers
on various aspects of Soviet rocket and satellite research.

* * *

A glance at the Bibliography will clearly show that Russia has a
well-established literature on rocketry and space flight.  This literature includes not only the classic works of her own pioneers, but also
translations of foreign mongraphs by Esnault-Pelterie, Oberth, Hohmann, Goddard, Sänger, and others.  The Soviets have also "liberated"
a vast amount of detailed material from German industrial firms and
scientific and technological institutes.  Russian textbooks on rocketry,
for instance, consider details of German developments that are not even
mentioned in American books on the subject.[10]

In the post-Tsiolkovskii period the names of M. K. Tikhonravov and
A. A. Shternfel'd stand out prominently in spite of the Stalin shadow.
Both are capable and prolific writers.  For several years the names of
popular-science writers B. V. Lyapunov and M. V. Vasil'ev, engineers
K. A. Gil'zin and Yu. S. Khlebtsevich, and scientist K. P. Stanyukovich have been appearing with increasing frequency as the authors of
articles and books on rocketry and space flight.  More recently Soviet

---

[10] See, for example, Bolgarskii and Shchukin, *Rabochie protsessy v zhidkostno-
reaktivnykh dvigatelyakh* (Working processes in liquid-jet engines), Oborongiz,
Moscow, 1953, 424 pp.

scientists have been reporting the results of their researches not only in the technical journals but also in the popular press, either in the form of interviews or as nontechnical essays.  Since 1951 a monthly journal, *Voprosy Raketnoi Tekhniki* (Problems of Rocket Technology), has been completely devoted to translations and surveys of the foreign periodical literature.  Since 1954 the Institute of Scientific Information of the USSR Academy of Sciences has been publishing a journal, *Referativnyi Zhurnal: Astronomiya i Geodesiya* (Reference Journal: Astronomy and Geodesy), which abstracts, among other things, foreign and domestic publications in the field of astronautics.  Moreover, the Soviets have, of course, their own classified literature, which in all probability is extremely interesting.

Prior to 1955 Soviet papers on space flight followed, in general, a fixed pattern.  (See Chapter 1.)  They began with an account of the historical contributions made by the early Russian astronauts; next came a discussion of the results of tests obtained by American and other foreign rocketeers, followed by a discourse on the problems involved in the launching of a satellite vehicle and on the variety and importance of the data to be obtained from an extraterrestrial laboratory; finally, they boasted about the great efforts that Soviet scientists were exerting in creating a scientific space station and in making cosmic flights possible for peaceful purposes.  It is interesting to note that (except in one or two cases) almost no mention is made of any specific Soviet developments or results.  Thus, for example, the article on rockets in the *Bol'shaya Sovetskaya Entsiklopediya*[11] includes two tables of rocket characteristics.  Table 1 lists the characteristics of some liquid-propellant rockets, including the German A-4 (V-2) and Wasserfall, the U. S. Viking No. 9 and Nike, the French Véronique, and the U. S. two-stage Bumper (V-2 plus Wac Corporal) rocket.  But no Russian rockets.  Table 2 gives the characteristics of some rocket missiles, including the German Rheinbote and a 78-millimeter fragmentation shell, and the U. S. Mighty Mouse and Sparrow missiles, Again, no Russian missiles.[12]

In recent years Soviet papers on astronautics have become more and more specialized, dealing with such topics as chemical and nuclear rocket engines, radio guidance, meteoric impacts, weightlessness, and orbit calculations, as well as with problems to be investigated during

---

[11] 2nd ed., Vol. 35, pp. 665-668.

[12] There is, however, a comprehensive table of Soviet missiles and their characteristics, prepared by Alfred J. Zaehringer, in *The Journal of Space Flight*, May, 1956. See Chapter 18.

the International Geophysical Year. Their tone has been somewhat conciliatory to the West, and the jibes at the capitalist countries, ever present in the earlier papers, are conspicuously absent.

Articles on the problems of astronautics by topnotch Soviet scientists and technologists began to appear in the official, serious scientific publications of the USSR Academy of Sciences in 1954. Typical of such articles are Shternfel'd's "Problems of Cosmic Flight," published in *Priroda* in December, 1954, which is primarily an exposition on flight trajectories from the earth to the moon, Mars, Venus, and Mercury (Chapter 5); Academician V. G. Fesenkov's "The Problems of Astronautics," which appeared in *Priroda* in June, 1955, and which was written from the point of view of an astrophysicist who touches on the possibility of using atomic energy as a source of power for space travel (Chapter 7); and "Contemporary Problems of Cosmic Flights," by A. G. Karpenko and G. A. Skuridin, published in *Vestnik Akademii Nauk SSSR*, in September, 1955 (Chapter 8). The last article is a comprehensive survey of the state of the art gleaned largely from papers presented at the Fifth and Sixth International Astronautical Congresses. It concludes, significantly, with the following statements:

"Together with the utilization of atomic energy for peaceful purposes and the development of the technology of semiconductors and new computing machines, the problem of interplanetary communications belongs with those problems which will open to mankind great areas of scientific cognition and the conquest of nature.

"The importance of this problem was clearly described by Academician P. L. Kapitsa, a member of the Commission on Interplanetary Communications: ' . . . if in any branch of knowledge the possibilities of penetrating a new, virgin field of investigation are opening, then it must be done without fail, because the history of science teaches that, as a rule, it is precisely this penetration of new fields that leads to the discovery of those very important phenomena of nature which most significantly widen the paths of the development of human culture . . . ' "

The Russian technical literature of recent years gives abundant evidence of continued progress in the various disciplines associated with space flight. One of the most important pieces of evidence was the publication a few years ago of tables of thermodynamic properties, ranging from 298°K to 5000°K, of such chemical species as $F_2$, $HF$, $CH$, $CH_2$, $CH_3$, and $C_2$. The first two indicate an interest in fluorine as an oxidant in chemical-rocket propellant systems, and the latter four an interest in hydrocarbons as possible propellants in nuclear rockets.

The subject of nuclear-powered rockets is treated by K. P. Stan-yukovich in an article entitled "Problems of Interplanetary Flights," which appeared in the August 10, 1954, issue of *Krasnaya Zvezda* (Chapter 4), and in a slightly more expanded form as a paper entitled "Rockets for Interplanetary Flights" in the book *Problemy Ispol'zovaniya Atomnoi Energii* (Problems of Utilizing Atomic Energy), published in 1956. Diagrams of nuclear-powered turbojet, ram-jet, and rocket engines illustrate G. Nesterenko's article, "The Atomic Airplane of the Future," published in *Kryl'ya Rodiny* in January, 1956 (Chapter 23), while R. G. Perel'man's article, "Atomic Engines," in the January, 1956, issue of *Nauka i Zhizn'* (Chapter 24), includes a sketch of a six-stage cosmic rocket in which the first stage is powered by a liquid-rocket engine, the second stage by a ramjet engine, the third stage by an atomic-rocket engine, and the three final stages by liquid-rocket engines.

In celebrating its 125th anniversary in 1955, the Moscow Higher Technical College, which is also known as the Bauman Institute and is the Russian counterpart of the Massachusetts Institute of Technology or California Institute of Technology, published a collection of nineteen papers on theoretical mechanics, several of which had direct applications to space flight. One that is particularly relevant was written by V. F. Krotov and is entitled "Calculation of the Optimum Trajectory for the Transition of a Rocket to a Given Circular Trajectory around the Earth."

Rocket guidance has been discussed by a number of Russian experts, notably by I. Kucherov in an article entitled "Radio-guided Rockets," published in *Radio* in August, 1955 (Chapter 22), and by Yu. S. Khlebtsevich, who wrote several articles on rocket flights to the moon, Mars, and Venus.

Some highly interesting and original ideas have appeared in recent articles in Russian popular scientific literature. One article proposes worldwide television broadcasting by means of three earth satellites symmetrically spaced in an equatorial orbit at an altitude of 35,800 kilometers. (See Chapter 31.) Needless to say, the author discretely avoids mentioning the military significance of such a system. Another article suggests the use of earth satellites for the experimental verification of the general theory of relativity. (See Chapter 32.) This article, written by V. L. Ginzburg, is a very lucid piece of non-technical scientific writing on a subject that is generally considered too abstruse for the layman to understand. The study of the biological problems of interplanetary flight continues to be the subject of considerable discussion and investigation. (See Chapters 11, 12 and 13.)

The two general subjects that have received the most attention insofar as the Soviet press is concerned are the artificial earth satellite and rocket flight to the moon. Prior to Sputnik I's establishment in orbit, the following scientists wrote papers on the problems associated with artificial earth satellites: K. P. Stanyukovich, "Artificial Earth Satellite," *Krasnaya Zvezda*, August 7, 1955 (Chapter 28); A. G. Karpenko, "Cosmic Laboratory," *Moskovskaya Pravda*, August 14, 1955 (Chapter 29); G. I. Pokrovskii, "Artificial Earth Satellite," *Izvestiya*, August 19, 1955 (Chapter 30); L. I. Sedov, "On Flights into Space," *Pravda*, September 26, 1955 (Chapter 9); and A. N. Nesmeyanov, "The Problem of Creating an Artificial Earth Satellite," *Pravda*, June 1, 1957 (Chapter 33). The first four articles were prompted largely by the White House announcement of July 29, 1955, while Nesmeyanov's article was a harbinger of Sputnik I.

In the Soviet literature there are repeated references to moon-rocket projects. For example, in an article entitled "Flight to the Moon," published in *Pionerskaya Pravda* on October 2, 1951 (Chapter 15), M. K. Tikhonravov, Corresponding Member of the Academy of Artillery Sciences, stated that according to engineering calculations two men could fly around the moon and back to earth in a rocket ship weighing approximately 1000 tons. Such a ship must have a velocity of about 11.1 kilometers per second. If an artificial earth satellite were available, then it would be possible to send a much smaller space ship — one weighing not more than 100 tons and having a velocity of 3.5 kilometers per second — from the satellite to the moon.

According to a German Press Agency report, the Soviet newspaper *Krasnii Flot* (Red Fleet) for October 12, 1951, asserted that a moon rocket had already been designed in the Soviet Union. It was said to be 60 meters long, to have a maximum diameter of 15 meters, a weight of 1000 tons, and 20 motors with a total power of 350 million horsepower. Heinz H. Kölle of Stuttgart's *Gesellschaft für Weltraumforschung* evaluated these data in an article entitled "Wird in der Sowjet-Union eine Mondrakete gebaut?" in *Weltraumfahrt*, January, 1952 (Chapter 16). He concluded that in the optimum case a manned rocket for at best a two-man crew and a single circumnavigation of the moon with subsequent return to the earth still lies too close to the outermost limit of present attainments:

"Even the unmanned moon messenger would require immense technical effort. The practical result would be trifling in comparison. On the other hand, the undertaking could be used psychologically and propaganda-wise, since successful execution and the corresponding accompanying fanfare would obviously demonstrate that Soviet long-range rockets would just as well reach any point on the earth's surface."

. Professor K. P. Stanyukovich, a man of many interests and of prolific pen, has made several contributions in this field. His article "Trip to the Moon: Fantasy and Reality" in the English-language propaganda journal *News: A Soviet Review of World Events*, for June 1, 1954, (Chapter 17), is more polemic than scientific. His article "Rendezvous with Mars" in the same journal for October 16, 1956 (Chapter 19), is not quite so belligerent toward the United States. In this later article he predicts flights to the moon in five to ten years and to Mars within fifteen years, the latter being accomplished not with chemical propellants but with nuclear propellants.

Perhaps the most widely publicized moon-rocket project in the Soviet Union is that proposed by Yu. S. Khlebtsevich, which made its first appearance in an article entitled "On the Way to the Stars" in *Tekhnika-Molodezhi* in July, 1954 (Chapter 3); later it was published in an expanded form as "The Road into the Cosmos" in the November, 1955, issue of *Nauka i Zhizn'* (Chapter 18). Khlebtsevich suggests landing a mobile "tankette-laboratory" on the Moon. The tankette, which would weigh not more than a few hundred kilograms and would be radio controlled from the earth, would explore the surface of the moon and report its findings back to earth.[12] Information so obtained would make possible the next stage — the mastery of the moon by man in the next five to ten years.

In February, 1957, the Soviet press gave considerable publicity to a space-flight project headed by Professor G. A. Chebotarev at the Institute of Theoretical Astronomy in Leningrad. (See Chapter 20.) According to Chebotarev's calculations it is possible, with the expenditure of only 16 tons of propellant, to launch a rocket vehicle weighing 50 to 100 kilograms with an initial velocity of 11 kilometers per second in an elliptical orbit around the moon. Flying solely under gravitational forces the vehicle would round the moon at a distance of 30,000 kilometers and return to the earth in 236 hours, after covering a total path length of about one million kilometers.

---

[12] This project has been made the subject of a Russian popular-science short film—of the Walt Disney type, but much inferior—and is No. 15 in a series generally entitled "Science and Technology." Since the advent of Sputnik I, the film has been shown in movie theaters throughout the United States.

One of the most startling disclosures in connection with Soviet space-flight activities is the paper entitled "Some Questions on the Dynamics of Flight to the Moon" by V. A. Egorov of the Steklov Mathematics Institute in Moscow. (See Chapter 21.) This paper is a summary of a systematic investigation undertaken from 1953 to 1955 to find satisfactory solutions for the fundamental problems in the theory of flight to the moon: specifically the problem of the form and classification of unpowered trajectories, of the possibility of periodic circumflight of the moon and the earth, and of hitting the moon. The paper also deals with the particularly important question of the effect of the dispersion of initial data on the realization of hitting or circumflight. More than 600 trajectories were calculated by means of electronic computers and were classified as hits, circumflights, or afflights (that is, approach trajectories which do not encompass the moon but allow one to see everything on its opposite side and to return to earth). This investigation is quite similar to studies of the general trajectories of a body in the earth-moon system that are being conducted in this country. The over-all results of the studies are in substantial agreement. Specific numerical comparisons can now be made, since the complete report is available.

\* \* \*

Two facts are obvious from the successful launchings of Sputniks I and II. First, there is no doubt that Russia has won a tremendous propaganda victory. Second, Russia unquestionably possesses rocket systems of proven operational reliability.

Since the Russians did not indicate beforehand what orbital elements they were striving to obtain for their scientific satellites, it is impossible to determine the guidance accuracy of their rocket systems. Suffice it to say that the Russians have propulsion and guidance capabilities of placing half-ton packages in orbit.

Nor have the Russians indicated the characteristics of the individual rockets in the systems used to launch the satellites. It would not be difficult, however, to construct rocket systems capable of placing Sputnik I and II payloads in orbit on the basis of information in Chapter 18, that is, by using first- and second-stage booster rockets having 120- and 35-metric-ton-thrust engines, respectively, and a third-stage rocket of the Wasserfall type which the Russians are known to have had under development.

That the Soviets might have been prodigal with their propulsive power in launching the Sputniks seems to follow from a statement made by Yu. A. Pobedonostsev in *Soviet Weekly* for October 10, 1957, in describing the launching of Sputnik I: "When the first stage engines stop, after one or two minutes, the whole first stage of the rocket falls away, and the second stage engines start, bringing the now smaller rocket up to a speed of between 11,000 and 12,500 miles per hour. From then on the rocket travels by inertia, and as it rises higher so its course flattens until it is flying parallel with the earth below. By that time, the rocket is more than 6000 miles away from where it started. It is at this point that the third stage engine cuts in, and brings the satellite's speed up to its final figure of well over 17,000 miles per hour."

It is obvious that the Soviets, in their struggle for world domination, are applying their sledge-hammer technique not only to terrestrial affairs but also to the conquest of cosmic space. Heretofore, trying to follow the maneuvers of the Soviet scientific bear was like trying to decide the outcome of Frank Stockton's classic short story "The Lady or the Tiger?" Not any more!

# Part One

# SPACE FLIGHT COMES OF AGE

# 1. The Way to the Stars

*V. Borisov*

"To set foot on the soil of the asteroids, to lift by hand a rock from the moon, to observe Mars from a distance of several tens of kilometers, to land on its satellite or even on its own surface, what can be more fantastic? From the moment of using rocket devices a new great era will begin in astronomy: the epoch of the more intensive study of the firmament." Thus wrote the originator of the theory and technology of interplanetary flight, the famous scientist Konstantin Eduardovich Tsiolkovskii.

But what kind of a device is capable of overcoming the force of terrestrial attraction and of taking travelers into interplanetary space? A number of people have tried to answer this question. Projects were made of constructing gigantic cannons — gunpowder, centrifugal, electromagnetic — but only Tsiolkovskii correctly solved this complex task by suggesting the use of a rocket motor for propelling interplanetary ships.

The interplanetary ship must go out beyond the limits of the atmosphere. It will have to fly in space where there is no air, without which no flying apparatus except the rocket can develop the thrust necessary for flight. Moreover, it will have to remain in flight a very long time, and interplanetary travelers will not be able to fly without fuel stored in great quantities. But where to find room for such a quantity of fuel?

The scientist pointed out methods of solving even this problem, which even today are of interest. In order to develop cosmic velocity without burdening the ship with unnecessary stores of fuel, Tsiolkovskii suggested launching composite rockets — original cosmic trains. People traveling to other planets must be placed in the head rocket of this train. Gradually, as fuel is spent, the tail rockets, one after another, must be uncoupled, returning to the earth.

"By a rocket train," wrote K. E. Tsiolkovskii, "I mean a combination of several similar reactive devices . . . only a part of this train

23

travels into celestial space, the remaining portions, not having sufficient velocity, return to the earth. . . . ."

K. E. Tsiolkovskii's ideas were caught up and developed by his
pupils and followers. Tsiolkovskii's successor, Yu. V. Kondratyuk,
creatively elaborating his teacher's ideas, wrote that the interplanetary
composite ship must comprise several rocket stages "of gradually decreasing size; mainly aluminum, silicon, and magnesium serve as construction materials; as far as possible, parts requiring special heat resistance are made of suitable kinds of graphite or carborundum; stages
becoming unnecessary because of their size, because of the reduced
mass of the rocket, are not discarded but are dismantled and go . . .
to be reduced and melted in order to be used later as the chemical
components of fuel."

Another successor of Tsiolkovskii's, engineer F. A. Tsander, also developed the idea of burning the no longer necessary metallic parts of
the rocket. In order to facilitate the flight of a cosmic ship out of the
atmosphere, he suggested as early as in 1924 to provide the ship with
wings. But now the atmosphere is already left behind. "The parts
of the airplane (propellers, chassis, surface controls, etc.) are pulled
into the body through slots which are in vertical side projections of
the body" and then the metal is melted and goes into the nozzle of the
rocket. . . . " . . . The liquid metal is atomized, partly vaporized,
and mixed with the injected oxygen, burning in the combustion chamber." Tsander makes the correct deduction that this "greatly increases the efficiency of the rocket."

Tsander passionately dedicated himself to the idea of interplanetary
flights. Evaluating his relation to his beloved work, *Pravda* wrote in
1934: "This man spent his life wonderfully! While still a boy, he
reads with interest books and stories on astronomy. With his first-
earned money he buys an astronomical telescope and often observes
the planets and the stars for several hours on end. While a university
student in 1908, he makes calculations on the reactive engine. Marri-
age: children are born; the name of his daughter is Astra, the name of
his son, Mercury. Every thought, every step manifests his aspiration
for interplanetary flight!

"At the end of 1920, at the Moscow Province Conference of Inventors, Tsander read a paper. V. I. Lenin, who was present at the
Conference, became interested in the paper and rendered Tsander his
support."

### ENERGY OF THE ATOMIC NUCLEUS

The achievements of modern science make it possible, in a different way, to solve the problems of storing fuel. It is necessary to utilize the energy hidden inside the atom. The magnitude of the thrust which is developed when a rocket engine is operating depends to a considerable degree on the velocity with which the gases, formed as a result of fuel combustion, escape from the rocket. By utilizing "atomic fuel," the exhaust velocity, which under ordinary conditions we try to increase in every way, can become an enemy instead of an ally. The point is that if in an ordinary rocket the exhaust velocity is about 2000 meters per second, then in the atomic rocket the particles which form during the nuclear disintegration fly with a velocity of 10,000 kilometers per second. In this case the energy obtained by the rocket will be so great that the cosmic ship can be vaporized.

Therefore, in order to utilize intra-atomic energy for interplanetary flight it is necessary to use a "moderator" — a special substance that reduces the velocity of propagation of the particles — or else to utilize an "intermediary" — a liquid which, while the engine is in operation, vaporizes and creates thrust.

### TRAVELERS IN THE COSMOS

Travel in the cosmos sets before science a number of complex problems. One of these problems is human physiology. We still have not made a trip into interstellar space but we already know what is in store for a man who has set out on such a flight. First of all, overloads beset him. At the moment when the ship will gain speed, the passengers will feel as though they are in a streetcar when it starts abruptly from a spot, with the only difference that this jolt will be hundreds and perhaps even thousands of times stronger.

Later the situation will change. If in the first minutes of flight the travelers are subjected to the action of overloads, they soon will completely lose the sensation of weight since the force of terrestrial attraction will cease to act upon them. Tsiolkovskii's scientific genius foresaw how man would feel in such a flight. He wrote about this vividly and with feeling: "We shall not have weight, only mass. We can hold any mass in our hands without experiencing the slightest weight. . . . Man does not press himself against anything and nothing presses on him; every spot is as soft as any down bed can be. . . . There is no top or bottom."

Just as graphically, the scientist describes the pictures which unfold before the eye of cosmonauts. "The sky is black. The patterns of the stars are the same as on the earth, only there is less red color in the stars, more variety in their colors. They do not twinkle, but they sparkle and to men with good eyesight they will appear as dead points (without rays). The sun also seems to be bluish. The earth appears as a star, like Venus, and our moon is hardly visible. The pattern of the constellations does not depend on our location in the planetary system, it is the same from Jupiter or from Mercury. But the size of the sun appears the same only from the earth's orbit.

"Because of the absence of an atmosphere, we see extremely distinctly the stars, nebulae, comets, planets and their satellites. We can see with the naked eye what from earth is impossible to see without a telescope. With the aid of the latter, however, we can behold what we have never seen from the earth. . . ."

### AND WHY IS ALL THIS NECESSARY

Perhaps the reader will ask the questions, "And why is this all necessary? Is it possible there is not enough space on the earth? Why is it necessary to fly into cosmic space?"

Even in his work "Goals of Astronavigation," Tsiolkovskii gave answers to these questions. Pointing out that the energy radiated by the sun is more than two billion times greater than the energy received from it by the earth and two hundred million times greater than all the planets of our solar system receive from it, the great scientist wrote: "That is the kind of energy that man can possess if he is able to establish himself in celestial space. One can hardly compare the achievement of this goal with the discovery of two thousand million new planets such as the earth!"

Tsiolkovskii was convinced that this time will inevitably come. In 1913, in a letter to engineer B. N. Vorobyev, he wrote: "Mankind will not remain on the earth forever, but in the pursuit of the world and space at first will timidly penetrate beyond the limits of the atmosphere and then will conquer all the space around the sun."

Tsiolkovskii's pupils also held the same humane and progressive opinions about the possibility of interplanetary flight. "For astronomers the future interplanetary ship must represent an astronomical flying laboratory," wrote F. A. Tsander.

"Let us look at the problem of mankind's flight into interplanetary spaces," wrote Yu. V. Kondratyuk. "What can we specifically expect . . . ? Undoubtedly the enrichment of our scientific knowledge with its corresponding reflection in technology."

The reactionary science serving Anglo-American imperialism sets forth entirely different goals for interplentary travels. It is not the study of the nature of surrounding worlds in the interest of science, but the search for strategic raw materials for a new war. It is not a research laboratory for the study of interplanetary spaces, but yet another extra-terrestrial base for attacking the Soviet Union and the countries of the People's Democracy. American imperialists, who are possessed by a mania of world domination, are threatening the entire universe and are making extravagant plans for transforming the entire solar system into an American colony.

Tsiolkovskii warned against this more than 20 years ago. He wrote: "Many visualize celestial ships with people traveling from planet to planet, the gradual population of the planets and the extraction therefrom of profits which ordinary terrestrial colonies yield. The fact will be far different from this."

Not long before his death, the founder of space flight, Konstantin Eduardovich Tsiolkovskii, wrote a letter to the People's Leader, Comrade Stalin, in which he bequeathed all his works to the Soviet people and to the party of the Bolsheviks — the true bearers of progress. These works came into reliable hands.

The insane plans of the imperialists are doomed to failure. The science of our country, having spoken the first word on interplanetary flights, will also be the first to realize this long-cherished dream of mankind. (*Znanie-Sila*, April, 1950.)

# 2: Interplanetary Communications

*Large Soviet Encyclopedia*

Interplanetary communications include the problem of flights within the limits of the solar system, with landing on other planets or flying around them. The basic condition for such flights is to obtain a cosmic velocity by which a body either becomes a satellite of the earth or moves away from it in a definite orbit. To do this in a vacuum it is necessary to ensure guided motion and to restrict overloading, which arises during change of velocity, within the limits permissible for man, mechanisms, and instruments. Peculiarities of interplanetary communications: motion beyond the atmosphere in the absence of a supporting medium in the field of gravity of the planets and the sun, in the presence in world space of ultraviolet solar radiation, cosmic rays, and meteoritic matter. To attain cosmic velocity, such technological means as shooting and throwing by means of a centrifugal machine were suggested, but they do not offer a solution to the problem. K. E. Tsiolkovskii was the first to suggest the use of rockets for interplanetary communications and demonstrated the possibility of achieving cosmic velocities by means of them (published in 1903).

A sketch of Tsiolkovskii's interplanetary rocket is given in Figure 1. The acceleration and, consequently, the amount of over-

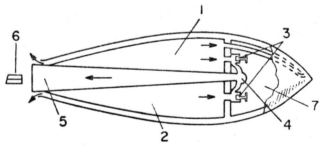

Figure 1. Sketch of Tsiolkovskii's interplanetary rocket: (1), (2) fuel, (3) fuel pump, (4) combustion chamber, (5) nozzle for gaseous jet exhaust, (6) gas rudders, (7) passenger cabin.

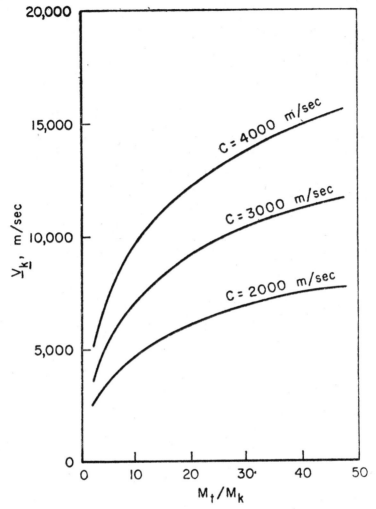

Figure 2. Relation of final rocket velocity $V_k$, to exhaust velocity, C, of combustion products and mass ratio, $M_t/M_k$ (in free space, i.e., beyond the field of gravity and in the absence of the atmosphere).

loading is regulated by change in fuel consumption; the direction of motion, by moving rudders which are fixed in the stream of the exhaust gases. Figure 2 shows the relation of final rocket velocity, $V_k$, to the exhaust velocity, C, of the products of combustion and the ratio of the mass of fuel, $M_t$ to the mass of the empty (after consumption of fuel) rocket, $M_k$.

If the force of attraction of the interplanetary ship to the planet is balanced by the centrifugal force, then the orbit is a circle. The velocity of such motion is called circular and is designated $V_k = \sqrt{gr}$, where $g$ is the acceleration of gravity at distance $r$ from the center of the planet (if $r$ is the earth's radius and $g = 9.8$ meters per second, then $V_k$ is necessarily 7912 meters per second). A body moving with this velocity cannot fall to the earth. As the rocket moves away from the planet, $V_k$ decreases, but the transition to a circular orbit requires a greater expenditure of energy than the attainment of a velocity of 7912 meters per second. Neglecting air resistance, the velocity required for complete release from the planet's field of gravity is equal to $V_p = \sqrt{2gr}$. In this case the relative trajectory of the body (rocket) will be a parabola; therefore, $V_p$ is called the parabolic velocity. For the earth, $V_p$ is, on the average, equal to 11,200 meters per second. The velocity required for the complete release of an interplanetary ship from the combined fields of gravity of the earth and the sun, which is obtained at a certain direction of flight, is equal to 16,662 meters per second. In the general case the trajectories of motion of an interplanetary ship are curves of the second order.

The maximum velocity of modern large liquid-fuel rockets is more than 2 kilometers per second for exhaust velocity $C = 2000$ meters per second and $M_t/M_k = 3$. From Figure 2 it is apparent that for an exhaust velocity of 4000 meters per second, a circular velocity is attained at $M_t/M_k = 7$; for $C = 11.2$ kilometers per second, it is attained when $M_t/M_k = 15$; for $C = 16.6$ kilometers per second, when $M_t/M_k$ is more than 50. Construction of a rocket with such weight characteristics is hardly possible. There are several ways of overcoming the difficulties connected with the necessity of putting a relatively large supply of fuel into the rocket. By using the principle of the multistage composite rocket, it is possible to reduce the relative fuel supply required to attain cosmic velocity. In such a rocket all the stages except one serve as accelerators, separating in flight, and by their consecutive operation the last stage attains the cosmic velocity. Another variant is also possible when the stages are connected not consecutively, but in parallel, and the motors operate simultaneously. The maximum velocity of the composite rocket depends on the number of stages n. By increasing n, however, the starting weight increases, the size of the relative payload decreases, and construction difficulties increase.

Utilization of the construction parts of a rocket as metallic fuel increases the relative fuel supply and can also facilitate the task of obtaining cosmic velocities. The maximum velocity of a rocket can be raised considerably by increasing the exhaust velocity. For this purpose it is possible, for example, to utilize the heat of atomic disintegration, by which a working fluid is heated; the vapors of the fluid flow through the nozzle with a great velocity, creating thrust. Building an atomic interplanetary rocket, however, requires the solution of a number of complex technical problems. The use of atomic energy for the purposes of interplanetary communications will yield in the future the possibility of reducing the necessary relative weight of fuel (possibly without resorting to the principle of the multistage rocket), of increasing the payload of the rocket, of reducing the time of interplanetary flights, and even of posing the question of cosmic voyages beyond the limits of the solar system; the use of atomic fuel will ensure greater reliability of interplanetary flights by increasing the maneuverability of the interplanetary ship, making it possible to compensate for accidental deviations, and also by making more probable in the future the possibility of landing on the planets and their satellites and returning to the earth.

To realize interplanetary communications, it is necessary to solve a number of very complex technological tasks: to design a cosmic rocket with a satisfactory $M_t/M_k$ ratio; to build a rocket motor with the necessary thrust; to make semiautomatic and automatic control apparatus, pilot-navigational instruments and radio equipment; to ensure normal living conditions for the crew (to provide protection from overloading, to attain "artificial gravity" during free flight with the motor shut off, to regenerate the air in the hermetically closed passenger cabin, to have space units for egress into airless space and on the surface of the planets); to protect the rocket crew against the danger of possible collision with meteors and from the action of ultraviolet solar radiation); to develop devices for landing on the earth and other planets; to create scientific research apparatus suited for flight conditions in world space. While the solution of a part of the tasks mentioned above is even now becoming sufficiently probable under the conditions of the development of advanced science and technology (for example, the problems concerned with the construction of the interplanetary ship itself), the others will require for their solution lengthier preliminary investigations. Modern theoretically proven possibilities of interplanetary communications: the launching of a multistage rocket with automatic instruments for the investigation of interplanetary space and the upper layers of the terrestrial atmosphere, the creation of an automatic rocket — an earth satellite — with a relatively small payload (instruments and radio transmitter). In the future will become possible: the launching of automatic rockets for flight around the moon, Mars, and other planets, for the investigation of the physical conditions on the surface of celestial bodies and of various astronomical and geophysical observations in cosmic space; the creation of an earth satellite — a research laboratory and extraterrestrial station for interplanetary ships; the utilization of radiant energy in world space for moving interplanetary ships and various energetic purposes (on stations beyond the earth).

An outstanding role in the creation and development of the theory and elaboration of the technical bases for interplanetary communications belongs to a native scientist. Tsiolkovskii scientifically founded the jet principle for flights in world space, derived the basic formulas of the theory of jet propulsion, described in principle the construction of the interplanetary rocket, advanced a number of constructive ideas relative to obtaining cosmic velocity (composite rockets). He first suggested the idea of creating an artificial satellite of the earth or the sun, "an ethereal dwelling," assembled from parts transported by rockets beyond the atmosphere. The extraterrestrial station can be used for various investigations in cosmic space, and also for replenishing the fuel supplies of rockets in interplanetary communications. This will considerably facilitate the realization of flights to the planets most remote from the sun. The use of an extraterrestrial station as the point of departure of interplanetary ships will considerably lessen the velocity required to reach one goal or another of interplanetary communications. Tsiolkovskii examined in detail the questions of life in world space, in the rocket, and on the extraterrestrial station, and suggested: to use plants to create a rotation of matter similar to that which takes place on the earth (purification of air and absorption of waste matter by plants, use of fruits for nourishment); to obtain under conditions of weightlessness (that is, in the absence of noticeable acceleration of flight) an "artificial gravity" of a desired magnitude by rotating the living quarters; to utilize changes in temperature (in shadow and under direct solar rays) to operate solar power plants in world space. Tsiolkovskii outlined the following path of gradual development of "technology outside the earth's atmosphere": rocket plane; flights to great heights and beyond the atmosphere, flights circling the earth; adaptation of plants in the rocket for air purification and food production; utilization of solar energy for flights in world space. From 1903 to 1935 he wrote fifteen scientific treatises dealing with the problems of interplanetary communications.

Soviet engineer F. A. Tsander and mechanician Yu. V. Kondratyuk played an important role in the development of the theory of interplanetary communications. To reduce $M_t/M_k$, Tsander suggested the construction of an interplanetary rocket in combination with an airplane, parts of which are used in flight as fuel, and investigated the problems of using metallic fuel in rocket motors; he examined certain theoretical questions of rocket flight and worked out the basis of the theory of long-range rocket flights with flight beyond the limits of the atmosphere. Kondratyuk worked out the theory of jet propulsion, and examined questions on fuel for rockets, on the construction of the rocket motor and the interplanetary rocket, on astronavigation, on braking of the rocket by the atmosphere while landing on the earth and on the design of a landing glider, and on the establishment of an extraterrestrial station — a satellite of the moon. Among foreign investigations of the problems of interplanetary communications, best known are the works of the German scientists H. Oberth "Die Rakete zu den Planetenräumen," 1923) and W. Hohmann ("Die Erreichbarkeit der Himmelskörper," 1925); the French scientist R. Esnault-Pelterie ("Consideration sur les resultats d'un allegement indefini des moteurs," 1913; "L'exploration par fusées de la tres haute atmosphere et la possibilité des voyages interplanetaires," 1928; and others); and the American scientist R. Goddard ("A Method of Reaching Extreme Altitudes," 1919). In these works are examined the questions of the theory of jet propulsion and interplanetary communications, possible designs of interplanetary rockets and of an extraterrestrial station, the conditions of flights in world space, and others. There are scientific-technological societies for interplanetary communications in a number of countries (the United States, England, France, and others).

The significance of the problem of interplanetary flight is great. Rocket flights to great heights allow even now the study of the structure of the very high layers of the atmosphere (distribution of temperature and pressure, composition and ionization of the air, etc.) and the phenomena occurring in them (interaction of cosmic particles with the atmosphere, solar radiation, propagation of radio waves, movement of air masses). There are many reasons for the great significance attached to the problem of interplanetary communications. The organization of a permanent research laboratory — an earth satellite — will make it possible to more fully study the physical conditions of world space, solar radiation, and cosmic rays beyond the atmosphere.   The rocket satellite can be used as a relay station for remote radio transmissions, television broadcasts, and photography of the terrestrial surface in map making; it will make it possible to carry out various investigations and observations of celestial bodies under conditions of airless cosmic space.   During flights of automatically controlled rockets with photographic, cinematographic, and television equipment, it will be possible to photograph from desired distances the planets and other celestial bodies and also to obtain data concerning their structure, atmospheres, surface physical conditions, etc. Extra-atmospheric flights will permit a better study of the sun and will yield many new experimental data on astrophysics and astronomy. By means of interplanetary communications it will be possible to utilize outside the atmosphere the energetic resources of the sun and the mineral resources of the planets for the mastery of world space. (*Bol'shaya Sovetskaya Entsiklopediya*, Large Soviet Encyclopedia, 2nd ed., Vol. 27, June 18, 1954.)

# 3: On the Way to the Stars

*Tekhnika-Molodezhi*

Which of our readers is not interested in the problems of astronautics — the science which studies questions of flight into cosmic space! This interest has grown recently, especially since, according to the apt expression of the late Academician S. I. Vavilov, the problem of interplanetary travels has passed from the irresponsible conduct of writers to the more responsible conduct of engineers, and when, according to the assertion of the President of the USSR Academy of Sciences, Academician A. N. Nesmeyanov, it has become feasible to send a rocket plane to the moon, to create an artificial satellite of the earth.

Recently, in Moscow, at the Chkalov Central Aeroclub of the USSR there was organized an Astronautics Section whose members set as their goal "to facilitate the realization of cosmic flights for peaceful purposes."

To meet our readers' interests in the problem of space travels, the editorial office arranged a meeting with the members of the Astronautics Section. The following participants took part in the conversation which developed: the Chairman of the Astronautics Section, N. A. Vavarov, Doctor of Physico-Mathematical Sciences Professor V. V. Dobronravov, Design Engineer I. A. Merkulov, Stalin Prize Laureate D. A. Seryapin, Doctor of Technical Sciences Professor K. P. Stanyukovich, Candidate of Technical Sciences Yu. S. Khlebtsevich, Laureate of International Encouragement Price in Astronautics A. A. Shternfel'd, and others.

### THE PAGES OF RUSSIAN GLORY

N. A. Vavarov began the conversation. Having opened the golden book of history of the conquest of the sky, he scanned the pages of Russian glory:

"It is difficult to find a real problem of more striking boldness and grandeur than flight into world space.

"Tales and ballads, songs and fairy tales, which arise in deep Russian antiquity, show that the Russian people from time immemorial have dreamed of mastering the air ocean. Winged people, flights on birds, flying carpets, and other poetical fantasies of Russian national folklore speak of the eternal dream — to fly off into the sky!

"Now these dreams are being realized. And a great Russian people has made a substantial contribution to the world's history of mastering the air ocean and interplanetary space.

"Russia is the birthplace of air navigation, as is manifested by documents on flights in an air balloon in 1731 by Ryazan official Kryakutnoi, who anticipated the French brothers Montgolfier by fifty-two years.

"Russia is the birthplace of the airplane, as is manifested by the patent issued in 1881 to A. F. Mozhaiskii, who anticipated by a quarter of a century the foreign inventors — the American Wright brothers.

"Russia is the birthplace of rocket navigation. The famous scientist K. E. Tsiolkovskii in 1903 published in the magazine *Scientific Review* the first part of his work, "Investigation of World Spaces by Reactive Instruments," in which for the first time in the world he established and proved the feasibility of flight in cosmic space. Only nine years later in France and sixteen years later in the United States were works published on this subject. We therefore rightfully consider Tsiolkovskii to be the founder of scientific astronautics.

"Tsiolkovskii's work was continued and developed by Soviet scientists Tsander, Kondratyuk, and others, who worked out separate problems of astronautics.

"On the problem of interplanetary flights, extensive work is also being carried out abroad, especially in the United States, but the purposes pursued there sharply differ from ours. They are clearly expressed in the American science fiction film 'Destination — Moon,' which shows a flight to the moon by a group of scientists headed by a general. The purpose of the flight is uranium ore which possibly exists on our planet's satellite. And the American general makes the statement from the screen, 'Who possesses the moon, possesses the world.'

Strategic raw material for manufacturing atomic bombs and other kinds of weapons of mass destruction is what primarily draws them into the cosmos. To convert the moon and the planets into American colonies — sources of profit for the monopolies — to create an artificial satellite of the earth and to make it an extraterrestrial military base in order to bring down death on the earth — such is the purpose of these merchants of death.

"We, however, see the purpose of interplanetary flights in another form. These flights will make it possible to take a step forward on the way to the knowledge of the world, which will make it possible to draw out of the treasure of the universe its colossal reserves of energy.

"Already today we can visualize roughly how the first jump from the earth into space will be accomplished.

"The most difficult segment of the path is its beginning — the first tens and hundreds of kilometers above the earth's surface. It is necessary to break through the dense layers of the earth's atmosphere, to develop great velocities. It seems most probable that at this stage of the flight one must employ several types of engines, selecting for each segment the most advantageous one.

"The space ship will take off from the earth powered by turbojet engines and will be equipped with large wings which will ensure its stability in flight and create its lifting power. This kind of engine is most effective up to speeds close to sonic and up to an altitude of the order of 20 kilometers. It will utilize the oxygen of the surrounding air, which means that it will require considerably less of the fuel and oxidizer necessary to attain cosmic velocities.

"Upon attaining the necessary velocity and altitude, the turbojet engines which have already played their role will be cast off. Ramjet engines, which are most economical at high altitudes, will come into operation. By their thrust the ship will ascend into the ionsphere to an altitude of the order of 50 kilometers and will develop a speed up to 1.5 kilometers per second. On crossing the sound barrier the external appearance of the cosmic ship will change sharply: all its leading edges will become tapered, adapted for supersonic flight. At this stage of flight the oxygen, stored in tanks, will also not be used.

"Finally the air-jet engines and the wings, which are no longer necessary, will be discarded. Now liquid-jet engines, which will give the rocket the final velocity necessary for flight, for instance to the moon, will begin to operate.

"Let this dream about mastering world space be realized sooner! Let the day come faster when we shall know what is as yet hidden in the mysterious depths of the universe!"

### DATES OF SPACE SHIP TAKEOFF

"I shall try to specify the dates of takeoff of 'the space ship,' " said V. V. Dobronavov, Vice Chairman of the Scientific-Technical Committee on Cosmic Navigation, "taking into consideration the present state of science and the prospects of its development.

"Many fields of science and technology are being developed now at extraordinarily fast rates, which are constantly increasing.

"As an example, we can point to the development of our knowledge in the field of the structure of the atomic nucleus.

"The discovery of radioactivity and of the electron belongs to 1898-1897 of the past century.  In 1905 the relationship between mass and energy was established.

"In 1932 the neutron was discovered and in 1939 a method of disintegrating the uranium nucleus with release of energy was found. But at that time the possibility of obtaining the intra-atomic energy seemed as yet very distant to the wide circle of scientific workers. Today, however, Soviet scientists and engineers already are having very considerable success in the field of peaceful application of atomic energy.  And it is indeed atomic fuel, in all probability, which will be utilized in the engines of space ships.

"Such, then, are the rates of development in some other fields of our technology.

"Casting a glance into the future, one can point out three periods of development of astronautics.  The first period is the creation of radio-controlled rockets (without crew) which will be able to fly away from the earth to a distance of 300 to 400 kilometers.  Basically, this task has already been solved by technology.

"The first period will end with the creation of an artificial satellite of the earth — a rocket which will move around the earth in an elliptical or circular orbit.  The most careful astronautical scientists name 1965 as the approximate date for accomplishing these steps.

"The following stage in the development of astronautics will be the creation of a space ship, manned by a crew of two or three men, that will be capable of moving in a circular orbit around the earth at a distance of approximately 500 kilometers.  The tentative date of the organization of such flights is 1975.

"The second period may end with a flight around the moon without landing on it (1980-1990).

"Finally, the first space flight to the moon with landing and, of course, with return will be accomplished about 2000.

"There is no doubt that all these calculations are approximate.  But, I dare say, we can expect these assumed dates to approach sooner than later."

### THE ROCKET ENGINE OF TODAY

The Chairman of the Scientific-Technical Committee on Rocket Technology, I. A. Merkulov, noted that the dates named by Professor V. V. Dobronavov are too pessimistic, but he did not attempt to make

them more specific. Without looking into the future, he discussed
the rocket engine of today.

"I think that the problem of cosmic flights will hardly be decided
as some isolated problem outside the general development of science
and technology. Flight into airless space will be a logical continua-
tion, a further development, of flights which began near the surface
of the earth, which now are performed even at great altitudes in the
stratosphere, and which in the future will extend also into airless space.

"Therefore, considering the technological basis of flights in world
space, jet technology, I shall speak about it not on a theoretical plane
— as a branch of technology which will serve us only in the distant
future — but shall try to dwell on it as an urgent task of technology
of our day which already has ensured outstanding achievements of
aviation and has made it possible to attain great flight velocities.

"I see the sources of astronautics not in the legends and fantasies
of novelists but in the power and strength of our air force. I want,
therefore, to begin my account of jet technology with the successes
of the Soviet Air Force.

"In the May 1 air parades, Soviet people see squadrons of jet fighters
flying with colossal speed over the columns of paraders. The speed of
these aircraft is several hundred kilometers per hour greater than the
speed of the fastest fighters with piston engines and air propellers.
Jet engines are not only being used widely on the fastest fighter airplanes, but have also become a part of bombarding aviation. In recent years many jet bombers have participated in the air parades.
The day is not far off when jet engines will be widely utilized in passenger aircraft also.

"Today jet airplanes have attained a speed exceeding the speed of
sound. When civilian aviation has acquired speeds close to this,
passenger aircraft will be able to cover the entire way from Moscow to
Vladivostok in six to seven hours, and a flight from Moscow to Leningrad will require half an hour.

"For more than half a century the development of aviation proceeded along the path of perfecting the flying qualities of propeller-
motor airplanes. During its development, propeller-motor aviation
has accumulated great technical achievements. And before our eyes
the creation of the new, qualitatively different, jet aviation took place.
With the transition from propeller-motor aviation to jet aviation the
speed of flight at once increased by a jump of 250 to 300 kilometers per
hour.

"The change from piston engines to jet engines was a real technological revolution in aviation.

"Modern jet technology is great and many sided. Scientists and designers have created many different types of jet engines.

"The most widely used jet engines in aviation at present are air-jet engines with a turbocompressor — the so-called turbojet engines. These engines are most effective for flight with speeds from 800 to 2000 kilometers per hour, when it masters altitudes over 40 to 50 kilometers, the only engine capable of ensuring flights of aircraft in these rarefied layers of the atmosphere will be the liquid-jet engine, or, in other words, the rocket engine.

"The rocket engine is the only engine known at the present time capable of operating not only in the greatly rarefied layers of the atmosphere, but also in airless cosmic space.

"Calculations show that its efficiency grows with increase in flight velocity, attaining a maximum when the velocity is of the order of 10,000 kilometers per hour and remaining very high at even greater speeds.

"Soviet scientist K. E. Tsiolkovskii mathematically investigated the flight of a rocket and derived the famous equation of its motion. Tsiolkovskii's equation shows that theoretically the rocket does not have limits on flight velocity. But to obtain great velocities a rocket must have a large relative supply of fuel and the exhaust velocity of the products of fuel combustion from the rocket nozzle must be very great.

"Calculations according to Tsiolkovskii's formula show that if, for example, the fuel weight amounts to 90% of the total weight of a rocket, then when the velocity of the exhaust gases is 4000 meters per second, the rocket, moving in airless space, can attain a flight velocity equal to 9200 meters per second, or more than 33,000 kilometers per hour.

"Hundreds of scientists and inventors in many countries of the world followed the path indicated by Tsiolkovskii. And, finally, came the long-awaited day of man's first flight in an apparatus with a liquid-jet engine (LJE). This flight was performed in our country. Soviet pilot V. P. Fedorov was at the controls of the airplane with LJE. The airplane was a glider in which was installed a liquid-jet engine designed by Engineer L. S. Dushkin. Successful summer tests of the first experimental airplane with LJE were an important step on the way to designing a fast jet fighter.

"In 1942 an airplane designed by V. F. Bolkhovitinov was built, using the liquid-jet engine of L. S. Dushkin.  Pilot G. Ya. Bakhchiv-andzhi, who tested this airplane, ascended into the air, performed the flight brilliantly, and landed successfully.

"In the past one and one-half decades since these flights, aviation has attained very important successes in building and testing airplanes with LJE.  Effective and reliably operating liquid-jet engines have been built.  Modern aircraft liquid-jet engines with a weight of the order of 150 kilograms are capable of developing a thrust up to 3000 kilograms.  At an airplane speed of 2000 kilometers per hour such an engine develops a useful tractive power of 22,000 horsepower.  It means that for every kilogram of weight such an engine will develop 150 horsepower, that is, 75 times more than the best piston engines with air propellers, which develop only about 2 horsepower for 1 kilo-gram of weight!

"These enormous powers developed by LJE made it possible for jet airplanes to attain speeds which would have been unthinkable when utilizing piston engines.

"In the aviation literature there is information about the fact that airplanes with LJE have already achieved a flight speed of more than 2400 kilometers per hour.  In the near future one may expect even greater successes from jet airplanes.  Thus, for example, if designers of liquid-jet engines succeed in increasing the velocity of gas exhaust from the engine nozzle to 4000 meters per second, then it will be pos-sible to build an airplane with a maximum flight speed of more than 10,000 kilometers per hour.  To move with such a speed, an airplane will require an enormous expenditure of fuel.  Therefore the fuel reserves aboard the airplane will have to comprise approximately 75% of its takeoff weight.  The total weight of such an airplane will be of the order of 40 tons.

"The character of the flight of such airplanes with LJE differs es-sentially from the flight of propeller-motor aircraft.

"At the start of motion, in order to avoid excessive air resistance in the lower dense layers of the atmosphere, the rocket airplane will gain altitude.  In the rarefied layers of the atmosphere the possibili-ties of motion with unprecedented speeds for the rocket airplane will open up.  At these speeds the rocket engine will work with high effi-ciency.  Flight to gain altitude will last until all the fuel is spent, in a number of cases; after this, motorless flight will begin.  Owing to the fact that at the moment the engines are switched off the air-plane will gain great altitude and speed, it will be able by further motion to travel enormous distances — several thousand kilometers.

"Flights in such jet airplanes will be of great significance for developing economic and cultural communications between cities of our immense country. At the same time they are a threshold to flights in airless cosmic space. Therefore, we can with complete justification say that the road to the realization of the majestic problems of astronautics lies in the all-out development and strengthening of our Air Force and our remarkable jet aviation."

### MAN IN COSMIC SPACE

Among the enthusiasts of astronautics there is a group of people whose specialty is far from the exact mathematical sciences and from technology. These are the physicians. They are united in a special Scientific-Technological Committee on Biology of Space Flight. The chairman of this committee, A. D. Seryapin, described what man will encounter in cosmic space.

"The previous comrades, speaking about the possibilities of cosmic travels, considered only the technological side of the question. Meanwhile, the biological problems play no lesser role here. Will man be able to visit the neighboring planets? Will he be able to live under the conditions of cosmic space? What measures must he take for his protection in flight? Modern medicine cannot as yet answer all these questions.

"Under terrestrial conditions man is subjected to the action of certain factors to which he has grown accustomed and has adapted himself in the course of his evolutionary development. Among these factors are terrestrial gravity, the rotation of the earth, the definite pressure of atmospheric gases, with a partial pressure of oxygen of 159 millimeters of mercury, and solar radiation.

"In flights in modern airplanes, even in the region of the stratosphere, the influence of certain of these factors changes sharply and, moreover, there arises a number of new factors specific only for the work of the pilot.

"Thus, for example, in the ascent to an altitude of 12,000 meters, where the barometric pressure is less than 150 millimeters of mercury, even the substitution of air by pure oxygen does not protect man from oxygen hunger. Flights above 12,000 meters can be performed only in a hermetically sealed cabin.

"In flights in interplanetary space, man will encounter a number of completely new factors. We can take into account and foresee only some of them today. To them belong the absence of the atmosphere, which under ordinary conditions ensures man with air for breathing and protects him against the effect of cosmic and harmful components of solar radiation, a decrease in force of gravity, an overloading created by the effect of accelerations in flight, etc.

"The task of ensuring the crew of the cosmic ship with air necessary for breathing must be solved at the expense of the reserves of liquid oxygen on board the ship, one liter of which in the process of evaporation transforms into 789 liters of gas. It will also be necessary to perform a chemical regeneration of the air in the cabin.

"There are propositions to utilize green plants for this purpose. One square meter of surface of the leaf of a gourd illuminated by the sun produces the same amount of oxygen as is required by two men during moderate work, and one square meter of surface of algae manufactures an amount of oxygen sufficient for one man. This method of air regeneration will require a peculiar construction of the ship because plants require much free area and light, without even speaking about a number of other conditions of their optimal growth.

"The second important factor which a crew may encounter in interplanetary space is the effect of solar and cosmic radiation. While the first does not even represent a serious danger because the skin of the ship offers complete protection against its harmful components, cosmic radiation may prove to be dangerous.

"The biological effect of cosmic radiation on the human organism has been studied very little. Work in this direction is the most important task for biologists.

"Nevertheless, one can hope that modern technology will find possibilities for protecting man from the effects of both primary and secondary radiation arising from the action of primary radiation on the air, jacket of the space ship, etc.

"Very important, but little studied, is the influence of the decrease in weight or complete weightlessness on the human organism. The complexity of study of this problem consists in the fact that to create even partial loss of weight under terrestrial conditions is extremely difficult.

"Recently, appropriate experiments were carried out on animals. The state of weightlessness was created in the 'free' fall of a rocket from an altitude of 149 kilometers to its entry into the dense layers of the atmosphere.

"Monkeys and mice were utilized as experimental animals. Monkeys were immobilized in a stretched position on mattresses or foam rubber. Mice were placed into a two-section cylindrical drum with a smooth surface. The experiments yielded very encouraging results.

During the decrease in the force of gravity, which lasted two to three minutes, no significant disorders of the cardio-vascular and respiratory systems of the monkeys were noted. The behavior of the mice during the two to three minute decrease in the force of gravity also indicated that no damage occurred to any organs. Apparently, living organisms can withstand a state of weightlessness for an even longer period of time.

"The effect of overloads on the human organism is not a less important problem during flight in cosmic space. Overloads are encountered while the cosmic ship is gaining velocity, changing direction of flight, and decelerating when landing. These overloads will be considerable, both in magnitude and in duration of their action.

"It has been proved that certain kinds of overload acting, for example, from the chest to the back can attain an eighty-fold increase without damage to the human organism.

"Such are the basic factors which man will encounter during flight into cosmic space. Their detailed study will still require very considerable efforts of biologists and physicians. One thing is certain: Soviet medicine in cooperation with Soviet technology will ensure safe conditions for man's life in a cosmic ship, and the time will come when flight from planet to planet will be just as safe from the medical point of view as flight from Moscow to Leningrad aboard a passenger airplane."

### "SUBMERGED ROCKS" ON THE ROUTES OF COSMIC SHIPS

A member of the Scientific-Technological Committee on Astronomical and Physical Problems, K. P. Stanyukovich, discussed the dangers that the "submerged rocks" on the routes of cosmic ships represent.

"I do not agree completely with A. D. Seryapin and with all who consider the realization of cosmic flights as a very simple affair. Many obstacles may arise in the way of future astronauts who undoubtedly will soon rush into the black abyss of cosmic space. Some of them we cannot even now imagine. It is entirely unclear, for example, how the influence of the magnetic fields of the universe, which develop parasitic eddy currents in the metallic body of an interplanetary rocket, will affect the velocity of the rocket and the precision of maintaining its assigned course. But I shall dwell on only one of these dangers, the most obvious at the present time — the possibility of collision of the cosmic ship with a meteor.

"In the space around the sun in which our cosmic ships will travel at first, there is, in addition to large celestial bodies, the planets, an enormous quantity of small ones: asteroids, comets, and meteors. At first glance, the population density of these bodies in space is small — a meteor with a mass of 1 gram is located 100 kilometers from another meteor of the same mass. But a cosmic ship with an external surface of 100 square meters will collide with such a meteor every few months of its flight. What will such a meeting mean for a cosmic ship?

"It is known that 1 gram of matter flying with a velocity of 3 to 4 kilometers per second explodes like a gram of TNT when stopped instantaneously. With an increase of initial velocity, the explosive effect increases correspondingly. Meteors move in cosmic space with velocities of 20 to 50 kilometers per second. Upon collision with such a meteor, a very high pressure develops at the point of collision — of the order of 100,000,000 atmospheres. Under such pressures a metal behaves like a liquid and even like a gas. Steel armor one meter thick cannot retard a meteor with a weight of 10 grams!

"For protection against meteors it will be expedient to make the wall of the cosmic ship double. The explosion wave resulting from the impact of a meteor against the first wall, having passed through the air space and the second wall, can be yet sufficiently strong inside the ship so as to make the presence of man impossible there. Evidently, it will be expedient to create a vacuum in the space between the walls. But in no case should one consider this problem as solved.

"Taking into account the danger of meteors, one must look at the problem of an artificial satellite of the earth in a new way.

"Semiscientific articles about the artificial satellite are frequently published in various American magazines. The creation of such a satellite is necessary for the atomic bombing of terrestrial objects, asserts *Collier's* magazine in an article by Wernher von Braun, one of the creators of the V-2.

"It is possible, although difficult, to create such a satellite. But it will be considerably easier to bring it down than to build it. Moreover, in my opinion, meteors will destroy it periodically, if only partially, once in several years.

"I have talked about small meteors. Larger meteors with weights from several kilograms to hundreds of tons are encountered quite rarely. Encountering these meteors is considerably less probable, but one should not forget about this danger. At present it is difficult to point out measures of fighting these meteors other than their early detection and a skillful maneuvering of the ship.

"Sailing on the sea and flying in the air entail their own dangers —

reefs, air pockets, unfavorable meteorological conditions. A ship in port and an airplane at the airfield frequently wait for good weather for sailing and for flying. For cosmic flights, also, a suitable 'weather service' must be created which would follow the distribution of meteor streams and accumulations in space and issue forecasts of 'flying' and 'nonflying' 'weather in the cosmos.'

"I want to express the hope that flight to the moon of a rocket with a crew can take place. But it is somewhat premature to speak about flights to other planets at this time. One must first learn how to cope with the dangers from meteors."

### RADIO-CONTROLLED ROCKETS

The speech of the Chairman of the Scientific-Technological Committee on Radio Telecontrol, Yu. S. Khlebtsevitch, opened new prospects for the realization of cosmic flights in the near future. "Radio-controlled rockets will open the way for man into the cosmos," he said.

"I shall recall two historical dates connected with two very great discoveries.

"The first date is May 7, 1895. Alexander Stepanovich Popov, at the session of the Physical Section of the Russian Physico-Chemical Society, demonstrated his storm indicator — a receiver for registering electromagnetic waves generated in thunder discharges. This day is celebrated as the birthday of radio.

"The second date is 1903. Konstantin Eduardovich Tsiolkovskii published his work 'Investigation of World Spaces by Reactive Instruments.' From this time began the development of problems connected with flights into cosmic space.

"Neither Russian scientists guessed how closely these new fields of technology would be connected with each other in the future.

"The late Academician N. D. Zelinskii said that a new discovery is often made at present at the junction of several sciences. It is about the new discovery that radiotechnology, automatics and telemechanics, in their utilization for the solution of space flight problems, give rise to what I shall discuss in my talk.

"Of course, Professor Stanyukovich, with good reason, dwelled on those difficulties and dangers which man may encounter in his flights in cosmic space. And, of course, these difficulties and dangers are so multiform that if we should begin at once to design rockets for flights within the limits of the earth or for a manned flight to the moon, then we indeed would put off for a long time the realization of flights of such rockets. For before sending man on a cosmic flight, it is necessary to obtain many data about the cosmic flight and about the physical conditions existing on other planets. Indeed, only on the basis of these data will it be possible to ensure the safety of takeoff, flight, and landing for the life of the rocket passengers dispatched to investigate other planets. How then to obtain this lacking data?

"Radar and radiotechnology, television, automatics and telemechanics will prepare scientific data for flights of passenger cosmic ships of the future. They will make it possible in a new way to approach the realization of the first flights of cosmic rockets and considerably advance the dates of realization of rocket flights to the nearest planets.

"Already today the achievements of these branches of technology make it possible to realize cosmic rockets which are unmanned. To control these rockets — their takeoff and behavior in flight — will be possible by radio from the earth by means of automatic instruments. It is also by radio that automatic equipment will transmit to the earth all data obtained by instruments in cosmic space.

"After obtaining all the necessary data by means of many automatically radio-controlled rockets, man himself will be able to perform flight to the moon and the planets of the solar system and will be assured of the possibility of returning to his native planet —earth.

"I imagine that even the first flights of cosmic rockets within the boundaries of the earth, for example, such as that from Moscow to Peking, at first will also be performed by means of radio-controlled unmanned rockets.

"Cosmic rockets intended for flights within the limits of the earth, as is known, will fly on elliptical trajectories.

"Mathematical analysis of rocket flight trajectories shows that in order to attain the assigned point of landing, it is necessary to strictly maintain the magnitude of the calculated final velocity in the takeoff segment. For an error of 1% in magnitude of final takeoff velocity in flights within the limits of the earth, a cosmic rocket will reach the assigned point of landing with an error of more than 2% of the flight distance. In other words, a cosmic rocket, having made an error of 1% in the final takeoff velocity, will land in the region of Peking with an error of more than 100 kilometers. Takeoff and landing last only a few tens of seconds. From this it follows that control of a cosmic rocket without special automatic equipment is impossible. During the few seconds of takeoff and landing, the astronaut will not have time to take his bearings correctly.

"Therefore, for takeoff and for landing of such rockets, automatically operating instruments and equipment must be developed for control of flight and transmission of the corresponding control commands.

"Science and technology of space flights, having passed through this stage of development, can then pass on to the mastering of rocket flights, even to the moon. Although at the time manned flights of cosmic rockets within the confines of the earth will not be a novelty, the first rocket on the Moscow-to-moon route also will be automatically controlled by radio. A special radar station constantly computing the coordinates of the rocket in space will follow its flight. As soon as substantial deviation of the actual rocket flight trajectory from the computed one is detected, radio signals will be transmitted from the earth to act upon the control instruments of the rocket.

"As the rocket approaches the moon there will occur the most crucial moment of the flight — the moment of the automatic landing on the surface of the moon.

"At this time a superpowerful terrestrial radar station, whose gigantic parabolic antenna is aimed at the moon, will come into operation.

"Altimeters aboard the rocket receive the short impulses of this radar reflected from the moon's surface. They determine the distance between the rocket and the lunar surface by measuring the interval of time between the moment of flight of the radiated impulse past the rocket and receiving the radioecho reflected from the moon. The automatic landing device aboard rocket, utilizing the data of the lunar altimeter, at the appropriate time turns the rocket with its tail section to the moon and, according to a special program, guides its jet engine in the regime of braking. Finally, the rocket reaches the goal of its journey and lands on the lunar surface.

"The rocket radio transmitter reports this portentous event from the moon to a large radio audience in the Soviet Union. There follows the routine work of discovering the secrets of the eternal satellite of the earth.

"From the cosmic rocket is separated a small tankette which, obeying the radio commands transmitted from the earth, begins its journey on the lunar surface. Above the tankette on the control rod is located a transmitting television camera. By means of this camera, scientists will be able to inspect structural details of the lunar surface, to select the path of safe motion of the tankette. Aboard the tankette are placed special measuring instruments permitting scientists on the earth to obtain all the necessary data on the properties of the lunar atmosphere and its surface. The image in the television camera and the data obtained by the instruments will be transmitted by radio to the earth.

"Very much work is still required, of course, for the solution of all these tasks. But at present radiotechnology, automatics, and telemechanics have already reached such a state that it is possible to solve these tasks.

"The apparatus of radiotelecontrol and radio communication can stand considerably greater accelerations and greater drops of temperature and pressure than man; it does not need many of the conditions which man needs for his normal life. All this considerably simplifies the solution of the problem of sending the first rockets to the moon and speeds up the date of the flight of a manned cosmic ship."

In conclusion, A. A. Shternfel'd, our eldest promoter of astronautics, Laureate of the International Encouragement Prize in Astronautics, Chairman of the Scientific-Technological Committee in Cosmic Navigation, took the floor. He dwelt on the question of routes of cosmic ships and navigational periods. (See *Tekhnika-Molodezhi*, No. 5, 1952, No. 2, 1953, and No. 1, 1954.) Summarizing the speeches of his comrades in the Astronautics Section, he said:

"In conclusion it should be pointed out that authors of science-fiction literature are far ahead of the practical activity of our section. Not only fantasists but also scientists have placed themselves behind the steering wheel of a magic dream boat and visited the moon, Mars, and the solar systems of remote galaxies. Quite recently, in March of this year, while reading an article of Academician Fesenkov, I was present, together with many readers of the magazine, at the birthday of 'Star Worlds.'

"But, today, after this talk, I can state that soon the strenuous work of engineers, physicians, and scientists of various specialties will be crowned by building the first cosmic ship. Following the dream, it will fly out into the black abyss of the cosmos, feeling the space around it with its invisible sensitive radar fingers.

"I am convinced that this will happen before the eyes of the present generation. Man will be among the first creatures whose leaden soles will leave their traces on the soil of the moon covered by eternal dust. The daily record of which this magazine will publish. I am convinced that these actual, dry, cursory records will be more fascinating, interesting, and fantastic than the boldest fantasies that have been penned by man who has never left the earth." (*Tekhnika-Molodezhi*, July, 1954.)

# Part Two
# PROBLEMS OF ASTRONAUTICS

# 4.  Problems of Interplanetary Flight

*K. Stanyukovich*

The dream about the possibility of flight to the moon and the planets was conceived in deep antiquity.  In numerous science-fiction stories and novels, writers of different times and nationalities have dispatched by various means their heroes now to the moon, now to Mars, and then again to Venus, or even to more distant planets of the solar system, and sometimes even beyond its limits.  The Russian revolutionist, Kibal'chich, who was executed by the Czarist government, proposed the world's first project of the cosmic apparatus.

The famous Russian scientist K. E. Tsiolkovskii developed a truly scientific project of the cosmic-rocket dirigible and the theory of its flight.  He proposed to use for this purpose an engine which now is known as the rocket.  In the forward part of the cosmic rocket were located liquid oxygen at a low temperature and some liquid hydrocarbon fuels.  By mixing oxygen and fuel in a certain ratio and igniting them, it is possible to obtain an intense combustion reaction.  As a result of this, the products of combustion will begin to move with great speed through the so-called nozzle, and the jet ship will start to move in a direction opposite to that of the exhaust gases.

K. E. Tsiolkovskii not only created the project of the rocket ship, but also laid down the principles of the theory of its motion.  He developed the fundamental formula which shows how the speed of the cosmic rocket can increase as its fuel gradually burns away, that is, as its mass decreases.  Tsiolkovskii showed for the first time that in order to overcome the force of earth's gravity, it was necessary to use precisely the principle of reactive motion, because only in such a way would it be possible to ensure so great a rocket velocity — 11.2 kilometers per second, which corresponds to 40,000 kilometers per hour — and to obtain a smooth increase in velocity.

The ideas of Tsiolkovskii have undergone great development, especially in the Soviet Union.  Thus, for instance, in 1929, Yu. V. Kondratyuk published a paper in which he proposed to utilize the metallic parts of a rocket as fuel.  Independently of him, the noted

Soviet engineer, F. A. Tsander, worked out the project of a cosmic rocket. At first the apparatus had to be an airplane, moving within the limits of the earth's atmosphere and attaining a cosmic velocity. Afterwards, according to Tsander's idea, the metallic supporting parts of the airplane must be pulled inside of the main body of the rocket and utilized as fuel. For this purpose, Tsander proposed to make these parts of the rocket of aluminum.

Soviet engineers, M. K. Tikhonravov, Yu. A. Pobedonostsev, I. A. Merkulov, and others, by their theoretical and experimental research, also helped progress in this direction. As far back as 1932, the first firing of a liquid-fueled rocket built by M. K. Tikhonravov took place in the Soviet Union.[1]

The construction of the interplanetary rocket involves tremendous difficulties. But there is no doubt that all these tasks will be successfully solved by science and technology. After all, the problems of the construction of rockets which rise to considerable height and which fly great distances already are solved. Such rockets were used for military purposes at the end of the Second World War. These were rockets operating on liquid fuel consisting of liquid oxygen and 75% ethyl alcohol. Total flight weight of the rocket, including a 750 kilogram explosive charge, amounted to almost 13 tons. The length of the rocket was 14 meters; maximum diameter of the body, 1.65 meters; diameter of empennage, 3.57 meters. This rocket rose to an altitude of more than 80 kilometers and developed a velocity of more than 1.5 kilometers per second. Its flight range was 300 kilometers.[2] At present, liquid-fueled rockets of such type, which are used to sound the upper layers of the atmosphere, attain heights of several hundred kilometers. Rockets intended for military purposes, however, can cover far greater distances than rockets of the Second World War period.

The thrust developed by a rocket depends on the velocity of discharge of the combustion products through the nozzle; that is, the thrust is proportional to this velocity. Moreover the exhaust velocity of the combustion products increases with an increase in combustion temperature, approximately as the square root of the magnitude of the temperature. Therefore, in order to create the greatest thrust, it is necessary to select the most "caloric" fuels that will inevitably produce a high temperature of the order of several thousand degrees in the combustion chamber. The task of the cooling and the thermal insulation of the "hot" aggregates of the rocket from its other parts is very complicated and difficult. These difficulties increase

with the increase in the dimensions of a rocket.[3]   And it is precisely
the dimensions of a rocket which must be increased in order to reach
still greater altitudes.

The building of an engine which will operate a long time under stable
conditions of combustion is an extraordinarily complicated task.   This
mainly explains why we do not yet have an interplanetary rocket, although the principles of its operation are sufficiently well known.   A
way out of this situation can be in utilizing the entire reserve of fuel
on a small segment of the path without striving for lengthy operation
of the engine — that is, in allowing greater accelerations of the rocket.
This will aid in sharply reducing its weight.

An exceptionally interesting solution of the problem is the project
proposed by K. E. Tsiolkovskii of the so-called compound rocket,
which, in his opinion, is designed to solve the task of flight into universal space.   This rocket consists of a series of separate rockets.   As
the fuel burns out completely in them, they separate from the still unused rockets.   At the same time the one or two remaining rockets must
acquire a speed of the order 10 to 15 kilometers per second required for
flight in cosmic space.   The operation of the engine of each of the individual rockets can be of short duration and the problems of controlling and cooling their engines can be solved (and actually have already been solved) somewhat more simply than the operation of a
single engine of one large rocket.

Step by step, overcoming numerous difficulties, scientists and engineers are perfecting the construction of compound rockets.   Evidently,
after long voyages of rockets within the limits of the upper layers of
the earth's atmosphere, which practically are already possible, it will
be possible to directly design rockets for flight around the moon and
return to the earth, and only after that for flights with landing on the
moon and subsequent return to the earth.

When landing on the moon, for braking, and later when taking off
from the moon, it will be necessary to expend fuel.   Inasmuch as the
velocity required to overcome the gravity of the moon is only 2.4 kilometers per second, the consumption of fuel for these operations will be
only 10% of the fuel consumption required for overcoming the earth's
gravity.

Landing on the earth is planned to take place with no significant expenditure of fuel.   For this purpose, provision is made to install into
the last remaining rocket a glider which, upon reaching the earth's
atmosphere, must separate from the rocket.   The braking increases
as the glider penetrates the depth of the atmosphere.   As a result, its

speed at the moment of landing must not exceed conventional airplane speeds.

Computations of the trajectory of interplanetary rockets, and especially computations of the most favorable trajectories in the sense of minimum expenditure of energy, have shown that if several days are sufficient to reach the moon, then the time necessary to reach Mars and Venus is calculated in terms of months, and sometimes even in years. During such long flights there exists the danger of the rocket's colliding with meteors and cosmic dust.

According to modern data, no less than five tons of meteoric material penetrates the earth's atmosphere every day. It is considered that in the space around the earth there is, on an average, for every 50 to 100 kilometers a meteor with a weight of from one to ten thousandths of a gram. As a result, a cosmic rocket with a surface of 100 square meters, in the course of 100 hours of flight, can collide with a meteor weighing approximately one one-thousandth of a gram. With a collision speed, measured in tens of kilometers per second, this meteor can easily break through armor plating 10 millimeters thick. A collision with a 10-gram meteor is still far more dangerous for a cosmic rocket. Such a meteor is capable of knocking out of the hull of a ship up to 10 kilograms of steel plating and of breaking through a steel hull up to 100 centimeters thick. It is true that such a collision can take place on an average once in 5,000 to 10,000 hours of flight.

The greatest achievement of science — the discovery of methods of producing atomic energy — undoubtedly will exert great influence on solving the problem of interplanetary flights. The conversion of jet engines to atomic energy will be of tremendous importance in building cosmic rockets.

In nuclear reactions a stream of extraordinarily fast particles is formed which move with speeds of the order of thousands of kilometers per second. Direct utilization of the products of nuclear decay for creating reactive force is not profitable as long as their mass is very small. From elementary theorems of mechanics, it is known that for a given energy, the impulse, or, in the present case, the reactive force, is proportional to the square root of the mass of the particles or gases which flow out of the nozzle of the rocket.[4] Therefore, in order to increase the efficiency of an engine which operates on atomic energy, it is necessary to distribute the initial energy over a considerably greater mass (inertial mass), the weight of which must correspond, in order of magnitude, to the weight of the rocket itself. A rough lay-out of a rocket with an atomic engine is shown on the figure reproduced here.

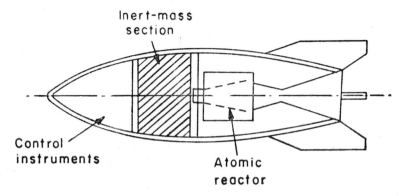

The inertial mass, for which a heavy [5] gas can be used, passes through an atomic pile, is strongly heated and is ejected from the nozzle with tremendous velocity. As a result, the velocity of the rocket's motion will be sufficient to overcome the force of the earth's gravity.

A similar redistribution of energy is possible in future atomic engines, in which the initial nuclear energy can be converted into thermal energy and thereby into kinetic energy of the gas stream flowing out of the nozzle. By decreasing the weight of the inertial masses, it is possible to increase the velocity of the rocket at lower efficiency.

In view of the small weight of "nuclear fuel," the time of operation of an atomic jet engine can be many times greater than that of a conventional engine. Because of the indicated characteristics of an atomic engine, one has to revise the assumptions concerning the most advantageous trajectories (from the point of view of economical utilization of fuel). The time required for a flight from one planet to another will be sharply reduced and the danger of meteoric collisions will be lessened.

K. E. Tsiolkovskii already thought and wrote about the possibility of creating an artificial satellite of the earth which would travel beyond the limits of our atmosphere and serve as a scientific and technical base for interplanetary rockets. Now even this problem is passing from the field of assumptions into the field of more concrete investigations. One of the problems in creating such a satellite will also be its protection from meteoric collisions, for it must move sufficiently long around the earth and serve as a transfer from short-range terrestrial rockets to long-range rockets.

Great are the achievements of modern science and technology. Science, said the President of the USSR Academy of Sciences, A. N.

Nesmeyanov, at the session of the World Peace Council on November 27, 1953, has reached a state when it is feasible to send a stratoplane to the moon and to create an artificial satellite of the earth. Our Soviet scientists and designers, who are devoting all their strength and knowledge to the cause of the further progress and prosperity of our Motherland, have made an enormous contribution to the solution of the very important problem of interplanetary flights. (*Krasnaya Zvezda*, August 10, 1954. The author is identified as "Professor" and "Doctor of Technical Sciences.")

[1] In 1920 Professor R. H. Goddard, the father of American rocketry, began active work on a liquid-oxygen-gasoline rocket engine. On March 16, 1926, he succeeded in making the first short flight with a projectile using a liquid-propellant rocket motor. (See G. P. Sutton, *Rocket Propulsion Elements*, John Wiley and Sons, New York, 1949, p. 33.)

[2] These data pertain to the German V-2 rocket missile.

[3] This is not necessarily so. The difficulties depend on the type of cooling employed in the rocket design.

[4] In this sentence by "impulse" is meant "total impulse," which is the product of the reactive force and the time the force acts, and not "specific impulse," which is the total impulse divided by the weight of the rocket propellant charge. The specific impulse, alternatively defined as the jet exhaust-gas velocity divided by the acceleration of gravity, is inversely proportional to the square root of the mass of the gases which flow out of the rocket nozzle.

[5] The use of the word "heavy" (*tyazhelii*) in this sentence is ill-chosen. For design purposes, it is desirable to have the working medium as dense as possible before it passes through the reactor and as light as possible when it passes through the rocket nozzle. In practice, hydrogen, the lightest of the elements, is generally considered the ultimate in rocket propellants in spite of the above requirements.

# 5. Problems of Cosmic Flight

*A. A. Shternfel'd*

The progress of modern rocket technology gives a basis for asserting that we are on the threshold of realizing cosmic flight. The increases in the velocity of flow of gases from the rocket and in the relative fuel reserve are, step by step, widening the radius of action of the rocket flying apparatus up to cosmic distances.

Already in our day astronautics has won a firm place among other sciences. On the basis of the contemporary data of this science, we can visualize how the first flights into world space, to the moon and to the planets, will proceed.

### ARTIFICIAL SATELLITES

When a rocket reaches a velocity of 7904 meters per second, it will be able to cover an arc of 170 degrees along the equator. When a rocket that has been launched horizontally develops a velocity of 7912 meters per second, it will be able to reach the antipodes. This small difference in the velocity will not just lengthen the radius of action of a rocket by more than 1000 kilometers — having reached its goal, the rocket will not fall to the earth, but will continue to revolve indefinitely around it. It will be transformed into an artificial satellite of the earth.

"Circular velocity" at the surface of a planet, or "the first astronautical velocity," is the minimum velocity at which a body no longer falls to the surface of a planet: the centrifugal force balances the force of gravity.

During the takeoff and the acceleration of the rocket to circular velocity, there will obviously be certain gravitational losses. The magnitude of these losses will depend both on the navigational methods and on the acceleration of motion. The greater the increase in speed, the smaller are the losses. The acceleration of motion can be taken to be equal to 40 meters per second per second. Calculation shows that if during such an acceleration one keeps the motion of the rocket constantly in a horizontal direction, then the gravitational losses of velocity will comprise only 3%, and the circular velocity will be attained after 3 minutes, 14 seconds.

In order to become practically free from the braking motion of air resistance, it is necessary to place the artificial satellite outside the limits of any dense atmosphere, that is, at an altitude of not less than 200 kilometers. At such an altitude, deviation of the artificial satellite from a given orbit, caused by the resistance of the medium, is insignificant and is easy to correct by switching on a miniature rocket engine from time to time.

Taking into consideration the contemporary state of astronautics, one should assume that the first artificial satellites will be automats which will send to the earth various instrument readings by means of radio signals. After these automatic "scouts," rockets with animals will follow. Only after the influence of cosmic flight on the living organism has been ascertained will a manned rocket fly into the cosmos.

Flight from the earth to an artificial satellite is a rather complicated task; it is somewhat like shooting at a target moving with an enormous velocity. But here there are certain peculiarities predetermining the success of the task: We know precisely the path of the artificial satellite, the velocity with which it moves, its location at any given moment. Thus we can calculate in advance the time of takeoff, determine the trajectory of the ship on the segment along which the rocket engines will operate (the so-called active segment), plot the program of accelerations and velocities, and, finally, foresee at which point in space the rocket must meet the artificial earth satellite.

It is most convenient that the takeoff should be accomplished always along the same trajectory. This is possible when the artificial satellite passes periodically over the takeoff site. And since the orbital plane of the artificial satellite does not change its position relative to the stars, this will take place, for example, when during a sidereal day a satellite makes a whole number of revolutions around the earth.[1]

Let us assume, for instance, that an artificial satellite makes 16 revolutions around the earth in one sidereal day. For this it must move in a circle at an altitude of 265 kilometers above the earth, performing a complete revolution in 90 sidereal minutes.

Thus, during the time that the earth makes one revolution around its axis relative to the stars, the artificial satellite will have just returned to the region over which it had already flown 24 hours ago.

From the altitude of such a flying laboratory, the earth will appear to an observer as an enormous disk occupying the greater part of the firmament — it will be seen as a sort of "little cap" of our planet with a diameter of 3700 kilometers. This "little cap" will move all the time. During a complete revolution of the satellite, the earth will make one-sixteenth of a revolution around its own axis, and the "little cap" will move 2500 kilometers along the equator; thus the whole terrestrial globe floats before the eyes of the observer. In prism binoculars with a 15-fold magnification, objects measuring 5 meters will be seen from there. Because of the headlong motion of the artificial satellite, however, the observations of the terrestrial surface will be hampered.

From this point of view, a satellite from which our planet would seem immobile would be most convenient as a flying laboratory; this would considerably facilitate observations.

Such a satellite would have the added advantage that it would be easier for its crew to communicate with the earth by means of directed radio waves or light signals. Finally, a flight to it could be accomplished at any time without waiting for a suitable location of the artificial satellite relative to the takeoff point.

To construct such an "immobile" celestial body is quite possible. What conditions must it satisfy?

Artificial satellites naturally obey the same laws of celestial mechanics that other celestial bodies obey. Therefore, the distance of the artificial satellite from the center of the earth predetermines the velocity of its motion and, thereby, its period of revolution around the earth.

This period increases with altitude because of the increase in the size of the satellite's orbit and the decreases in its velocity. An artificial satellite, soaring at an altitude of 265 kilometers, flies around the earth in 1½ hours; whereas the moon, which is almost 400,000 kilometers from the earth, will require about four weeks for this. Evidently, there is also a particular distance at which rotation of a satellite will be accomplished in exactly one day. It will take place at a distance of 35,800 kilometers from the surface of the earth.

Let a satellite set at such an altitude be over the equator, and let it move in the same direction as the earth. Then it will be immobile with respect to a terrestrial observer. From such a satellite the visible diameter of our planet will be approximately forty times greater than the diameter of the moon visible from the earth, which, as we know, subtends an angle of about ½ degree.

If the orbit of the satellite does not lie in the plane of the equator, then the satellite revolving at the specified distance (35,800 kilometers) will be seen daily from different points of the earth in a certain direction at the same time.

Artificial satellites can be located so that they, in turn, will fly around the entire globe or will fly only above certain territories. Simple reasoning shows that it is impossible to build an artificial satellite that will fly over territory of only one country, except when the equator passes through that country.

Artificial satellites can be useful for meteorological observations, in particular, for the investigation of the distribution and character of the cloud cover of the earth; for observations on the movement of ice floes in the Arctic and Antarctic, and also in the adjacent seas and parts of the oceans; for warning about the origin of forest fires in sparsely populated regions; and as relay stations for short-wave broadcasts, television for example, and other purposes.

Certain investigators have proposed to establish on artificial satellites enormous mirrors reflecting solar rays to the earth and thus to heat and illuminate great areas of the terrestrial globe. These projects are insufficiently developed, however.

Finally, according to the idea of K. E. Tsiolkovskii, artificial satellites will be able to play a great role as intermediate stations — jumping-off places for the further penetration of man into world space.

For this purpose it would be most effective to utilize a satellite revolving above the torrid zone; only, in this case, the direction of motion of the cosmic ship leaving an intermediate station may be practically parallel with the direction of motion of the earth in its orbit, which is very important for takeoff into world space.

For the realization of cosmic flights, the mobility of the intermediate station is its main advantage. Because of this, in landing on the station, a rocket preserves its velocity, which it uses for the takeoff on its further journey. Thus, for example, leaving the artificial satellite for the moon, Venus, or Mars, the rocket must develop a velocity of only 3.1 to 3.6 kilometers per second, instead of 11.1 to 11.6 kilometers per second for takeoff from the surface of the earth.

In certain variations of cosmic ship design, an interplanetary station can also be of use during the return to earth. In this case, the crew will transfer to a cosmic glider on which it will make its landing.

The air of the hermetically sealed living quarters and laboratories of the artificial satellite, possibly of somewhat different composition than that of the earth, will be conditioned. Shielding against harmful ultraviolet radiations of the sun and against cosmic rays offers no difficulties. So far it is not known, however, how to make the skin of the satellite sufficiently light and capable of protecting the crew from penetration by meteorites. The upper layers of the atmosphere can serve as partial shielding if the satellite is located sufficiently low above the surface of the earth, at such an altitude where, on the one hand, the air is already sufficiently rarefied so that it does not hinder the motion of the artificial satellite and where, on the other hand, the air is sufficiently dense for protection against the "fastest" small meteorites.

In the literature, the possibility of using the moon as an interplanetary station is often cited. The comparatively great potential of the gravitational field of the moon, however, and the remoteness of its orbit from the earth exclude such a possibility. This would have some sense only if especially high quality fuel and construction materials were found on the moon. In other words, as an intermediate interplanetary station, an artificial satellite has a number of advantages when compared with the moon.

In the first place, it can be located sufficiently close to the earth to permit making a flight with a smaller expenditure of fuel.

In the second place, the absence of the artificial satellite's own field of gravity will permit economizing the fuel required to make the landing on the moon and the subsequent takeoff from its surface.

The first artificial satellites apparently will fly around the earth in a circle at an altitude of 200 to 300 kilometers. Later on, satellites will make flights in elliptic orbits. Their perigee (that is, the point closest to the earth) distance will evidently remain at the same level, while the apogee distance will gradually increase. If in the first stage, raising the "ceiling" of the artificial satellite will encounter great difficulties, then as the power of the rockets is increased this task will be rendered easier and easier. Indeed, increasing the initial velocity at the earth's surface, for example, from 7.9 to 10 kilometers per second will raise this ceiling by 3 equatorial radii, while a further increase of 1 kilometer per second in this velocity will result in raising the "ceiling" by 25 earth radii.

### FLIGHT TO THE MOON AND TO THE PLANETS

Still another little step — increasing the velocity by 0.1 kilometer per second — and the moon will be within the radius of attainability of a cosmic ship (Figure 1). If one launches on the earth a rocket with such a velocity, then it will ascend only 0.5 kilometer. If such an experiment, however, is repeated from aboard a ship that has just

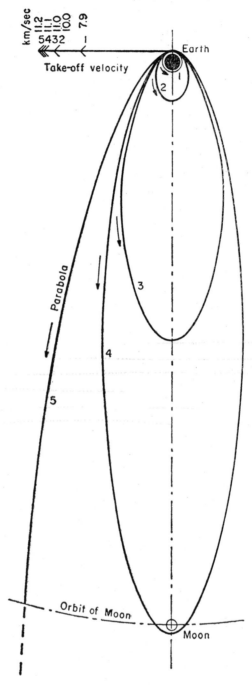

Figure 1. Variation of orbit of artificial
satellite with initial velocity.

64

taken off with a velocity of 11 kilometers per second, then the rocket will outstrip the ship by 200,000 kilometers.

Another increase of 0.1 kilometer per second in the takeoff velocity of the cosmic rocket will decrease the duration of the earth-to-moon flight from five to two days.

Although 0.1 kilometer per second is less than 1% of the initial velocity of the rocket, this is sufficient to increase the velocity of the rocket in crossing the lunar orbit approximately 700% (from 0.18 to 1.45 kilometers per second).

In the above cases we disregarded the influence of the gravitational field of the moon; since the mass of the moon is 81.3 times smaller than the mass of the earth, the perturbing effect of the moon's field of gravity will be negligible. The study of the influence of this factor is a rather complicated and laborious matter. Therefore, we shall resort to certain simplifications.

Let us assume that the earth and the moon are stationary with respect to each other and that the flight is taking place along the shortest straight line. At the same time, it is sufficient to impart to a space ship such a velocity as would permit it to fly a little farther than the neutral point between the two celestial bodies, since at that point the gravitational forces of the earth and the moon are equal in magnitude and opposite in direction. Having passed the neutral point, a body will continue to move in the direction of the moon under the influence of its attraction.

Calculations show that in this case, during the flight of a ship from the earth to the moon, the work performed by the field of gravity of the moon is extremely small in comparison with the work spent in overcoming the field of gravity of the earth; the ratio is less than 1/500 (in the case of the return, the analogous value for the field of gravity of the earth is approximately 23 times larger). At the same time the velocity that the ship develops while landing on the moon amounts to 2.27 kilometers per second. It is necessary to impart such a velocity to the ship during its takeoff from the surface of the moon to the earth.

In its flight to the moon, the ship cannot free itself completely from the earth's gravitational field, since on the orbit of the moon, the earth's attraction is still quite appreciable; in flight to the planets, however, in view of their remoteness, such freedom is a necessary condition.

In practice, it is possible to calculate that near a planet or satellite only the gravitational force of the given celestial body acts on the ship, but in interplanetary space, that is, along almost its entire route, only the gravitational force of the sun acts on the ship.

The radius of the sphere of attraction of the earth — i.e., the space where its attraction is stronger than that of the sun — does not exceed six one-thousandths of the distance separating the earth from the sun. The spheres of attraction of Mars, Venus, Mercury, and all the satellites are considerably smaller. This explains precisely why cosmic ships along almost their entire route are subject only to the force of attraction of our sun in interplanetary space.

What, then, is the minimum initial velocity required for a catapulted body to completely overcome the attraction of the earth, that is, to fly into interplanetary space?

Mathematical calculation shows that the work necessary for moving a body from the surface of a planet to infinity is equal to the work which would be necessary to raise a body to an altitude equal to the radius of the planet, under the condition that the intensity of gravity does not change as the body draws away from the center of the planet. In order to make it possible for any body to fly completely away from the surface of a planet, it is necessary to impart to it on the surface of the planet such a velocity that its kinetic energy will be numerically equal to the work just indicated; this velocity will be 41.42% greater than the circular velocity. A body possessing such a velocity will, in general, move to infinity along a parabola; therefore, this velocity is called parabolic; but when a body is thrown strictly vertically upwards, it will move along a straight line. Both circular and parabolic velocities have different magnitudes for different points on the earth. If we disregard the influence of the rotation of our planet, then the parabolic velocity is equal to 11.189 kilometers per second for the points on the earth's equator.

The takeoff velocity of a cosmic ship, of course, is added to the peripheral velocity of rotation of a planet around its own axis. At the terrestrial equator the peripheral velocity is equal to 465 meters per second. Therefore, the direction of takeoff must be chosen so as to coincide with the direction of the earth's rotation. In this case, to remove a body to infinity, it is sufficient to impart to it a velocity of only 10.724 kilometers per second.

The parabolic velocity on Mercury, Venus, Mars, and Pluto is smaller than that on the earth; whereas on the giant planets it is considerably greater.

If a velocity greater than the circular velocity but less than the parabolic is imparted to a body, it will then move in an elliptic orbit.

In the cited calculations it is assumed that the body is under the influence of the force of gravity of the earth alone. A cosmic ship, however, leaving the earth will be subjected simultaneously to the attraction of the earth and that of the sun. Therefore, for a body to be able to travel beyond the limits of our solar system, a velocity greater than the parabolic must be imparted to it. We shall call this velocity the escape velocity. The magnitude of the escape velocity depends on its direction; it will have its smallest value, equal to 16.662 kilometers per second, when the direction of the velocity coincides with the direction of the earth's motion around the sun.

How is this velocity computed?

Since the earth moves around the sun with a velocity of 29.766 kilometers per second and the parabolic velocity relative to the sun is equal to $29.766 \sqrt{2} = 42.095$ kilometers per second, it would be sufficient for a space ship to acquire an "additional velocity" equal to the difference between the above-mentioned velocities, that is, $V_a = 12.329$ kilometers per second, in order to escape from the sun's gravitational field. If the mass of the ship is equal to $M$, then its kinetic energy is equal to $\frac{1}{2} M V_a^2$. On the other hand, in order to escape from the earth's gravitational field, the ship must possess a velocity $V_f = 11.189$ kilometers per second at which its kinetic energy is equal to $\frac{1}{2} M V_f^2$. Consequently, the escape velocity, $V_e$, must be of such magnitude that the kinetic energy of the ship, $\frac{1}{2} M V_e^2$, is equal to the sum of the above mentioned energies. Whence, $V_e = (V_a^2 + V_f^2)^{\frac{1}{2}} = 16.662$ kilometers per second.

Therefore, if a rocket flies from the earth with an escape velocity in the direction of its orbital motion, then it will be able not only to reach any of the outer planets, but also to completely leave the solar system. If, however, the rocket flies away with a velocity of 16,662 meters per second in a direction opposite to the earth's motion, then it will follow an ellipse with a perihelion distance equal to 0.207 astronomical units.

Knowing the orbital velocity of a planet and also the parabolic velocity on its surface, it is possible by means of a geometrical construction to determine all the remaining velocities mentioned above. Figure 2 shows how these velocities are determined for the earth. They can also be obtained for all the other planets of the solar system by an analogous construction. These are astronautical "profiles"; they not only characterize the principal astronautical velocities of a given planet, but also show to what extent the gravitational fields of the sun and of the planet itself affect these velocities.

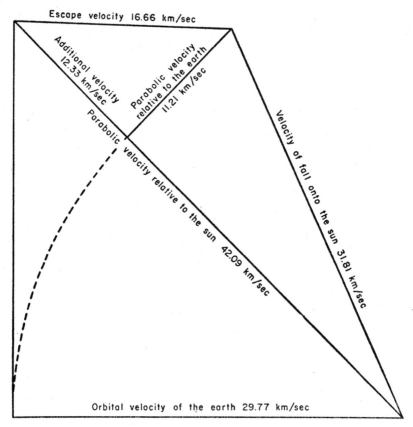

Figure 2. Relation between required velocity of motion
of cosmic ship and orbital velocity of the earth.

A ship following a semielliptic trajectory at its start from the earth
will require a minimum rate of acceleration. The velocity that must
be braked during the descent will also be a minimum.

The flight along a semiellipse is very lengthy, but it is sufficient to
slightly increase the takeoff velocity in order to considerably reduce
the duration of the journey. Thus, for example, a velocity of 5.69
kilometers per second is required for the return from Mars to the
earth along a semiellipse. The duration of the flight is then 258.9
days. If, however, one increases the velocity 12.3% and flies along
a shorter arc (Figure 3) tangent to the orbit of Mars, then the time of
flight would be reduced one and one-half times (to 172.8 days).

Another disadvantage of the semielliptic trajectory is the fact that a
small decrease in the initial velocity considerably decreases the radius

of accessibility. Thus, for example, if the take-off velocity to Mars along a semielliptic trajectory is reduced 2.3% the ship will not even fly halfway between the orbits of the earth and Mars.

Under terrestrial conditions, the faster a missile travels, the faster it will hit the target. But under cosmic flight conditions, this is not always so. It is true that the faster a ship travels in interplanetary space relative to the sun, the faster it will reach the moon, Mars and Jupiter. As far as the inner planets are concerned, however, a ship that travels in interplanetary space more slowly will reach its destination sooner.

In proceeding to Venus along a semiellipse, the flight time is 146.1

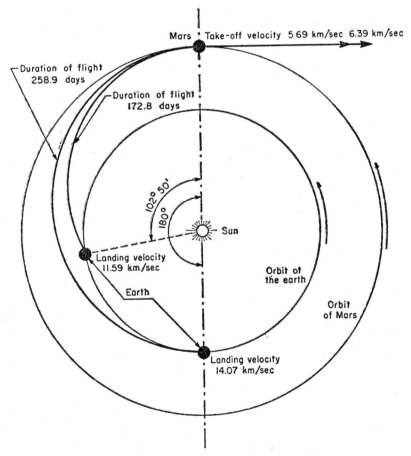

Figure 3. Dependence of duration of Mars-earth
flight on initial velocity of ship.

days (Figure 4). In this case the initial rate of travel relative to the sun in interplanetary space is equal to 27.3 kilometers per second. But, if the initial speed of the ship is reduced with respect to the sun,

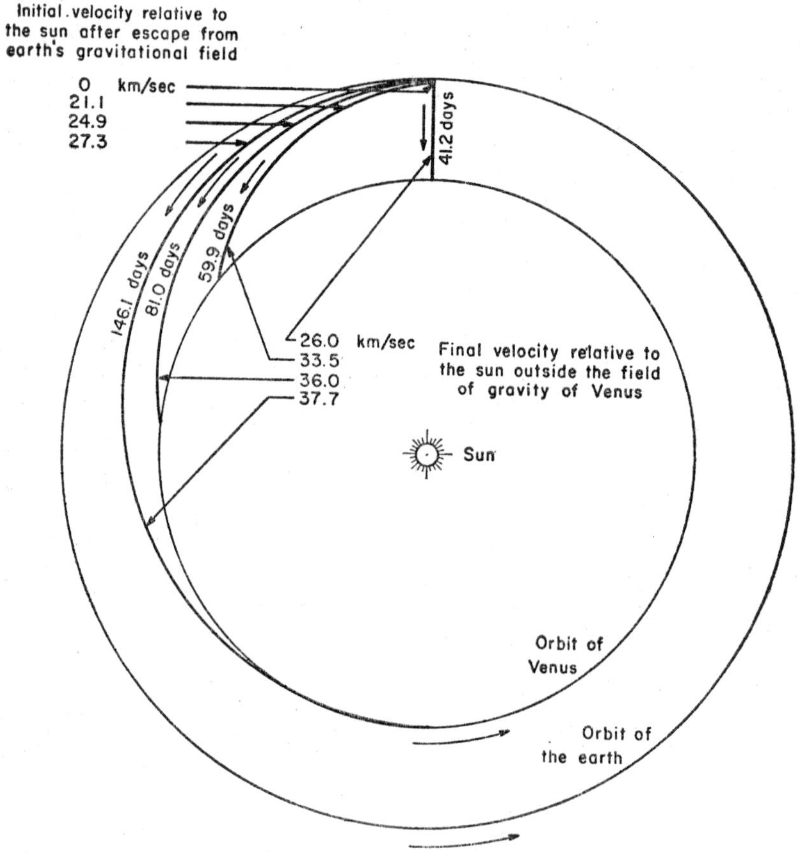

Figure 4. Dependence of duration of earth-Venus flight on initial velocity.

the ellipse described becomes more and more "flattened out." Finally, if, after the rocket escapes from the earth's gravitational field, its velocity reduces to zero, the ellipse will become a straight line; the rocket will begin to fall vertically into the sun, intersecting the orbit of Venus on its way. Simultaneously, with the shortening of the ellipse, the arc connecting the earth with Venus is also reduced. At the same time, as mathematical analysis shows, this arc reduces faster than the average velocity of the ship's motion. As a result, a paradoxical phenomenon is obtained: the smaller the ship's velocity in space with respect to the sun, the sooner it will reach its destination.

In Figure 4 we see how, as a result of reducing the initial velocity to 24.9 and 21.1 kilometers per second, the duration of flight reduces to 81.0 and 59.9 days, respectively. Here also are shown the corresponding velocities with which the ship intersects the orbit of Venus. The smallest velocity is equal to 26.0 kilometers per second. It corresponds to flight on a straight line with zero initial velocity; the duration of flight is 41.2 days.

But from the above one must not, of course, conclude that less powerful rockets are required for the fastest attainment of Venus, for example. On the contrary, the directions of the rocket takeoff and of the earth's motion are opposite and the velocity of the ship in space will be the smaller, the greater the acceleration it develops during the takeoff. And if, in the case of flight along a semiellipse, it were sufficient to reduce the velocity of the rocket with respect to the velocity of the earth by only 2.5 kilometers per second, then in flight along a straight line the velocity must be braked to 29.8 kilometers per second.

With the development of the technology of cosmic flight, the speeds of cosmic ships will increase, and, thereby, the times of flights will decrease. At the same time, during flight to the outer planets, the ellipses that the ships will follow will gradually become longer and longer until, at the aphelion, the ellipse will "break up" and become a parabola tangent to the orbit of the earth, with the sun at the focus.

We note that a ship departing from Mercury along a parabolic trajectory tangent to its orbit with an escape velocity of 20.275 kilometers per second will intersect the orbit of Venus after 23.8 days, and after another 14.3 days will reach the earth (Figure 5).

Flights with even greater velocities in parabolic orbits belong, of course, to a more distant stage in the development of astronautics, and for the present we shall not dwell on this problem.

Let us consider the remaining trajectories connecting the earth with our celestial neighbors, Venus and Mars, from the point of view of possible dates of takeoffs and landings. It is possible to divide these trajectories into three groups:

1. Elliptic and parabolic trajectories tangent to the earth's orbit and intersecting the orbit of a neighboring planet.

2. Elliptic and straight trajectories intersecting the earth's orbit and tangent to the orbit of Mars or of Venus.

3. Elliptic trajectories intersecting both orbits.

All these routes, of course, correspond to the perfectly definite dispositions of planets. On the other hand, rigidly fixed dates of the pos-

sible departures and arrivals of cosmic ships are connected with the
given configuration of the planets.

If these dates are compared and a timetable is compiled of the
possible takeoffs from the earth and from Mars (or Venus) and of
the landings on these planets, then a striking result is obtained: Be-

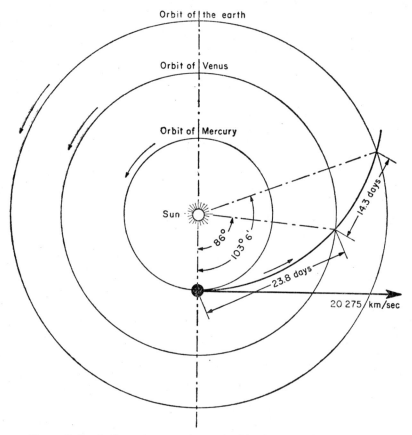

Figure 5. Parabolic trajectory of cosmic ship departing from Mercury.

tween these dates there will be intervals, "dead seasons," during
which not a single ship will be able to depart from the earth to Mars,
for instance, or to land on that planet, and, conversely, it will be impossible to take off from Mars or to land on the earth. Thus, results of calculations have shown that under such assumptions a Martian ship could not at all have reached the earth on the day and the
year of the fall of the Tungus meteorite (June 30, 1908). We know
also what we should think of all kinds of "flying saucers" from the

neighboring planets invading terrestrial space at the very height of the dead interplanetary navigational seasons.

### TAKEOFF AND LANDING OF THE COSMIC SHIP

In all the above cases it is assumed that at the takeoff the velocity is imparted to the ship instantaneously, and subsequently the flight is accomplished by inertia.

But if we maintain a constant velocity by means of a rocket engine during the entire flight, then, of course, there is no necessity for so great a rate of acceleration; in this case, the flight can be accomplished at any initial velocity.

This latter reasoning, however, is true only from a theoretical point of view. Realization of such a flight is impossible in practice because fuel expenditure would then increase to fantastic figures.

Thus, for example, in order to escape from the earth's gravitational field at a constant velocity of 850 kilometers per hour, the weight of fuel carried by a rocket ejecting gases with a velocity of 4 kilometers per second would have to exceed the net weight of the rocket by $5 \times 10^{28}$ times, and at a flight velocity of 1,800 kilometers per second, by $4 \times 10^{13}$ times.

But if during the takeoff the rocket is accelerated to a great velocity and the flight continues at the expense of the acquired kinetic energy, then a colossal economy of fuel is obtained, and construction of a space ship becomes possible.

Indeed, in order to impart a parabolic velocity to the rocket, it is sufficient for it to have a fuel supply exceeding its own weight only fifteen times (here, as before and in the following, the velocity of the gas exhaust from the rocket is assumed to be equal to 4 kilometers per second.) At the same time, it is assumed that air is absent and the necessary velocity is imparted to the ship instantaneously, that is, with an infinitely great acceleration. But in reality, the magnitude of this acceleration is restricted by the power of the engine, by the strength of the materials from which the ship is constructed, and, primarily, by the endurance of the human organism with respect to great accelerations (on the average, the acceleration endured by man does not exceed 40 to 50 meters per second per second). Thus, the interplanetary ship acquires the necessary velocity not at the very surface of the earth but practically beyond the limits of the terrestrial atmosphere where the earth's gravitational field is considerably weaker than at its surface. Let us assume, for example, that the acceleration of the jet thrust of the cosmic rocket is constant and equal to 40 meters per second per second. Then, in a vertical takeoff, after 5 minutes, 16 seconds, at an altitude of 1565 kilometers, the rocket will attain a parabolic velocity, which in this case is only 10.025 kilometers per second, i.e., 1 kilometer per second less than at the surface of the earth.

But as a result of gravitational losses, the rocket spends as much fuel as would be required in free space [2] to develop a velocity of 12,640 meters per second (40 meters per second per second x 316 seconds). The ratio of the weight of fuel to the weight of the empty rocket in this case increases to 24.6.

Vertical takeoff, however, is advantageous only for the beginning of the active segment of the trajectory, where the density of the air and its resistance are still considerable. But in the rarefied layers of the atmosphere it is more advantageous for the rocket to develop velocity in horizontal flight, since in this case gravitational losses of velocity are considerably smaller. For example, during flight with jet acceleration, which is four times greater than the acceleration of gravity, these losses amount to 25% for vertical flight and 3.48% for horizontal flight.

The success of cosmic flight depends not only on the possibility of obtaining great velocities, but also on the precise control of these velocities and their direction to a fixed point in space.

In flying to the moon, at the perigee a difference of ±1 meter per second in the velocity of takeoff from the earth will alter the range of a cosmic ship ±3797 kilometers. This figure increases to ±4244 kilometers for the mean distance to the moon, and to ±4717 kilometers for the apogee distance.

During flight to the planets and their satellites, a change in velocity of 1 meter per second changes the radius of action tens and hundreds of thousands of kilometers. After all, in 0.1 second the ship's velocity increases four to five meters per second. One must also not forget that changes in the shape of the trajectory accompany the changes in the magnitude of the velocity.

Figure 6 shows how the aphelion distance (the aphelion is the point of the orbit fartherest from the sun) changes during flight to the planets on semiellipses as a result of deviations of ±1 meter per second in takeoff velocity.

The solid line represents the deviation in velocity of takeoff at the surface of the earth, and the dotted line the deviations in this velocity after the ship has escaped from the earth's gravitational field and is affected only by the sun's gravitational field.

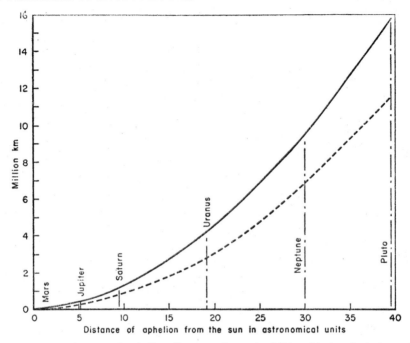

Figure 6. Variations of aphelion distance of cosmic ship's orbit for deviations of ±1 meter per second in initial velocity near the surface of the earth, considering (solid line) and ignoring (dotted line) the earth's gravitational field.

Deviation in the instant and the angle of takeoff also involves serious consequences. If, on the mean distance to Mars, an arc 66,250 kilometers long corresponds to an angle of 1 minute, then on the orbit of Pluto, this arc length increases to 1,716,000 kilometers.

All these quantities point to the importance of the precise control of the velocity of a space ship and its direction at the end of the active segment at the surface of the earth.

Special automatic instruments will be required for measuring with the necessary speed the direction of the motion of the space ship and its coordinates. The regime of engine operation and the manipulation of air and gas control surfaces must be performed automatically in exactly the same way. Finally, the moments of launching and switching off the engines must be executed with such precision that even for this an automatic device will be required.

Thus, the entire control of flight of the cosmic ship will be performed automatically in accordance with a previously set program. The pilot must, of course, follow the working order of the automatic devices, check the results of their operation, and make the proper decisions.

Theoretically, it is possible to use the engine for braking the rocket. In the early stage of cosmic navigation by rocket, however, there will not be sufficient fuel for braking the velocity both when landing on the earth and when landing, for example, on Mars or on Venus. The resistance of the gaseous envelopes of these planets will have to be utilized for this purpose.

Braking of the ship's velocity by the earth's atmosphere will begin at an altitude of less than 200 kilometers. The ship will describe around the earth a number of decreasing ellipses whose perigees are submerged in the earth's atmosphere.

The descent will, evidently, be performed in a gliding flight. The glider will enter the upper layers of the atmosphere with wings extended. As the glider descends into the increasingly dense layers of the atmosphere, the surface of the telescopic wings will have to be diminished. Later on, however, as the soaring speed is reduced, it will again be necessary to push the wings out to increase their lifting power and to land with the wings fully extended. During the last stage of the descent, the cosmic glider can also be intercepted by a super-high-speed airplane on whose "back" it can land.

One frequently is asked the question: What, then, is the main difficulty in the way of realizing cosmic flight?

The difficulties are, of course, numerous and diverse; each of them is a link in a common chain. One may say, however, that there is one principal difficulty which arises in the search of experts in the most diverse fields of science and technology who are working on the solution of the problem of astronautics. This difficulty consists in solving the problem of fuel economy.

The solution of the problem of building a cosmic ship boils down, in the main, to reducing the fuel required to a quantity that the rocket, starting from the surface of the earth, could carry. (The question of fuel cost so far has not at all been taken into consideration.)

Liquid fuel offers the possibility of reducing the weight of a rocket. This is the main reason why designers refuse to use solid propellents for extra-long-range rockets, substituting liquid fuel for it. An unceasing struggle is being carried on to raise the velocity of the exhaust gases from rockets: a comparatively small increase in this parameter considerably decreases the necessary amount of fuel.

But in this field the prospects are extremely limited. In the best case, the exhaust velocity of thermochemical fuel products of combustion will reach 4 kilometers per second (at present this velocity is equal to about 2.5 kilometers per second). This is why designers are looking forward to the atomic rocket, which as yet has not been built but which holds great promise.

Use of a composite rocket requires less fuel, and designers are also working on this problem.

In order to reduce fuel expenditure, the engine of a cosmic ship, as we know, will not operate continuously, as do terrestrial means of locomotion, but only during the short period of the takeoff. At the same time, designers are working on the complications connected with the creation of engines of great power, and physiologists on the extreme overloads that man can endure.

After the engine is switched off, the effect of gravity aboard the cosmic ship will cease. Perhaps this force will have to be replaced by a centrifugal force; the astronauts are prepared to tackle this problem, too.

Departing from considerations of fuel economy, scientists propose to divide cosmic flight into stages, after having created an interplanetary station. But how much this complicates the realization of interplanetary flights!

So far, no one has succeeded in creating a suitable armor for rockets against meteorites. This promises even greater difficulties, but they, too, no doubt, will be overcome.

One can say, then, that when a rocket's construction has been made sufficiently strong and light, when the expenditure of fuel has been sufficiently reduced by the mutual efforts of experts in various fields of science and technology, and when automatic and telemechanic devices have been improved and made more precise, the question of interplanetary travels will have been solved.

Recently the Presidium of USSR Academy of Sciences resolved to establish the K. E. Tsiolkovskii Gold Medal for outstanding work in the field of interplanetary communications. The medal will be awarded once every three years for the best research of Soviet scientists in astronautics. Such high encouragement of scientific work in this very complicated field of knowledge undoubtedly will be conducive to a speedier solution of the problem of cosmic flight. (*Priroda*, December, 1954. The author is identified as "Laureate of the International Encouragement Prize in Astronautics.")

---

[1] 24 sidereal hours equal 23 hours, 56 minutes, 4.091 seconds of mean solar time.

[2] By this term is understood the space devoid of resisting media and sufficiently remote from celestial bodies so that it is possible to disregard the forces of their attraction.

# 6.  Problems of Flight Into Cosmic Space

*N. Varvarov*

Before the second half of the last century man's dream of visiting distant, mysterious worlds was a fantasy without any actual possibility of realization.  Only at the end of the nineteenth century, through the work of the Russian scientists, the Narodnik revolutionary N. I. Kibal'chich and K. E. Tsiolkovskii, were ways of solving this complex problem first discovered.  Independently, they both pointed to the rocket engine as the only possible means by which flights through the boundless spaces of the universe could become a reality.

Today, as a result of the great achievements of science and technology — the mastery of processes of transforming nuclear energy, the creation of powerful jet engines, the unprecedented successes in the development of the means of electronic automatics — favorable conditions are created for the successful solution of this grandiose problem.  "Science," said Academician A. N. Nesmeyanov, President of the USSR Academy of Science, "has reached a stage where it is feasible to send a rocket to the moon, to create an artificial satellite of the earth."

Modern rockets are already reaching altitudes of 400 kilometers and more and flight ranges of several thousand kilometers.  A cosmic ship for flights into space, however, has not so far been successfully built.  Just what difficulties lie in the way of solving this problem?

First of all, let us remember that enormous distances separate the earth from the other planets of the solar system.  In order to reach even the closest planets in a flying machine, tremendous energy must be expended to surmount not only the enormous distances but also the gravitational fields of the earth, the other planets, and the sun.  It is known that the greater the velocity with which an object is thrown the farther it will fly.  The velocity, in its turn, depends on the amount of energy expended in the throw.  If a velocity of about 8 kilometers per second is imparted to a rocket beyond the limits of the atmosphere, and if its motion is directed parallel to the earth's surface, it will not fall back to the earth but will become a small artificial satellite.

Given a velocity of 8 to 11 kilometers per second, the rocket will move in cosmic space along a closed elliptical curve, and its path can be calculated in such a way that it will be able to reach the moon. If the rocket is given a velocity of about 12 kilometers per second, however, it will fly as far as Mars or Venus. With a velocity of about 17 kilometers per second the rocket will not only be able to reach Pluto, the most distant planet in the solar system, but will travel beyond the limits of the solar system.

K. E. Tsiolkovskii showed that the velocity of a rocket flying in a vacuum and in a medium without gravity (outside the field of gravitation) depends on only two quantities: the velocity of the rocket engine's exhaust gases and the amount of fuel expended.

Calculations show that with an exhaust gas velocity of four kilometers per second, the amount of fuel necessary for a rocket flight to the moon must be twenty times more than the weight of the rocket itself and its payload. From this it is obvious how thin and, at the same time, how strong the rocket shell must be to hold so much fuel. If we consider that an exhaust gas velocity equal to 4 kilometers per second is at present the maximum velocity that the best chemical fuels known to us can develop, and also the fact that at present an exhaust velocity of only about 3 kilometers per second has been attained, it will become clear how difficult it is to solve even the first problem — sending an automatically controlled rocket to the moon. These difficulties, however, can be surmounted with present-day technological means.

One of the basic factors that prevents the realization of space flight today is the large relative fuel supply that is necessary to attain cosmic speeds.

To avoid the difficulties associated with storing a large fuel supply in the rocket, K. E. Tsiolkovskii proposed to build the rocket not as a massive single unit, but as a multiunit rocket consisting of several separate rocket stages, each with its own engines. Each stage comes into operation in turn, and after its fuel is exhausted, it detaches itself from the rest and falls to the earth. To this idea of the noted scientist we can now add several improvements that will allow an even more substantial gain in fuel economy and, consequently, a decrease in its relative supply.

By installing turbojet and ramjet engines, which use oxygen from the atmosphere, in the separate stages of the rocket, the consumption of the oxidant can be reduced. The general construction scheme of a rocket for flight to the moon may then be approximately as follows:

the first stage (in order of operation) must have turbojet engines; the second, ramjet engines; the third and subsequent stages, liquid-rocket engines.  If we consider that the exhaust gas velocity increases with the increase in temperature in the combustion chamber approximately as the square root of the magnitude of the temperature (which leads to enormous thermal stresses in the combustion chamber and, because of this, to a short period of engine operation), then the great advantage of the multistage rocket over the single-stage rocket will be quite obvious.  This advantage consists in the fact that it is possible to speed up the operation of the engines of each stage, forcing them to work a short interval of time under high thermal stresses in the combustion chambers.

Economy of fuel can also be obtained when the ascent of the rocket is strictly vertical, which enables it to pass through the lower, denser layers of the atmosphere more quickly.  Besides, it must be kept in mind that the faster the rocket takes off, the less fuel will be required, in the end, to reach the necessary velocity.

If one takes into consideration the factors pointed out above, and of certain other factors which ensure a minimum expenditure of fuel to gain the requisite velocity, then it is possible even today to build a composite rocket, operating on thermochemical fuel, that will be able to fly to the moon.  By utilizing such fuel, however, the rocket will fail to return to earth.

Broad new prospects for solving the problem of interplanetary communications open up in connection with the possibility of using atomic energy in rocket engines.  Such engines can be of two types.  The first assumes the use of the energy of nuclear reactions for heating some working substance — gas, liquid, or molten metal.  By heating hydrogen, for example, by this method, it is possible to raise its temperature to several thousand degrees, as a result of which the exhaust gas velocity can reach 12 kilometers per second.  With such an exhaust velocity the initial weight of a rocket flying to the moon and back must be 10 times its final weight, which is a quite acceptable value for present-day technology, since for modern rockets the mass ratio is already about five.

According to another variant, direct utilization of the products of nuclear disintegration is considered for creating the reactive force.  As we know, during nuclear reactions a stream of extraordinarily fast particles is formed, which move with velocities of the order of several thousand kilometers per second.  Precisely this stream is proposed to be used as a propelling force.

Of course, the realization of these problems is far from being an easy task. There will be needed new alloys that have extraordinary strength, that are capable of withstanding very high temperatures for a long time, that are resistant to radioactive effects, and that rapidly give off heat to the surrounding space. It is essential to find lightweight means of protection against radioactive radiations, etc.

Even under the conditions of utilizing only chemical fuel, however, a flight to the moon and back will probably be possible in the near future. Calculations show that this can be solved if there is an artificial satellite of the earth that can serve as an intermediate refueling station, as it were, for rockets traveling to the moon. We can assume that as rocket technology develops, the range and flight velocity of rockets will increase more and more. If, however, a rocket reaches a velocity of 8 kilometers per second beyond the boundaries of the atmosphere and if its motion continues along an orbit parallel to the earth's surface (by inertia, and without expenditure of fuel), then it will become a miniature artificial satellite of the earth. Instruments on the rocket-satellite will communicate the conditions that exist there. This will make it possible to send there a rocket with a crew of research workers. Later on fuel supplies and individual parts of an extraterrestrial station that the astronauts will assemble into a single construction will be delivered in freight rockets.

Creation of such a cosmic laboratory will permit scientists to carry out investigations that are otherwise impossible under ordinary terrestrial conditions. Biologists, for instance, will be able to study conditions of life in the absence of the force of gravity; astrophysicists will be able to observe the ultraviolet and X-ray spectra of the radiations of the sun and the stars and to study more thoroughly the processes that take place in these celestial bodies; radiophysicists will be able to investigate the ionosphere more completely and to determine the most advantageous regimes of radio communication with future cosmic ships, etc.

Automatic rockets will take off from the artificial satellite to explore the moon, and after flying around it, will return with the necessary information. An artificial satellite of the moon, possibly, will be built with the help of automatic rockets. When flight around the moon has been mastered, and when astronauts with the help of automatic rockets will have studied the conditions for landing on it, an expedition of research workers will be sent there. In the same way, apparently, the conquest of the nearest planets — Venus and Mars — will take place.

In order to make space flight a reality, a number of complex problems besides those enumerated above will have to be solved. The most important among them are: the question of meteorite danger; the creation of an artificial force of gravity; the protection of the interplanetary rocket crew from the harmful radiations of the sun and the stars, from the icy cold of cosmic space, and the high temperature of the solar rays; and many others. Suitable automatic controls and other instruments ensuring the navigation of the ships in cosmic space must also be built. There are also other questions on which work remains to be done.

The solution of the problem of space flight will be of extraordinary importance for the further development of science. Scientists will obtain the possibility of thoroughly studying the universe, to carry out such physical, chemical, and other experiments that are inconceivable under terrestrial conditions, to establish where, besides on earth, life exists and what level it has attained.

American imperialists and their henchmen dream of putting to a different use the possibilities connected with the prospect of creating an artificial satellite of the earth, as well as other achievements of modern science and technology. They would like to create extraterrestrial bases from which they could launch atomic attacks against countries of the democratic camp and to destroy selected targets. As technical calculations show, however, these extravagant plans cannot be realized — for reasons that do not depend on the imperialists. Such plans can intimidate only the weak — and kindle war hysteria.

Soviet scientists are persistently investigating questions connected with the problems of flight in cosmic space. The Presidium of the USSR Academy of Sciences recently adopted a resolution to establish the K. E. Tsiolkovskii Gold Medal for outstanding work by Soviet scientists in the field of interplanetary communications. In order to coordinate and direct all work concerned with the solution of the problem of mastering cosmic space, a permanent interdepartmental Commission on Interplanetary Communications attached to the Astronomical Council of the USSR Academy of Sciences has been created. The astronautics section organized at the Central Aeroclub of the USSR, which unites in its ranks scientists and engineers, sets itself the task of aiding in every possible way the solution of the problem of space flight in the interests of the further progress of science and for the welfare of mankind. (*Sovetskii Flot*, May 29, 1955. The author is identified as "Chairman of the Astronautics Section of the V. P. Chkalov Central Aeroclub of the USSR.")

# 7.   Problems of Astronautics

*V. G. Fesenkov*

At present man is, without a doubt, on the threshold of a new epoch of interplanetary voyages.   The first experiments of flight beyond the limits of the earth's atmosphere have already been made.   In various countries — in Europe, in America, in Greenland, in Alaska, in the center of the Pacific Ocean, at the equator — rockets are ascending with automatic instruments and reaching altitudes of hundreds of kilometers.

Already extremely valuable information has been obtained on the physical and chemical composition of the highest atmosppheric layers, that is, on the pressure, density, temperature, content of different gases, state of the earth's magnetic field, the intensity and composition of cosmic rays, the abundance of meteoric dust and its effect on the metallic shell of the rocket and on solar radiation in the ultraviolet and roentgen ray region of the spectrum.   By means of rockets the solar constant was measured anew, new phenomena were discovered — namely, the terrestrial atmosphere's own radiation, its changes during the day, the presence of clouds at an altitude of about 70 kilometers — and the percentage content of dissociated molecules of oxygen was investigated.

Many times photographs of the earth's surface have been made from an altitude of hundreds of kilometers, which give an idea of what our planet looks like from cosmic space.

Finally, in 1954, the first attempts were made to send aloft in the head of a rocket living beings — monkeys and mice — the former being under continuous automatic control with respect to heart activity and general condition.   A movie film was obtained which showed the behavior of a monkey from the moment of the launching of the rocket, during its ascent to great heights, and to its landing by parachute.

Thus, experimental proof was obtained of the possibility of utilizing rockets capable of moving in a vacuum as passenger ships, for which the surrounding air medium is, to a certain degree, an obstacle but not a necessary condition of travel.

In special literature of recent years the task of creating an artificial satellite of the earth as a very convenient intermediate station for flights into interplanetary space is considered, and the most favorable routes of flight around the moon and to the moon itself, and also to Mars with return to the earth, are calculated and route estimates of similar travels are also made.[1]

Thus, we may assume that in the realization of interplanetary travels mankind is in approximately the same position it was almost 50 years ago with respect to aircraft construction and the conquest of the air space.

Without doubt, for interplanetary travels there will be utilized such powerful means as atomic energy, although this has its own specific difficulties, so far not overcome, which consist mainly in the enormous temperature developed by the atomic reactions and the absence of the directivity of action. However, with conventional engines used in contemporary rockets, the exhaust velocity of jet gases for certain kinds of fuel (oxygen and hydrogen) amounts to 3.5 kilometers per second and even 4 kilometers per second.

In the light of contemporary technology of rocket engines and the rapid rate of development of new designs which attain greater altitudes above the earth's surface, one might think that in all probability in the near future, approximately in 10 to 20 years, the first flights of man into cosmic space will be realized.

Numerous universities and scientific societies of various countries are occupied with the problem of interplanetary travels, developing them from different points of view. In England, for example, there exists, and is actively working, the British Interplanetary Society which includes about 2500 members and has published thirteen volumes of its works. There are similar societies also in other countries. These societies are united by an international organization which organizes annual congresses for discussions of the most urgent tasks. In the United States in recent years several types of rockets have been built. Judging by data in the literature, in five to seven years one can expect to realize an extraterrestrial laboratory as a preparatory stage for cosmic travels.

A great deal of work in astronautics has already been carried out and continues to be carried out in our country, which is the original birthplace of this new branch of science. First of all, one should recall the noted revolutionary Nikolai Kibal'chich, who wrote a remarkable memoir in which he first substantiated the possibility of interplanetary travels and pointed out the technological means necessary for this in the form of rocket engines. This memoir remained buried for a long time in the archives of the Czar's secret police and was made known only after the October Revolution.

In fact, the pioneer in the field of astronautics who exerted great influence on the development of scientific thought throughout the world in this direction was Konstantin Eduardovich Tsiolkovskii, who back in 1903 wrote his "Investigation of World Spaces by means of Reactive Instruments," which was followed by a series of other works.

Under the Soviets, K. E. Tsiolkovskii published the works: "Rocket in Cosmic Space" (1924), "Cosmic Rocket" (1927), "Cosmic Reactive Trains" (1929), "Reactive Airplane" (1930). Tsiolkovskii's ideas were developed by his followers, of which one should note the enthusiasts in this field, F. A. Tsander ("Problem of Flight by Means of Rocket Apparatuses," 1932), Yu. V. Kondratyuk ("Conquest of Interplanetary Spaces," 1929), A. Ananov ("Interplanetary Navigation," Paris, in French, 1935), A. Shternfel'd ("Flight into World Space," 1939), and especially Professor N. A. Rynin, who wrote a fundamental encyclopedia on astronautics in nine volumes.

To popularize and further develop the ideas and methods of astronautics, there was recently established at the Astronomical Council of the USSR Academy of Sciences an interdepartmental commission which sets forth the rather broad tasks of ensuring cosmic flights. Besides that, at the V. P. Chhalov Central Aeroclub an Astronautics Section was organized early in 1954. In the near future, a magazine devoted to questions of astronautics will be published in Moscow.

The presidium of the USSR Academy of Sciences has established a gold medal for the most outstanding works in the field of astronautics, which will be awarded every three years. One can rest assured that Soviet investigators will do their level best to be the first to solve in practice the problems of interplanetary communications.

\*     \*     \*     \*

Let us dwell in some detail on the essential peculiarities of rocket motion. The basic feature of a rocket consists in the fact that it represents the only presently known possibility of rapidly moving in airless space, since this motion takes place as a result of the ejection of mass from the rocket. All other types of engines realize their motion by means of reaction against the surrounding external objects. Another essential feature of the rocket consists in the fact that the velocity developed by it may considerably surpass the velocity of the

gases exploding in it (that is, the velocity of any artillery projectile)
if only the expended mass will be sufficiently great.

The artillery missile, which back in the nineteenth century was considered by many as the only possible means of breaking away from
the earth, cannot fly faster than the gases expand in the muzzle of the
gun.  Under the most favorable circumstances this velocity is two
to three kilometers per second, which is entirely insufficient to escape
from the earth.  Meanwhile, the velocity of the rocket theoretically
can be as great as desired.  Practically, however, it is impossible to
realize the ejection of the predominant mass of the rocket and therefore its maximum velocity usually is not many times greater than the
exhaust velocity of the gases from the nozzle, which, thus, may be increased as expediently as possible by inventing the necessary fuel.
The best results are obtained with two- or three-stage rockets.  The
idea of a multistage rocket consists in the fact that as the fuel is spent
and the tanks occupied by it are emptied, the mass of the tanks, having become useless, is also discarded.  A two-stage type of rocket
was, for example, realized in the form of a combination of a heavy V-2
rocket, carrying a lighter Wac Corporal rocket.  At the moment when
the first ascends to the greatest altitude it can attain, the second rocket
takes off, separating from the first, which is completely discarded.  The
combined effect of these two rockets is considerably greater than that
which can be achieved by each of the rockets separately.  Thus, for
example, the V-2 rocket, taken alone, with a maximum velocity of 1.6
kilometers per second attains an altitude of 185 kilometers.  The Wac
Corporal rocket with a maximum velocity of 1.2 kilometers per second
has a maximum altitude of 70 kilometers, but these two rockets combined into one two-stage rocket reach an altitude of 400 kilometers
and even more.  The principle of the staged rocket recalls several
methods applied earlier to reach the earth's pole, when a great mass of
people carry food and leave it in separate warehouses, keeping only as
much as is necessary for the return trip, and only the remaining
small group, using the warehouses thus established, finally attacks the
pole.  The projected artificial satellite of the earth, which will revolve around the earth in a circular orbit with a period of approximately two hours and which will be an exceptionally valuable cosmic
laboratory must serve as an intermediate warehouse for refueling.  In
order to attain a circular velocity and, consequently, to come in contact with this satellite, the rocket must expend half as much energy as
it requires for the final escape from the earth's gravity and departure
into cosmic space.  During the return trip to the earth, a new refueling

will be necessary on the way so that this return can be accomplished with complete assurance, since an expenditure of energy is required for proper braking.  At the same time, the artificial moon will be a convenient station for astronomical observations of various cosmic bodies, particularly of planets, under the conditions of ideally quiet images and at the same time in all the regions of the spectrum.  From such a moon it is also possible to observe the general circulation of, and the various processes in, the earth's atmosphere and, in general, all kinds of changes on the earth's surface.

Another advantage of the rocket as compared with the simple projectile consists in the fact that its velocity increases gradually and attains a controlled maximum only several minutes after the beginning of the flight.  It is understood that it is more advantageous to utilize as great accelerations as are possible, but these accelerations must not exceed the acceleration of the earth's gravity more than several tens of times.  On the other hand, an artillery projectile must secure its maximum velocity at the moment it leaves the barrel of the gun, which the projectile passes over in an insignificant fraction of a second.  Because of this, the acceleration developed in the muzzle of the gun attains an enormous magnitude in comparison with the usual acceleration of gravity.  The conventional cannon with a barrel length of several meters, has an attainable acceleration roughly 50,000 times greater than that of the earth.  Under similar accelerations, a man located in the missle will be flattened at once.  Thus, it is only the rocket that presents the practical possibility of flight of living beings beyond the limits of the earth into cosmic space, but even here it is necessary to pay serious attention to creating the most favorable conditions with respect to an easier possibility of surmounting the harmful effects of great accelerations.

Experience shows that for a short time, measured in seconds, it is possible to endure rather great accelerations without harm to life.  It is possible to expect that during immersion in an incompressible fluid the permissible accelerations can be considerably greater.  In this respect, experimental medical research is necessary.

* * * *

The problems of astronautics directly affect the most diverse scientific disciplines — astronomy, mechanics, physics, chemistry, and, to a considerable degree, physiology and medicine also.  Some of them cannot be solved without a previous consultation of organizations which work on the design and manufacture of rockets, whereas other problems of a more theoretical nature require a knowledge only of the general principles of rocket propulsion and the purpose of rockets for cosmic flights; therefore, these problems can and must be considered by our scientific institutions and experts even now without further delay.

Let us consider the problems which mainly have a theoretical character based on a knowledge only of general principles of rocket motion. The solution of these problems is nevertheless important, because the results obtained thereby will make it possible to formulate the conditions which must be taken into consideration by designers in building cosmic ships, without even mentioning the fact that similar results may prove to be necessary for the realization of rocket flights in cosmic space.

The entire complex problem of cosmic travels can be divided into three unequal stages, each of which requires the cooperative work of various experts: (1) takeoff and entrance into cosmic space, (2) travel in interplanetary space, and (3) return to the earth or, analogously, a visit to the surface of another planet.

The realization of all these tasks involves numerous difficulties that cannot be fully coordinated, and this requires that each time the most rational palliative solution must be found.

Let us consider, for example, the problems arising in connection with the takeoff from the earth, and the entrance into cosmic space. The takeoff from the earth is carried out by means of the jet impulse of the gases which escape from the rocket nozzle. The greater the exhaust velocity of these gases and the greater the loss of the mass of the rocket, that is, the greater the expenditure of fuel, the greater this impulse will be. It is vitally important that having freed itself from the earth's gravity, the rocket should preserve the greatest store of fuel possible for its further journey and for its return to the earth. At the same time, it should try not to move away from the earth as far as possible but should try to develop the necessary relative velocity of not less than 11 kilometers per second.

To guide the rocket directly along a radius from the earth is not advantageous, because it will not be able to utilize the rotation of the earth, which can act as a sort of sling to aid in launching the rocket and in the development of a velocity of 400 meters per second at the equator, a fact which should not be disregarded. Secondly, launching a rocket directly along the radius is also not advantageous because in this case there will be a maximum gravitational back-drift to the center of the earth, which, for example, in 100 seconds will develop a velocity of a whole kilometer per second and in 1000 seconds, or 17 minutes, will create a reverse rocket velocity equal to 10 kilometers per second, or, in other words, will be able to fully annul the rocket's forward motion from the earth. Horizontal launching of a rocket is also not advantageous, since in this case resistance in the terrestrial atmosphere proves to be the greatest and can considerably brake the momentum of the rocket.

Moreover, the rapid acceleration that a rocket must develop in going from zero velocity to 10 to 11 kilometers per second can be extremely painful for passengers. As is already known, during even slight changes in the sensation of gravity (for example, when the sea is rough, or during descent or ascent in a fast elevator, unpleasant sensations, changing into actual sickness, are felt. During the ascent of a rocket, the passengers will feel the sensation of gravity much more strongly, since they will be subjected to accelerations at least 10 to 15 times greater than the earth's acceleration of gravity during the entire period of the takeoff from the earth and flight into cosmic space. This sensation will at once be replaced by the sensation of complete weightlessness when the jet impulse of the rocket ceases and the rocket is subjected only to the action of ordinary gravitational fields. Taking into consideration all these inconveniences at the start of the journey, it is necessary to work out, in the most thorough way, just what must be the conditions of the most expedient launching tolerable for the passengers, during which the rocket upon attaining the necessary velocity will still preserve the maximum possible store of fuel, that is, its maximum possible mass.

The problem is described by a system of differential equations which are solved by a numerical method under various initial conditions. It is necessary to know what is the coefficient of resistance which the rocket experiences during its motion in the atmosphere, or at least to consider different values for this coefficient. It is necessary to assign a definite law for the change in the acceleration of the rocket, that is, its jet impulse, which can be controlled automatically from its launching until it attains a maximum value. Under these conditions, the solution of the equations must determine the direction of the launching of the rocket — that is, the angle which the jet impulse makes with the vertical line and at which the loss of mass is a minimum and the rocket, entering cosmic espace, still preserves the maximum amount of fuel.

At the same time, one must take into consideration the rotation of the earth around its axis and calculate the moment of launching so that the rocket, having entered cosmic space, will begin to move at a certain angle with the earth's orbit, depending on the goal assigned.

In this takeoff from the earth, the greatest difficulty is in connection with the maximum expenditure of energy during a minimum of time. Subsequent cosmic travel does not present any special difficulties if only there will be assured the possibility of existence inside the rocket for a sufficiently long time — weeks or even months. The main point is that it is possible to move in cosmic space by utilizing the gravitational fields existing there, in exactly the same way as sailing vessels travel over enormous distances by utilizing winds favorable for them. Suppose, for example, that we want to travel to Mars. For this we must launch a rocket in such a way that it goes out into space tangent to the earth's orbit and impart to it a velocity which exceeds the orbital velocity of our planet by only 2.9 kilometers per second. To attain this velocity will require one-sixteenth of the energy required for takeoff from the earth. At the same time, the rocket will move around the sun with a velocity of 32.7 kilometers per second, thus permitting it, by describing an elliptic orbit under the influence of the solar attraction, to cross over into the orbit of Mars, which it will reach in 259 days. The moment of launching must be calculated in such a way that Mars will be at the very point of its orbit at which the rocket will arrive. If it turns out to be impossible (for men) to remain inside the rocket for such a long time, it is possible to equip the rocket with automatic instruments which will photograph the surface of Mars at very small intervals in exactly the same way as automatic surveys of the earth's surface from cosmic space are made, and then the rocket will return to the earth, where the readings of the automatic instruments and cameras can be recorded. Generally speaking, a trip to Venus or any other body of the solar system can be performed in the same way. As mentioned before, this will require a very insignificant expenditure of reactive energy. The main task is to find the possibility for the travelers' existence inside the rocket for this long period. With this will be connected various other problems, primarily the problem of supplying the travelers with the foodstuffs and the necessary atmosphere inside the rocket, since the content of oxygen, carbon dioxide, and moisture must be maintained at a uniform level throughout the journey.

In addition, one must make provision to protect the rocket from, or at least to evaluate the degree of danger resulting from, possible collisions with meteorites, since such collisions will be tantamount to hits by strong explosive missiles.

It is also necessary to consider in advance the question of consequences of the prolonged effect of cosmic rays both on the shell of the rocket and on the passengers inside, taking into consideration that the intensity of the cosmic rays will, under these conditions, be incomparably greater than even in cosmic space itself, owing to the great development of a secondary component.

In connection with this, one must also consider the question of how well the shell of the rocket will be able to hold the gases inside without allowing their escape into the void outside, despite sharp temperature changes in various parts of the rocket — within the limits of from 100 degrees centigrade on the side facing the sun to almost absolute zero on the side in the shade.

Everything mentioned above appears to be necessary to ensure the very existence of the passengers inside the rocket during long cosmic flights. It is superfluous to say that it is necessary to thoroughly think through all the questions of man's living under conditions where the force of gravity is completely absent, but where the force of inertia is present in full measure; where there is neither top nor bottom, nor any support for locomotion or the placing of objects.

For astronavigation all this is still insufficient, however. It is necessary to know how to control the motion of the cosmic ship; how to compare its course with those previously computed, and at the time when this still does not require a considerable expenditure of energy; and how to correct the small deviations from the true course. For this the travelers must know how to determine their own position in cosmic space, which, in principle, presents a new problem. As we know, on the earth the coordinates are determined with respect to the equator of the terrestrial globe or to the plane of the ecliptic orbit. In the rocket this natural system of coordinates is absent and one must employ an entirely different method. One must not demand of cosmic travelers, however, that they conduct lengthy observations and calculations and thus transform the rocket into a kind of astronomical observatory for determining their position and verifying the correctness of the plotted course. It is necessary that the time signals and all the information relative to their position in space, even all the exhaustive references relative to their motion, be obtained from the earth by the travelers and that they themselves should communicate their inquiries and transmit their own impressions to earth. For this it is necessary to ensure two-way radio communication between the rocket

and the earth. Inasmuch as the rocket in all probability will not be
visible from the earth in the reflected rays, and even light signals
from it can be perceived only with difficulty, it is necessary, obviously,
that the call radio signals should be transmitted from the rocket continuously and automatically, for example, on a wave of 1 meter, which
freely penetrates the earth's atmosphere, and at the same time with a
solid angle of not less than 20 to 30 degrees. Large radio telescopes
located on the earth will be able to catch these signals, to fix the location of the rocket on the firmament, and by means of consecutive observations to follow its movement in space along the determined, immediately computed, orbit. Information so obtained must be immediately transmitted to the rocket, together with the necessary directions regarding the correctness of the course taken. In addition to this,
the rocket itself must possess the means of exactly determining its
distance from the sun, for example, by the size of the sun's diameter,
and to plot the projection of its path in the starry field, determining
thereby the plane of its motion. It is especially important to supply
the travelers with the means of determining the velocity of their motion, which is not felt directly, just as we do not feel our motion
around the sun, although this velocity is about 30 kilometers per second. The rocket's velocity relative to the comparatively near bodies
— the planets — can be measured most simply by means of radar, and
its velocity relative to the most distant ones — the sun and other
planets — perhaps by means of a special interferometer, which determines the Doppler shift of individual spectral lines and thus the velocity in a radial direction.

It is very important to solve the task of the return trip of the rocket
to the earth without expenditure of fuel. This can be achieved by a
rational utilization of the braking properties of the terrestrial atmosphere.

It is well known that meteors and meteorites which fall into the atmosphere of the earth with cosmic velocities up to 70 kilometers per
second, despite their mass, are fully braked in our air envelope, which
is like an armor that protects us from impacts of such cosmic projectiles. Ordinary small meteors pulverize completely and burn up at
an altitude not less than 80 kilometers, and even the most massive
bodies of this kind — for example, the well-known Sikhote-Alin meteorite, which entered the atmosphere with a velocity of 14 to 15
kilometers per second and an initial mass of not less than 2000 tons —
still completely lose their cosmic velocity and fall to the earth comparatively slowly. Separate masses of the Sikhote-Alin meteorite,

which formed numerous craters and holes, had a velocity of not more than 400 meters per second at the moment of impact. When meteorites fall they fuse and break into small fragments. The rocket must be guided in such a way that its braking will not be too rapid, as in the case of meteorites, and thereby lead to its destruction. For this, one must guide the rocket so that it at first will pass through the entire atmosphere at a considerable altitude above the earth's surface in the very rarefied air layers and thereby decrease its velocity to the elliptic with respect to the earth, that is, less than 11 kilometers per second.

The rocket will thereby inevitably return and again will find itself in the earth's atmosphere, and having passed through the atmosphere at a somewhat lower altitude, it will again lose a part of its velocity. A number of consecutive returns of such a kind and the gradual loss by the rocket of its initial energy will finally lead to such a decrease in velocity that for a safe landing only a small fraction of reactive energy will be required. The conditions of such a motion on several loops of the spiral must be calculated mathematically beforehand. On approaching the earth, the astronavigator must know in advance how he must plot the course of the cosmic ship in order to pass through certain layers of the earth's atmosphere with a definite velocity.

These directions must be obtained by means of a previous calculation, which, in principle, does not differ from the calculation applied to the motion of bolides in the earth's atmosphere. In the given case, however, one must also take into consideration the rotation of the earth around its axis, and, for the part of the rocket's trajectory outside the earth, to make an approximate calculation of lunar disturbances which are capable of changing somewhat the flight altitude of the rocket over the earth's surface in its successive entrances into the atmosphere.

One could make analogous calculations, although with a much smaller degree of assurance, relative to the atmospheres of other planets (for example, Mars) which also undoubtedly possess a braking capability.

Without stopping here on the most complex problem of astronautics, which will not be solved in practice for a long time yet, it is precisely on our visits to surfaces of various planets, first of all to the moon and Mars, that I shall note only that such visits to the other planets in the solar system will involve many new difficulties. There is no doubt that it is far more comfortable and simpler to remain in the close quarters of the rocket in cosmic space than to find oneself on some strange planet, even on such a planet as Mars, although the latter, more than any other planet, resembles our earth.  There is no doubt that even on Mars we shall encounter enormous difficulties.  The atmosphere on Mars is, in all probability, completely devoid of oxygen and its pressure so low that breathing in it is impossible.  There can be no combustion at all there.  Life, as we know it, thus may be completely impossible on Mars without some sort of safety chambers, and yet there we shall have to deal with the cruel cold of Martian nights when the temperature drops to 100 degrees below zero and even lower.

We cannot as yet contemplate seriously direct visits to other cosmic bodies, but flight into cosmic space with the possibility of coming close to various planets of the solar system, in all probability, will follow very soon when we succeed in escaping from the earth's gravity.

In conclusion, the contemporary state of the problem of cosmic travels can be characterized in the following manner:

1.  At present rockets are used with great success for various investigations in the high atmospheric layers and the altitude of their flight increases every year, even now attaining hundreds of kilometers. Contemporary technological capabilities permit flight into cosmic space in a circular orbit relative to the earth, which gives a basis for setting the problem of creating an artificial earth satellite as a convenient intermediate station for further flight.

2.  Work on the utilization of atomic energy for cosmic travels is carried out with extraordinary intensity, and the success of this work will make feasible all the tasks of astronautics, at least with respect to the power of jet engines.

Because of this, one must acknowledge as extremely urgent the development of various problems connected with interplanetary problems and the conquest of cosmic space.  Astronomers, mathematicians, physicists, chemists, physiologists, and physicians already now can undertake the development of individual problems.  The development of scientific apparatus and the problematics of research work in cosmic space also can serve as the subject of discussion among the experts.

Before the scientific workers of our country at present has been set the task of solving a number of problems connected with the conquest of cosmic space.  There is no doubt that every scientific worker will do his best to bring his share of participation into this needed work. (*Priroda*, June, 1955.  The author is identified as "Academician.")

[1] See, for example, *Priroda*, No. 12, 1954, pp. 13-22 (for translation see Chap. 5).

# 8. Contemporary Problems of Cosmic Flight

*A. G. Karpenko and G. A. Skuridin*

The problems of mastering cosmic space are attracting the attention of the world scientific community. Increased interest in these problems is connected first of all with those colossal successes in the development of rocket technology and jet aviation which were achieved recently, and also with the discovery of the possibility of utilizing atomic energy for peaceful purposes.

In many countries numerous committees and commissions and scientific associations and institutes have begun to work on the various questions of cosmonautics. The thought of the conquest of cosmic space has seized the minds of many thousands of famous experts — engineers and technologists — and the very task of the realization of cosmic flights has acquired an international character.

The International Astronautical Federation (IAF), which comprises more than 18 national societies of different countries of the world, including six American ones, was organized in 1948. The Federation at present has more than 7000 members.

Such a range and concentration of scientific efforts around the problems of interplanetary communications attests to the scientific possibilities which are opening before mankind in the matter of the cognition and mastery of the universe.

There is no doubt that the better coordinated the work of the representatives of the various branches of science and technology, the more rationally will the collective efforts of scientists be spent; and the more clearly defined the tasks standing before them, the more successfully will the development of this many-sided problem proceed.

In this connection, a permanent Interdepartmental Commission, including many of the greatest scientists of our country, was created under the Astronomical Council of the USSR Academy of Sciences to coordinate scientific work on the mastery of cosmic space.

Just what are the ways of realizing this — one of the most fantastic ideas of man? This question was given a scientifically founded answer as far back as in the beginning of this century by one of the most remarkable scientists — K. E. Tsiolkovskii, who devoted his whole life to the great idea of cosmic flights (the twentieth anniversary of his death is commemorated this year).

In his work "Investigation of World Spaces by Reactive Instruments" (1903), Tsiolkovskii showed for the first time that only the rocket can be the sole means of realizing interplanetary flights.

By means of very simple reasoning, the scientist derived the basic laws of rocket motion. In accordance with these laws, the maximum speed acquired by a rocket during its motion in space, free of the influence of external forces, is defined by the formula:

$$v_{max} = v_o + v_r \ln (M_o/M),$$

where $v_o$ is the initial velocity of the rocket, $v_r$ the relative velocity of the stream of particles, $M_o$ the initial mass of the rocket, and $M$ its remaining mass.

From this formula it follows that the velocity attained by the rocket is linearly dependent on the exhaust velocity of the products of combustion and is proportional to the logarithm of the ratio $M_o/M$.

In spite of the extreme simplification of the problem, the derived formula made it possible to answer one of the fundamental questions of the theory of rockets — the possibility, in principle, of the practical attainment of cosmic velocities (8 to 17 kilometers per second).

At the same time, Tsiolkovskii understood perfectly well that the main difficulty in the way of realizing interplanetary flights boils down to overcoming the forces of gravity and that, in the first place, it is necessary to explain the influences of these forces on the character of the motion of the rocket and also to compute the fuel supply required for overcoming the "armor of gravity."

The expression found by Tsiolkovskii for the maximum value of the velocity of a rocket during its motion in a field of external forces has just as simple a form as his first formula:

$$v_{max} = -v_r(1 - q/p) \ln (1 + M_2/M_1),$$

where $M_1$ is the mass of the rocket with its entire contents, except the fuel, $M_2$ the mass of the fuel, $q$ the acceleration of gravity, $p$ the constant acceleration imparted to the rocket by the jet stream.

Thus both these formulas point to the fact that the greater the relative velocity of the jet waste products and the greater the general store of fuel relative to the mass of the rocket at the end of the active section, the higher the velocity of the rocket will be toward the end of the burning of the fuel.

In addition, by making use of these formulas, K. E. Tsiolkovskii for the first time calculated the efficiency of the rocket, which turned out to depend not only on the ratio $M_2/M_1$, but also on the value $p$, the assumed constant acceleration of the rocket during its motion in the field of gravitational forces. (Constant acceleration of the rocket can be assured if its mass in the process of fuel combustion changes exponentially.)

Thus the theory of the uniformly accelerated motion of a rocket in a gravitational field was worked out for the first time.

Tsiolkovskii, however, did not exaggerate the value and significance of his theoretical calculations, which for the first time gave a scientific basis to the idea of mastering cosmic space. He knew perfectly well that the practical realization of a cosmic rocket with its technical and scientific difficulties is beyond the powers of a single man.

Tsiolkovskii wrote that this purpose was to stimulate interest in the question under consideration, "to point out its great significance in the future and the possibility of its solution."

Tsiolkovskii's historical merit is vividly described by the following lines of a letter addressed to him by the famous German expert, H. Oberth: "You have kindled the light and we shall work until the greatest dream of mankind will be realized."

Soon after the publication of Tsiolkovskii's first scientific works, there began to appear in many countries followers of his ideas, who took the next steps in the development of rocket technology. Among them one should note such scientists as Esnault-Pelterie, Goddard, Oberth, and our Russian investigators Yu. V. Kondratyuk and F. A. Tsander. The circle of ardent followers of Tsiolkovskii's ideas is widening every year.

*     *     *     *

Recently it was proved that only by means of the rocket is it possible to build an apparatus capable of overcoming the earth's gravitational force.

It is evident from Tsiolkovskii's formulas that the greater the exhaust velocity of the combustion products and the smaller the portion of the initial mass of the rocket that remains after the burning of the fuel, the greater will be the velocity attained by the rocket when the fuel is completely expended. It is precisely this law of jet propulsion that determines the main directions of investigation that will be able to bring about the realization of cosmic velocities.

One of the most practicable methods at present of increasing the velocity of the exhaust gases from the nozzle of the rocket is that based on increasing the working temperature, since it is known that the higher the initial temperature when the molecular weight of the combustion products is the smallest possible, the greater their exhaust velocity.

But the high temperature of the combustion products requires special heat-resisting materials for the walls of the combustion chamber, the problem of obtaining which is one of the most important ones in modern rocket technology. Chemists, metallurgists, crystal-physicists, as well as experts in adjacent fields of science, are participating in its solution.

Other methods of accelerating the ejected particles are frequently discussed in the scientific-technological literature. It is proposed, for example, to utilize ion accelerators by means of which it is possible to impart a velocity of several thousand kilometers a second to the particles.

At the Fifth International Astronautical Congress Ernst Stuhlinger (American Rocket Society, Huntsville) presented a paper on the possibility of utilizing an electrical propulsion system for interplanetary ships. In his scheme he suggested utilizing cesium and rubidium as fuels: Their vapors ionize on colliding with an incandescent platinum grid; the resulting positive ions and electrons are then separately given an identical velocity on leaving the accelerator; and combining, they mutually neutralize each other to form fast-flying molecules of gas. In the presence of an additional source of electrical energy — photoelements or atomic batteries, for example — the engine of such a rocket can, in principle, with a small expenditure of matter develop sufficient thrust to impart a very great velocity to the rocket during its lengthy time of travel in cosmic space. A similar rocket was designed by D. Romick (American Rocket Society, Washington) at the same Congress.

This trend of research deserves attention inasmuch as it points out the possibility of investigating new methods of increasing the velocity of the ejected particles.

Equipment of the cosmic ship with its means of radio communication and its complex automatic control of the rate of fuel combustion in the rocket engines and the direction of motion of the rocket in cosmic space will require a great amount of different radio components. For example, the replacement of vacuum tubes alone by the very portable semiconductor crystal devices that are widely used in practice will lighten the cosmic ship several kilograms. This will lead to a great economy of fuel and, in the end, will make it possible to increase the velocity of the rocket. Therefore, any achievement in the field of physics and the technology of semiconductor instruments will also be an achievement towards realizing interplanetary communications.

The operation of the rocket control devices, of the means of radio communication with the earth, etc., will require considerable expenditure of electrical energy. As its source it will be possible to utilize the powerful light flux in which the rocket will be traveling within the limits of the solar system. Photoelements operating on the same semiconductor principle as crystal diodes and triodes are the best transformers of light energy into electrical energy. As is known, such photoelements have already attained an efficiency of 10%.

Thermoelements, whose efficiency can be just as high, can also play an essential role in this direction. From 10 square meters of the illuminated surface of a rocket it is possible by means of semiconductor devices to obtain electric current with a power up to 1 kilowatt. Under these conditions, during 100 days of flight of a cosmic ship, utilization of photoelements and thermoelements will make it possible to economize approximately 1000 kilograms of fuel, which will lead to a decrease of several tens of tons in the initial mass of the rocket. Consequently, any achievement in the field of increasing the efficiency of semiconductor photoelements and thermoelements will be a great contribution to the solution of the problem of cosmic flights.

A most significant achievement in decreasing the mass of the rocket and its equipment (in the period of developing cosmic velocity) would be the realization of the idea of composite rockets — "cosmic rocket trains" — worked out by Tsiolkovskii, and the idea of utilizing the elements of construction of the rocket itself as fuel, described by the talented engineer F. A. Tsander in his well-known work, *The Problem of Flight by Means of Reactive Apparatuses.*

The essence of these two ideas boils down to the following: If a combustible liquid serves as the rocket fuel, then logically the mass of the tanks for this liquid also becomes a part of the mass of the rocket. As the fuel is spent, the tanks should be dropped or, as Tsander suggested, burned, along with the unnecessary auxiliary equipment. The heat generated in this process must be absorbed by the fuel from the gaseous products of combustion.

Much work still has to be done before the practical expediency of the latter suggestion will become apparent.

*    *    *    *

The problem of utilizing the gravitational fields created by the earth, the sun, and the planets is absolutely essential for cosmonautics. The fact is that a correct choice of the direction of flight, taking gravitational forces into account, can ensure the ship's motion in space along complex trajectories without significant expenditure of fuel. Furthermore, performing a successful maneuver while the ship is flying near a massive moving body, a planet for example, it is possible to achieve an increase or a decrease in the ship's velocity only at the expense of the perturbing action of this body, that is, without expenditure of jet fuel. Insignificant deviations from the plotted course can lead to undesirable results and afterward will require for their correction a considerable expenditure of fuel, which is especially valuable under space conditions.

Therefore, a constant knowledge of one's location in space — knowing how to control the cosmic ship's movement by comparing its trajectory with the course computed beforehand — is one of the basic conditions of cosmic navigation.

The task of the precise determination of coordinates in interplanetary space is considerably more complex than the analogous task under conditions on the earth with its natural system of coordinates. Observation of remote stars from a cosmic rocket with its lightened instruments could hardly ensure the necessary precision. In this case, knowing how to find one's bearings in space with respect to the comparatively near planets and the sun must play an important role.

It will be possible to put into practice more reliable means of determining the ship's position in cosmic space by means of modern photoelectrical methods of automatic control. This will make it possible not only to ensure determining the ship's coordinates but also to bring its trajectory into conformity with the previously computed course.

At present in many countries of the world much attention is being paid to the creation of automatically controlled rockets, as well as astronavigational equipment. Thus, according to a report in the newspaper *Herald Express*, an optical system fixed on two previously selected stars, the light from which will be focused on a special light-sensitive screen, has been proposed for one of the rockets under construction in the United States. The functions of this screen are analogous in many respects to the functions of the retina of the human eye. Any change in the direction of motion of the cosmic ship will cause a displacement of the light spots, as a result of which the "retina" will give an impulse to the rocket's control relay. The impulse will operate until the spots of the stellar light occupy the position determined by the plotted course.

The determination of its velocity, which is the basic factor in the whole problem of interplanetary communications, bears a direct relation also to the problem under consideration of controlling the motion of the cosmic ship. Will this velocity be determined by radar methods or will it be more advantageous to use optical methods, or, finally, perhaps, shall we succeed in designing an instrument which will make it possible to integrate automatically and with great precision all the accelerations of the ship, including those caused by gravitational forces? — the answer to this question must be resolved in the immediate future.

\*　　\*　　\*　　\*

Study of the moon's surface by radar methods points to the rich possibilities in the realization of interplanetary radio communication. This problem, however, remains incompletely solved to the present. The rigid requirements imposed on the mass of the cosmic rocket payload make the problem of radio communication of the rocket with the earth one of the most complex technological tasks.

Communication by radio over hundreds of thousands and even millions of kilometers will require exceptionally powerful transmitters and very sensitive receiving instruments. It is much simpler to build transmitters of great power for short waves, but in this case there arises a new difficulty in establishing radio communication with a fast flying cosmic ship — the great shift of frequencies caused by the Doppler effect. As a result of this shift the frequency of the radio waves goes beyond the limits of the narrow band which is determined by the conditions of remote communication.

The question of the danger for astronauts that cosmic and meteor particles present has not yet been solved in practice or in theory. Flying into the terrestrial atmosphere with velocities reaching several tens of kilometers per second, meteoric particles "burn up" as a result of friction with the air at an altitude of more than 50 kilometers from the surface of the earth and only very few of them, comparatively large in size, succeed in reaching the earth and even then possess small velocities (hundreds of meters per second). This explains the lack of experimental data on the interaction of fast particles with an obstacle. We still have not only to calculate the probability of collision of meteorites with the ship, but also to ascertain the smallest size and lowest velocities at which they are dangerous to the metallic and transparent walls of the rocket.

This work must be preceded by many observations of meteorites in the upper layers of the atmosphere, by theoretical calculations on determining the penetrating power of such particles in their interaction with different substances, and also, possibly, by experimental investigations. Carrying out the latter entails for the present the insurmountable difficulty of obtaining under laboratory conditions large particles with velocities of the order of 10 to 40 kilometers per second.

The velocity of a space ship upon its return from an interplanetary journey will exceed 11 kilometers per second. In order to brake a ship flying with such velocity, one must either switch on the rocket motors, or utilize the braking effect of the atmosphere.

Braking by means of jet thrust directed in a direction opposite the rocket's motion would require such an expenditure of fuel that it would hardly be possible to hope for a quick solution of the idea of conquering cosmic space.

The second method of braking is based on passing the rocket first through the rarefied layers of the atmosphere, where its velocity will be somewhat reduced. At the same time the rocket will pass from a parabolic orbit to an elliptic one. A further decrease in velocity will occur during the flight of the rocket around the earth along a spiral-like trajectory. After several revolutions the rocket's velocity will be reduced to such a degree that subsequently it will be possible to safely utilize ordinary aerodynamic methods of landing.

Here we shall have to solve one of the interesting problems of mechanics — that of determining the motion of a body along a spiral-like trajectory in a resisting medium, taking into account the forces of gravity which depend on a predominant central mass around which the motion is taking place.

\*    \*    \*    \*

The most active period in the development of rocket technology began in the middle of World War II when in the arsenal of Hitler's army there appeared a new weapon — the ballistic V-2 rocket. Soon after the explosion of the first of these missiles, liquid-fuel rockets capable of covering distances of hundreds of kilometers began to appear in other countries also.

Rocket technology began to be intensively developed in the United States, where, at present, several types of long-range rockets have been elaborated, including rockets for high-altitude flights beyond the stratosphere. The best known rockets in the latter category are the Viking Numbers 9, 10, and 11, the Wac Corporal, the Aerobee, and Bumper Number 5.

The Viking Number 9 rocket, launched December 15, 1952, attained a height of 218 kilometers. The high-altitude one-stage Viking Number 11 rocket launched at the White Sands (New Mexico, U. S.) proving grounds on May 24, 1954, attained a record (for the given type of rocket) an altitude of 254 kilometers. The flight lasted 10 minutes, maximum flight velocity was 6880 kilometers per hour, and the starting weight of the rocket was 7.5 tons. Especially interesting and effective were the launchings of the two-stage rockets, particularly of the Bumper rocket Number 5, whose first stage is an "A-4" motor and whose second stage is a Wac Corporal. The latter was mounted in the warhead of the A-4 rocket. When the first motor had ceased operation, the jet engine of the Wac Corporal switched on. As a result of such a combined flight, the Bumper Number 5 was able to attain an altitude of 400 kilometers and to develop a maximum velocity of 2200 meters per second or 8000 kilometers per hour. Today, however, it is possible to attain even greater altitudes.

The basic program of high-altitude investigations is the study of the physical composition of the terrestrial atmosphere, the nature and properties of the ionosphere, and also those processes which lead to its formation. With the aid of numerous automatic devices installed in such rockets, much interesting information was obtained about the upper layers of the atmosphere, about its temperature and density, about the content of various gases in it, about the degree of ionization, and about the processes taking place at this altitude, all of which is extremely interesting to science.

Various animals were also raised in the rockets to the attained altitude. Their behavior and state of health were studied under such unusual flight conditions when at the moment the engines first began to operate, they had to live through a manifold increase in weight caused by the acceleration of the rocket, and later a complete loss of weight at the moment of subsequent motion by inertia.

Such a state of weightlessness lasted several tens of seconds. Instruments which registered the heart activity, breathing and other vital functions of the animals by means of radio signals and tele-recording reported data which no one had been able to observe before.

In experiments with the Deacon rocket launched from a balloon, it was established that animals can endure without harm short-time accelerations up to 3 to 4 $g$ for 45 seconds, and up to 15 $g$ for 1 second ($g$ is the acceleration of gravity equal to 9.8 meters per second per second).

In the paper presented by K. Gatland before the British Interplanetary Society, February 6, 1954, it was pointed out that the effect of great accelerations on the human organism and on animals was studied by means of the centrifuge. Experiments were conducted on a man who was subjected to accelerations up to 15 $g$ for 5 seconds.

\*     \*     \*     \*

The possibilities of modern jet technology, on the one hand, and the greatest prospects of scientific investigations that open up in this connection, on the other, spur scientists and designers to the next step in the conquest of cosmic altitudes — to the creation of an artificial satellite of the earth.

As far back as 1932, F. A. Tsander pointed out: "The establishment of interplanetary stations around the earth and other planets will be very important . . . Interplanetary travels will become much cheaper with the construction of these stations, since everything that is necessary for further flight to another planet can be maintained on the interplanetary station."

Again, only a cosmic rocket that, when properly equipped, is turned into an automatic laboratory in the cosmos can be such an artificial satellite.

Various projects of cosmic flight utilizing an artificial satellite of the earth have been discussed on the pages of the world press. One of them is the project of a miniature satellite proposed by Professor S. Singer of the University of Maryland. This satellite, which weighs 45 kilograms and is 60 centimeters in diameter, according to its author, will revolve around the earth at an altitude of 320 kilometers. A three-stage rocket with an initial weight of 16 tons and a first-stage thrust of 30 tons will be required to deliver the satellite into its orbit.

In order to observe the satellite from the earth, it is proposed to utilize sodium vapors emitted by it, whose bright illumination by sunlight will make it possible to see the satellite at the mentioned altitude.

One should also mention the projects of Von Braun and G. A. Crocco. According to the first project, the artificial satellite must revolve at an altitude of 1730 kilometers with a velocity of 7.08 kilometers per second and perform a complete revolution in two hours. Von Braun assumes that the creation of such a satellite is possible if one takes advantage of three-stage rockets propelled by hydrazine and nitric acid. The first two stages are accelerators and only the third is an interplanetary ship. The starting weight of these rockets must amount to 7000 tons.

The project of G. A. Crocco is based on the idea of interplanetary trains with refueling during flight in cosmic space. He also proposed a program of concrete measures for building an artificial satellite, including the training of the technical personnel who are expected to work on it.

Despite the achieved successes and intensive development of the ideas of cosmonautics, one should nevertheless acknowledge that the question of interplanetary flight is still in the theoretical stage. This stage is, however, passing with such an impetuous speed that even today nobody will venture to say that the practical realization of the idea of interplanetary flight is utopia.

This was especially evident at the Sixth International Astronautical Congress which took place in August of this year in Copenhagen. Soviet scientists were also present at the Congress in which delegates of 18 countries participated.

The day before the Congress opened, the National Academy of Sciences in Washington and the National Science Foundation of the United States made an official announcement concerning plans for launching an artificial earth satellite during the International Geophysical Year (1957-1958).

According to the Associated Press report of July 29, from Baltimore (Maryland), the type of artificial earth satellite which the United States intends to build for scientific purposes corresponds in detail to the proposal of S. Singer, who was mentioned above. S. Singer maintains that it is possible to launch around the earth a small rocket laboratory that will cost two-thirds as much as a large bomber.

In S. Singer's opinion, it will be possible by means of this "flying laboratory" to carry out the following investigations: measurements of the light reflected by the earth from which to determine the total layer of cloudiness (this will permit forecasting weather for a long period, perhaps for an entire season); tracing magnetic storms to their source, that is, the sun; and the study of the nature of cosmic rays, which will make possible a deeper acquaintance with the nature of nuclear forces. By means of luminescent sodium, one will be able to study from the earth the trace left by the satellite, and in this way gather data on the movements of winds and other phenomena in the upper layers of the atmosphere. It is believed that the first and subsequent satellites will be launched from the proving grounds at White Sands (New Mexico, U. S.).

As the United Press reports, coordination of the work will, apparently, be entrusted to Joseph Kaplan, Chairman of the Committee established by the National Academy for United States participation in the International Geophysical Year.

Of all the papers presented at the Congress the most interesting were those of Ehricke and Tousey (U. S.) and of Kölle (German Federal Republic).

In Ehricke's paper a plan was suggested for creating an artificial satellite of the earth which can be launched to an altitude of 150 kilometers. This satelloid, in the words of the speaker, will require only 15 kilograms of a mixture of gasoline and oxygen in order to fly once around the earth.

In Kölle's paper a program was worked out for realizing interplanetary flights calculated for 30 years.

According to Tousey's project, a sphere 53 centimeters in diameter, moving in an orbit in the plane of the equator at an altitude of 300 to 1400 kilometers, will be visible to the naked eye when the sun descends nine degrees below the horizon (provided the sphere is illuminated by the sun). When the sun is two degrees below the horizon the sphere will be visible through binoculars "if only one knows precisely where and when to look," as Tousey says.

Soviet scientists held a press conference at which Academician L. I. Sedov spoke. "It seems to me," he said, "that the time has come when it is possible to direct our combined efforts to the creation of an artificial satellite and to switch the military potential in rocket technology to the peaceful and noble purposes of the development of cosmic flights."

At the Congress a special Commission was established to work out a program of international investigations and experiments in the field of creating an artificial earth satellite and the realization of interplanetary flights. The work of this commission will proceed within the framework of UNESCO.

It is easiest to make a satellite move in the plane of the equator in the direction of the earth's rotation. In this case its linear velocity, which amounts to 463 meters per second at the equator, would be utilized. But it will be more interesting to choose a slightly elliptical trajectory passing over the poles. With such a choice of direction of motion, a satellite will be able to fly at different altitudes with respect to the surface of the earth, to intersect all the latitudes of the terrestrial globe rotating under it. This means that with each new revolution it will fly over different segments of the earth's surface and enter different places of the space around the earth.

A long-lived satellite must, obviously, revolve around the earth at an altitude where the resistance of the atmosphere is almost completely absent, that is, at an altitude of not less than 1500 to 2000 kilometers above the surface. It is possible, however, that for the first of the satellites an altitude will be chosen within the limits from 200 to 1000 kilometers where the resistance of the air, which is rarefied many billions of times in comparison with the density of the air at the earth's surface, is also insignificant. Months and even years will elapse before the satellite will lose a significant part of its initial velocity as a result of such very weak air resistance. During this time it will be possible to carry out physical, geophysical, and astrophysical investigations which are either impossible near the terrestrial surface or do not yield sufficiently complete results here.

The complex of the contemplated investigations must include as wide a circle of interconnected phenomena as possible so that with their aid it would be possible to more completely reveal the processes which are taking place in the upper layers of the atmosphere, in interstellar space, on the sun, and on the planets.

Data of such investigations will be not only of general cognitive value but also of practical significance in the solution of the subsequent problems of mastering cosmic space.

Some scientists assume that the creation of an artificial earth satellite will also open new prospects for the solution of many important tasks of national economy. Among the latter, they consider the possibility of utilizing the satellite for observing the general movement of clouds in the atmosphere and of ice in the Arctic Ocean, which will permit making more precise forecasts of the weather and conditions for Arctic navigation, and the possibility of utilizing the satellite for relaying telecasts and for the solution of a number of other special problems of radio communications.

Besides the role that the artificial earth satellite must play in interplanetary communications, it will have to assume the role of the greatest cosmic scientific laboratory.

What kind of scientific problems then can be set forth in connection with the utilization of an artificial earth satellite?

First of all, it is necessary to learn more fully the properties of the ionosphere and the causes of its formation, that is, to ascertain the mechanism of the formation of the ionized layers of air at the boundary of its collision with different radiations invading the limits of the earth. In this respect cosmic rays — those fast-flying electrons and nuclei of various chemical elements from space — are of considerable interest. Flying into the limits of the atmosphere with tremendous velocities, sometimes approaching the speed of light, and colliding with molecules of gas, they often break them into positive ions and electrons. Interacting with the nuclei of the chemical elements which they meet on their way, cosmic rays sometimes generate new particles, mesons, or give rise to hard gamma rays, which in turn can simultaneously generate electrons and positrons.

Thus, every fast-flying cosmic particle is capable of forming a whole cascade of other charged particles, participating thereby in the formation of the ionosphere.

Cosmic rays attract the attention of investigators also because of the fact that, by their coming to us from remote interstellar spaces, they can serve as messengers of processes inaccessible to our direct observation. In particular, a study can be organized of the influence of the magnetic field of the sun and the oscillations caused by magnetic storms on the intensity of cosmic rays; "after thrashing out which," as Alven writes, "we shall come to the exceptionally interesting problem of the origin of the tremendous energy of cosmic rays and their isotropy." The latter question is especially important since the isotropy of cosmic rays indicates their exceptional role in the energy balance of the universe.

Two hypotheses were suggested to explain the phenomenon of the isotropy of cosmic rays. According to the first, cosmic radiation is isotropic throughout the entire universe.

The second hypothesis assumes that cosmic rays are a local galactic phenomenon and that the components of the cosmic-ray particles move along spiral lines around the lines of force of the magnetic field of the galaxy.

In this connection the measurements made photographically at great altitudes acquire an exceptional importance. These measurements have shown that primary radiation consists of nuclei of atoms, and the relative composition of these atoms in cosmic rays is approximately the same as their composition in interstellar matter.

The study of this question under transatmospheric conditions will give science new material for judgment about the origin and energetics of cosmic rays.

It is possible that such questions, as yet unsolved under terrestrial conditions, as the question of the composition of primary cosmic radiation (for example, the percentage content of the nuclei of atoms of lithium, beryllium, and boron in the flux of cosmic particles) can also be investigated by means of suitable instruments installed in the satellite.

By means of miniature ionospheric stations installed in the satellite it will be possible to study, in particular, the electronic and ionic concentrations in the ionosphere at different altitudes, the frequency of collision of electrons, the length of their free path, and their stability and uniformity in the latitude of the electronic concentration at the altitude of stable equilibrium.

Knowledge of all these data as well as information about the indices of refraction of meter, decimeter, and centimeter radio waves in the various layers of the ionosphere, and the influence of the ionosphere on the polarization of radio waves of the standard range will help in solving the question of establishing radio communication between the earth and the other planets.

Observations of the earth's magnetic field and of its changes with time will allow scientists to penetrate more deeply one of the great riddles of nature — the mystery of the origin of terrestrial magnetism.

Questions connected with the problem of the origin of the solar system also can receive very wide illumination by means of investigations carried out on the artificial earth satellite. For this purpose it would be expedient to collect cosmic dust and larger particles in order to determine their amount and chemical composition.

Compact radar installations in the satellite will ensure the possibility of observing in a fixed volume the movement of meteoric particles by the ionized tracks they leave behind them that reflect short-wave radiation well. Knowledge of the flux density of these particles will facilitate the solution of the meteorite problem which is discussed, together with other tasks arising on the way to realizing interplanetary communications.

Among the interesting phenomena of nature are those connected with the luminescence of the terrestrial atmosphere. Of exceptional interest are the investigations of the earth's own atmospheric emission with the transitions of observations from the night to the day part of the earth's surface. The combination of observations above the chosen regions of the sky from the satellite (beyond the atmosphere) and from the terrestrial surface will make it possible to pick out the luminescence of atmospheric origin.

Besides this, observation from the satellite would make it possible to more fully study the spectrum of the cosmic component of the luminescence of the night sky.

Finally, there are the numerous problems of the sun. On the artificial satellite, one will be able to observe continuously that which now draws investigators to observe the solar corona, which is most accessible only during a total solar eclipse and which lasts only a few seconds. At the same time it is extremely desirable to follow the successive changes in the solar corona, the development of coronal arcs and fans, especially over the active regions of the sun, and the origin and displacement of the coronal protuberances. The most remarkable feature of the astrophysical investigations from the artificial satellite will undoubtedly be the accessibility of observations of the ultraviolet and roentgen spectra of the radiations of the sun and the stars, which are impossible under terrestrial conditions because of the complete absorption of these rays by the atmosphere. In all these investigations, when the satellite is suitably stabilized, automatic slow-motion cinematography can play an exceptional role.

Obviously experiments concerned with the study of conditions of life in the absence of gravity will be especially interesting. On the artificial satellite all bodies will be in a state of weightlessness since the force of gravity acting on them will be counterbalanced by the centrifugal forces caused by the revolution of the satellite around the earth. Living organisms will perceive this state as a state of continuous free-fall, with all the sensations resulting therefrom.

How will such a state affect the vital functions of animals, their physiological processes? How will the life of plants proceed under these completely unusual conditions when the force of gravity will no longer restrict their growth? Biologists and biophysicists will be able to find answers for all these and other interesting questions when a laboratory in the cosmos will be at their disposal.

Together with the utilization of atomic energy for peaceful purposes and the development of the technology of semiconductors and new computing machines, the problem of interplanetary communications belongs to those problems which will open before mankind great areas of scientific cognition and the conquest of nature.

The importance of this problem was clearly described by Academician P. L. Kapitsa, a member of the Commission on Interplanetary Communications: " . . . if, in any branch of knowledge, possibilities of penetrating a new virgin field of investigation are opening, then it must be done without fail, because the history of science teaches that, as a rule, it is precisely this penetration of new fields that leads to the discovery of those very important phenomena of nature which most significantly widen the paths of development of human culture." (*Vestnik Akademii Nauk SSSR*, September, 1955.)

# 9.   On Flights Into Space*

*L. I. Sedov*

The development of modern science and technology is creating the conditions necessary for transforming astronautics from a bold dream of mankind into a genuine science of flight in cosmic space.  The time is not distant when the brilliant foresight of the great Soviet scientist Konstantin Eduardovich Tsiolkovskii, who scientifically established the principle of flights in interstellar space and who first suggested the idea of creating an artificial earth satellite, will come true.

The interest which the scientific community of the whole world is showing now in the important problems of astronautics that are being developed in a number of countries, including the Soviet Union, is quite understandable.

Recently in the USSR, much attention has been devoted to research problems connected with the realization of interplanetary communications, and first of all to the creation of an artificial satellite of the earth. An interdepartmental committee for coordinating and controlling scientific and theoretical work in the fields of organizing and carrying out interplanetary communications has been established at the USSR Academy of Sciences.

The report made at a press conference in Copenhagen on the work of Soviet scientists in the field of astronautics evoked considerable interest among the newspapermen and the participants in the International Congress of Astronauts.

The Congress has undoubtedly promoted the establishment of creative contact between the scientists of various countries and an increase in exchange of scientific and technical information in the field of astronautics.  Much attention was devoted, in particular, to the

---

* This interview appeared in *Pravda* on September 26, 1955.  It was prefaced by the following remarks:

The international Congress of Astronauts took place in the Danish capital of Copenhagen. Soviet scientists Academician L. I. Sedov and Prof. K. F. Ogorodnikov attended the Congress as observers. Upon his return to Moscow, Academician L. I. Sedov stated in an interview with a *Pravda* correspondent.

creation of an artificial earth satellite. As it turned out, work on creating such a satellite is being carried out in a number of countries.

In the United States of America, for example, there are under way plans for launching into the upper layers of the atmosphere a small artificial earth satellite designed for scientific observations during the International Geophysical Year, which will extend from July 1, 1957, to December 31, 1958. Ehricke, the German expert in the field of rocket propulsion, who is at present working in the USA, told the Congress of Stratonauts about his plans for creating an artificial earth satellite (satelloid) which can be launched to an altitude of 150 kilometers. Such a satelloid, according to Ehricke, will offer good premises for a thorough study of the possibility of launching a manned earth satellite.

Up to the present, observations in the upper layers of the atmosphere have been carried out by means of gas-filled weather balloons which ascended to an altitude of approximately 30 kilometers. The layers of the atmosphere located higher were investigated by means of rockets. According to information published in the foreign press, the highest altitude reached during such experiments was 400 kilometers. Information was obtained by this method on pressure, density, temperature, and composition of the upper layers of the atmosphere and on the directions of the winds in them.

A number of rockets were equipped with chambers for experimental animals. Mice and monkeys, lifted to a great height, were placed in the chambers where they had freedom of movement. A moving picture which recorded the behavior of the rocket-borne animals, was shown at the Congress. The film recorded separate moments of the fall of the rocket when the mice were seemingly "suspended" in the center of the chamber. Before the landing, a parachute opened and the rocket, together with its "passengers," fell smoothly to the earth. It turned out that under the conditions of upper-layer flights the animals suffered no ill effects.

The atmosphere protects the earth from harmful radiations and particles coming from cosmic space and from the dangerous effects of strong ultraviolet radiation. At the same time, the atmosphere deprives scientists of the possibility of observing a number of phenomena revealing the laws of the development of the universe. To acquire many important data, scientists must place instruments outside the earth's atmosphere in order to obtain, with their aid, the signals which characterize the phenomena under investigation. At present, some information of interest to us has already been obtained by using rockets launched to a great height. But their flights and the corresponding measurements are restricted by the extremely short period of time and by the segment of space. Only by means of artificial satellites of the planet will it be possible to determine the conditions and difficulties which man will encounter in realizing his future flights into cosmic space.

It will be necessary to impart to the satellite, during its motion along a circular trajectory around the earth, a velocity that will give it a centrifugal force sufficient to balance the force of gravity. Revolving around the earth at an altitude of several hundred kilometers, it will develop a velocity of 25,700 kilometers per hour. A satellite delivered to this altitude by multistaged rockets will be able to continue its motion in the orbit without the aid of an engine.

Such a satellite will perform a flight around the earth in one and a half hours. It is assumed that the duration of the satellite's revolution around the earth can amount to several months or even years. Later on, because of the gradual effect of the resistance of the atmosphere, it will approach the earth, will heat up on entering the denser atmosphere, and finally, will burn up like a meteor high above our planet. Scientists also are considering the possibility of the preservation and the landing of the satellite on the earth.

Let us note that an artificial satellite, by the character of its motion around the earth, will to a certain degree resemble the earth's natural satellite, the moon, which is located at a distance of approximately 400,000 kilometers from our planet.

As was pointed out at the Congress, under favorable conditions it will be possible to see an artificial satellite through binoculars or even with the naked eye. The basic means of observing it, however, will be various instruments, including telescopes, theodolites, and electronic devices.

Use of an artificial satellite will make it possible to carry out a number of important observations concerning the earth's magnetism, the aurora borealis, luminescence of the air, physics of the ionosphere, solar activity, cosmic rays, etc.

At the press conference in Copenhagen, I expressed an opinion about the possibility of launching an earth satellite in the next couple of years. In my opinion it is technically possible to create artificial satellites of different dimensions and weights. It seems to me that the time has come when it is possible to unite the efforts of scientists and engineers in various countries to create an artificial earth satellite and to switch the military potential in rocket technology to the peaceful and noble purposes of developing cosmic flights. I think that such work would serve the cause of strengthening peace. The press conference of the Soviet scientists evoked great interest. It was widely reported in foreign newspapers and radio broadcasts. But, unfortunately, they contained gross distortions. Some foreign newspapermen, eager for sensation, distorted the real state of affairs beyond recognition. We later received a number of apologies from them.

Many reports devoted to the development of various scientific problems connected with the motion of an artificial earth satellite in the upper layers of the atmosphere were delivered at the Congress. They also discussed questions of the aerodynamics of highly rarefied gases, questions of stability of motion, methods of launching a satellite to a great height with the necessary velocity.

The reports also contained "predictions" about the development of interplanetary communications in the next thirty years. Thus, for example, the report of the German scientist Kölle of Stuttgart foresees such a program of interplanetary flights, according to which it will be possible from 1966 to 1970 to start serial production of rocket earth satellites for cargo and people and to build an experimental space station; from 1971 to 1977, to plan, prepare, and carry out an expedition to the moon; and from 1978 to 1985 to send an expedition to Mars. According to Kölle's calculations, approximately fifty billion dollars will be required to finance this program.

A popular-science artistic cinema film entitled *Man in Space*, released by the American director Walt Disney and the German rocket-missile expert Von Braun, chief designer of the V-2, was shown at the Congress. Films were also shown on the flights and tests of modern rockets, on new rocket installations, and on experiments with modern jet airplanes. It would be desirable that new popular-science films devoted to the problems of interplanetary travels be shown in our country in the near future. It is also extremely important to increase the interest of the general public in the problem of astronautics. Here is a worthwhile field of activity for scientists, writers, artists, and for many workers of Soviet culture.

During the work of the Congress we became acquainted with prominent European and American astronauts and established friendly contacts with them. We should mention the fine organization of the Congress and the unusually cordial reception accorded the Soviet scientists by the Danish people and the participants of the Congress. (*Pravda*, September 26, 1955.)

# 10. Study of the Upper Atmosphere by Means of Rockets

*S. M. Poloskov and B. A. Mirtov*

The study of the upper atmosphere now being carried out by the USSR Academy of Sciences is of considerable magnitude. On the occasion of the International Geophysical Year, it has been decided to augment the work, and the additional studies will include direct observation by means of rockets.

The Academy of Sciences of the USSR will take part in a series of studies in this particular field. In the course of the International Geophysical Year it is expected that results on the following subjects will be obtained:

1. Structure parameters of the upper atmosphere — temperature, pressure, and composition.

2. Movements of the upper atmosphere.

3. Study of the electrical properties of the upper atmosphere (ionosphere).

4. Study of cosmic radiation.

5. Study of the ultraviolet part of the sun's spectrum.

6. Study of the solid composition of interplanetary material (micrometeorites).

7. Study of corpuscular rays from the sun.

We have already begun work on some of these problems. It is proposed to develop the work further. Let us enumerate some of the more important results obtained during the study of the upper atmosphere by direct methods.

The fundamentally new character of our work in the field of structure parameters lies in the fact that the measuring instruments are carried, not in the rocket itself, but in automatically jettisoned containers. For this purpose, special mortars are installed on two sides of the rocket, where the containers are located. The mortars are themselves faired into the main structure. At the required altitude the containers are fired out of the mortars some distance from the rocket, and measurements are then made under much more favorable conditions.  The gases given off by the rocket interfere with measuring the parameters of the undisturbed atmosphere.

Another distinctive feature of our work is the fact that we are obliged to recover all the containers by parachute.  The recovery system has been well proved.  All necessary measurements are made by photographing electrical instruments included in the appropriate circuitry.  The exposed film is rolled into an armored casette and is preserved intact, even when the container makes a bad landing.

I will now describe briefly the container and the apparatus carried within it.

### THE INSTRUMENT CONTAINER

The instrument container is a metal cylinder two meters long and 0.4 meter in diameter and weighs about 250 kilograms.  The bottom part of the cylinder is hermetically sealed and contains the storage batteries, measuring devices (milli- and micro-ammeters), the camera, and the program mechanism which controls all these instruments.

The upper part of the cylinder is reserved for glass spheres, designed to collect samples of air, and for manometers.  This part of the cylinder is so designed that the apparatus contained in it is open freely to the surrounding air.

The wires connecting the spheres and manometers to the program switch and power supplies come from the hermetically sealed portion to the upper part of the cylinder by way of a suitable socket.  The parachute is attached to the perforated top part of the container; and, in order to prevent accidents, the former is carried in a pressurized container.  The container is jettisoned automatically in the descending phase of the trajectory at a height of 10 to 12 kilometers above the earth's surface.  At this altitude the parachute comes into operation.  To obtain a good landing, the rear portion of the container carries a spike, equipped with special points, which buries itself in the ground on landing and keeps the container vertical.

### PARTICULARS OF THE EXPERIMENTS

*Atmospheric Composition at Altitudes of 80 to 95 Kilometers.*

In order to solve this complex task successfully, it is necessary, first to obtain a pure and unaltered sample, and second, to be able to analyze it accurately.  The first part of the problem has been solved by using glass flasks varying from $\frac{1}{2}$ to 3 liters in capacity.  These flasks, which are evacuated, are equipped with special taps which

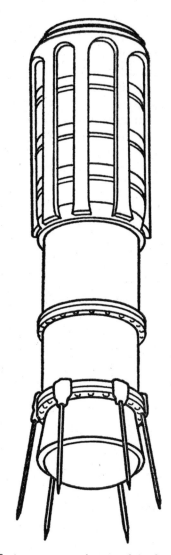

Instrument container used in Soviet
atmosphere rocket research.

open and close automatically at chosen altitudes. The taps are high-vacuum, large-diameter taps, without any entry tube.

The second part of the problem is solved by spectral analysis of the gas mixture. This method allows the analysis of tenths and hundredths of a cubic centimeter of gas mixture under normal conditions. The air is subjected to an analysis for oxygen ($O_2$), nitrogen ($N_2$), and argon (A). In the analysis the relative error of the measurement for $O_2$ and $N_2$ does not exceed five to seven per cent, and for argon, three to four per cent. To carry out this analysis the gas is displaced with mercury from the sphere into a capillary-analyzer tube 0.4 millimeter in diameter, in which a pressure of five to ten millimeters of mercury is created. By passing a high-frequency current through external electrodes, the gas is made to glow. The spectrum of this light, together with that from special calibrating mixtures, is photographed in a spectrograph and then a careful photometric study of the photographs is made. We must point out the fact that the air samples are collected at the summit of the trajectory, or thereabouts. In this case the speed of the container does not exceed 50 to 70 meters per second, so that the pressure inside the flask corresponds to the ambient pressure. It is for this reason that the container is superior to the rocket itself, in which samples can only be collected at high speeds, because of the release of gas from the rocket.

*Pressure at Altitudes From 50 to 110 Kilometers.*

Pressure measurements are made with thermal and ionization gauges. The results of these methods of pressure measurement agree approximately with the known results obtained in the U. S.

*Determination of the Speed and Direction of Winds at Altitudes From 60 to 80 Kilometers.*

We have determined the speed and direction of wind by the creation and observation of artificial clouds at fixed altitudes.

Special smoke-producing containers are used to form these clouds. These containers, like the ones containing the instruments, are ejected from the rocket by mortars. This is after one or more of the containers, as required, have been put into the mortar. The smoke container is made up of five cylinders each containing 15 kilograms of smoke material. These cylinders are provided with delay fuses. The container explodes at the desired instant, forming a cloud of smoke at a predetermined altitude. The cylinders, by exploding almost simultaneously but at different altitudes, enable a sufficiently complete picture to be obtained of the movement of masses of air within the layer in which the artificial clouds were formed. Movements of the artificial clouds are photographed by cine-theodolites set out in the area beneath the release point. Each cloud is photographed by at least two theodolites, having a base of several tens of kilometers. This, after development of the films, allows the speed as well as the direction of the clouds to be determined with great precision. This method, however, has an upper useful limit of about 80 kilometers altitude. Above this limit, the smoke cloud (the particles which form it having a dimension of 0.5 micron) does not persist in the atmosphere but starts to fall and to disperse rapidly, making observation impossible. The same clouds formed at or below 80 kilometers persist for an adequate length of time. Their speeds are subject to important variations, but are always high — of the order of 60 to 100 meters per second. The direction of the wind shows a seasonal character; in the summer from east to west, in winter from north to south.

### OTHER STUDIES

In addition to the work described above we are studying micro-meteorites, which are detected by their impact on sensitive plates. This work has so far not produced sufficient results to make discussion feasible.

In order to study the gaseous and ionic composition of the upper layers, we intend in the near future to use radio frequency mass spectrometers, which possess a number of advantages over the air-sampling method. Finally, in order to study winds and temperatures of the upper layers of the atmosphere, we will use the sound-detection method, which will be a second independent method of measuring the parameters of the atmosphere.

In the course of this communication I do not only want to speak of what we propose to do during the course of the International Geophysical Year and, in general, in the near future; I should also like to draw your attention to several problems, fundamental ones in my opinion, that will have to be resolved with maximum success and effectiveness both by the aid of direct methods and by a combination of direct and indirect studies of the upper atmosphere.

We shall be extremely grateful to those taking part in the meeting who might give their opinions on the questions we are raising or who could express new thoughts.

In the near future and in the course of the International Geophysical Year, we propose to study:

1. The structure parameters of the upper atmosphere (pressure and

temperature) and its composition at different altitudes, using various types of equipment. It is foreseen (and this applies to all sections of our research) that work will be carried out at different altitudes up to approximately 1000 kilometers and at different geographical locations (all at the same high latitude).

2. Movement of the upper atmosphere (winds).

3. Micrometeorites (meteoric dust).

I wish to indicate how we propose to combine the direct and indirect methods in the course of our work in the three directions indicated.

We propose to organize optical and radar studies of meteors in order to obtain data by another, independent method on the densities and movements in the upper atmosphere and on the number of microparticles and their speed and deceleration.

We propose (and I wish to speak on behalf of the Academy of Sciences), if we are successful, to begin work in other directions also.

On this question we are presently consulting with other establishments and scientific workers in our country. We are always happy to have the opportunity to discuss the problems which interest us with our foreign colleagues as well.

In order to make the most logical use of this opportunity I would like to express our thoughts on the question of what at the moment we consider to be the most essential and fundamental problems in the study of the upper atmosphere by means of rockets.

There is no doubt at present that the physical conditions existing in the upper atmosphere depend to a large degree, or, more correctly, are determined fundamentally by, the effect of of the outermost layers of the sun on the earth's upper atmosphere and the sporadic changes occurring in the upper atmosphere and at the earth's magnetic poles are essentially determined by the changes occurring in the active region of the outer envelope of the sun: photosphere, chromosphere, and solar corona.

From this it follows that fundamental regard should be paid to the study of the actions and interactions which undoubtedly exist, but which have not been sufficiently established at present, or even established at all, between the changes which take place in the active regions of the sun, and the changes which occur in the physical condition of the upper atmospheres. These changes are connected with upper-layer ionization and also with the conditions for propagation of radio waves; and with the variations of the earth's magnetic pole, the intensity of cosmic rays as far as the sun is concerned, the changes in sky luminosity by day and night, and the intensity, the duration and form of the aurorea borealis, and the change of ionic composition and structure parameters of the atmosphere, etc. In this respect the general problem can be divided into two parts:

1. Study of the role of the sun's ultraviolet radiation.
2. Study of the role of the sun's corpuscular currents.

Let us examine these problems from the point of view of the question, What new contribution can be made by rocket research?

### STUDY OF THE ROLE OF THE SUN'S ULTRAVIOLET RADIATION

For some time it has been known quite certainly that, with a quiescent sun, the source principally responsible for ultraviolet radiation — in the line spectrum as well as in the continuous spectrum — is the solar corona, and that the chromospheric protuberances are responsible for the intense sporadic outbursts of ultraviolet radiation; therefore it is natural that one should be extremely interested in two problems.

(a) The first problem is that of obtaining, while the sun is in its quiescent state, as exhaustive measurements as are possible on the ultraviolet solar spectrum at all possible wave lengths. It is known at present, as a result of research carried out in the U. S., that the ultraviolet spectrum of the sun is known in sufficient detail. Similar work has been carried out in the USSR. We are not aware, from the method point of view, of any particular difficulties, and at present it is hoped to obtain measurements more complete and of greater precision by the use of spectrographs of considerably greater resolving power. In the remote ultraviolet it is more desirable to obtain those regions of the spectrum corresponding to most intense rays of the solar corona. I am speaking of the Ne VIII, Mg X, and other lines.

It will be even more interesting, however, and it will have a fundamental significance and will constitute an entirely new result, if measurements can be obtained on the ultraviolet radiation over the whole of the accessible region of spectrum during chromospheric eruptions. This will obviously raise a series of considerable difficulties both in method and technique because the eruption phenomena are of short duration and occur suddenly in such a way that their appearance cannot be predicted. Furthermore, the vigorous eruptions are very rare phenomena. Since they are connected with sun spots, however, their probability is considerably greater in the period of maximum solar activity, that is to say, in the period of the International Geophysical Year.

(b) The second new problem for rockets is the study of the eruption spectrum and the photography of the outermost corona at the moment of a total eclipse of the sun. It is known that on October 12, 1958, in the Pacific Ocean area, a total eclipse of the sun of long duration will take place. This eclipse will occur at the maximum of solar activity during the International Geophysical Year.

It is probably very difficult, but not impossible, to organize observations of these solar eclipses by means of rockets. Paralleling the complete geophysical program, one can imagine these rockets obtaining measurements of the eruption spectrum and of the corona, and photographs of the external corona, and ensuring the ultimate recovery of the scientific results. It appears difficult to us to underestimate the scientific importance of such an experiment.

### STUDY OF THE ROLE OF CORPUSCULAR RADIATION FROM THE SUN

It cannot be contested that the corpuscular rays from the sun play an immense role in the formation of the upper layers of the atmosphere and cause to a great extent a series of phenomena of sporadic character which occur in the upper atmosphere. It is sufficient to cite by way of example phenomena such as the aurorae borealis, the disturbance of normal conditions in the ionosphere and at the magnetic poles, etc.

Can there be any doubt, however, that at present the problem of the physics of corpuscular solar currents has been studied very insufficiently? The centers of the solar surface, which form the source of the corpuscles and the mechanism of emission, are insufficiently studied. The nature of the particles has not been established with authenticity.

Several hypotheses exist on the physical conditions existing in a corpuscular beam in interplanetary space during its path from sun to earth.

The conditions of the penetration of the corpuscular rays into the earth's atmosphere and the phenomena which occur as a result are studied in an entirely insufficient fashion. In this respect rockets represent an invaluable research tool. First, they allow study at high altitude of physical conditions existing in a practically undisturbed beam and, as a result, of the behavior of corpuscular rays at characteristic altitudes and at different latitudes. Second, just as in the study of the role played by ultraviolet rays from the sun — perhaps to an even greater extent — it would be extremely desirable to proceed to the study of corpuscular radiation from the sun, both when the sun is in its quiescent state and when there are chromospheric eruptions, and other events that occur on the sun's surface — during and after the existence of the great floccular fields, for example. It would be particularly interesting to carry out such experiments at high latitudes and, in particular, in the zones of maximum intensity of the aurora borealis.

It seems to us that the study of the sun's corpuscular radiation by means of rockets presents no insurmountable obstacle from the scientific and technical viewpoint.

In conclusion, concerning particles emitted by the sun, I would like to draw your attention to cosmic rays — the most rapid of these particles. It seems to us that it would be extremely interesting to carry out the experiments for the study of cosmic rays at high latitudes during periods of chromospheric eruptions, in order to detect electrons in the primary cosmic rays. I would point out, although probably there are many who know it already, that the question of electrons in cosmic rays is of primary importance in bringing some light to bear on the nature of cosmic rays. This affects all of modern radio-astronomy. It has been established at present that, for causes that are unknown, the electronic component of cosmic rays is removed at the limit of the solar system. That will obviously not apply, however, to electrons which, if they exist, are emitted from the sun in the direction of the earth. (Presented at the Congrès International des Fusées et Engins Guidés, Paris, December 3-8, 1956.)

# Part Three

# BIOLOGICAL FACTORS

# 11.  Problems of Weightlessness

*P. K. Isakov*

One of the works of our famous native scientist, K. E. Tsiolkovskii, bears the title: "On the earth and outside the earth in the Year 2017." Today, in connection with the accelerated progress of science and technology, there is every reason to think that the date mentioned by the scientist for realizing flights of man into cosmic space will be brought considerably closer to our time.  Whereas, at the beginning of the twentieth century, individuals worked on these questions, to-day, many tens and even hundreds of investigators, a great number of universities, and scientific societies of various countries are working fruitfully on the problems of organizing and ensuring cosmic travels. Today in this field there is almost no question left that is not a matter of scientific discussions, or is not subjected to thorough scientific consideration and even often to direct experimental study.  One may assume that within the next year and a half an extraterrestrial laboratory (artificial satellite of the earth) will be created as a preparatory stage for cosmic flights, and that in five to ten years, man will appear in cosmic space.

One of the important features of cosmic flights will be the weightlessness of the contents of the cosmic ship over large segments of its path in interplanetary space.  K. E. Tsiolkovskii gave the first scientific description of this feature as early as 1911-1912.

Specific study of the problem, however, began only recently.

It is known that every body under the action of gravity exerts a definite pressure on its support.  At the same time, it does not matter in what position it finds itself with respect to the latter: whether it stands directly on it, or is suspended from it.  In each case a force is created which is called the weight of the body.

The weight of any body located on the earth is constant only under the conditions of a certain limited part of the earth's surface.  As soon as the body is moved outside the boundaries of this area, its weight will change.  Thus, if some cargo, weighed in Moscow, is moved to one of the drifting stations of the North Pole, then a clearly manifested increase in weight will be discovered. Of course, it is necessary to use a spring-balance to detect this difference. Ordinary balances will not show any difference in the given case since the weights used for measuring will change in the same ratio as the cargo.

Why do such changes in weight occur? The fact is that the magnitude of the pressure of a body on its support is the result of the action of two factors: the earth's attraction and the centrifugal force created by the rotation of the earth around its axis.

Our planet is flattened at the poles. The distance from the earth's surface to its center is less here than at the equator. Since the force of the earth's attraction is inversely proportional to the square of the distance from the center of the earth, it has a greater magnitude at the poles. The effect of the centrifugal force arising from the rotation of the terrestrial globe is also different.

The greatest linear velocity of the earth's surface is in the region of the equator, and the smallest in the region of the poles. The centrifugal effect lowers the weight of a body because the force with which a body moves away from the earth is directed opposite the force of the earth's attraction. Thus, bodies at a pole weigh even more because the effect of the centrifugal force here is less pronounced than at other points of the earth's surface.

The centrifugal effect is especially noticeable in the motion of bodies on the earth's surface. Thus, a train running from Moscow to Vladivostok weighs less than a train running in the opposite direction. In the first case its velocity is added to the linear velocity of the earth's surface, in the second case it is subtracted from it. The same thing, only in a more sharply pronounced form, takes place also in the motion of airplanes to the east or to the west. Suppose an airplane weighs 10,000 kilograms; then such an airplane flying east in the region of the equator with a speed of about 1000 kilometers per hour will weigh 100 kilograms less than when flying in the region of a pole. Of course, the pilot at the same time will also weigh correspondingly less.

An even greater change in weight takes place during the motion of artillery projectiles. At a velocity of 2500 meters per second, their weight decreases approximately 10%, which is noticeably reflected in the range of flight.

A further increase in the velocity of motion of bodies leads to a still greater decrease in their weight. At a velocity of 8 kilometers per second (about 29,000 kilometers per hour) the weight will disappear completely. An apparatus moving with such speed around the earth will no longer be attracted by it, since the force of gravity in this case will be balanced by the centrifugal force.

But the weight of bodies changes not only with the speed of their motion within the limits of the earth's surface. In ascent above our planet, the force of its attraction, as mentioned earlier, decreases in inverse proportion to the square of the distance. Of course, to detect a noticeable difference in the weight of the body, it is necessary to raise it to a suitable altitude. Thus, at a distance of 6400 kilometers from our planet, the weight of a body is one-fourth of its weight on the earth's surface.

All this only confirms the position that under conditions of the uniform motion of a cosmic ship in interplanetary space, all objects inside such a ship become weightless. True, the law of mutual attraction of bodies is operative in any region of the universe, and, hence, also for the bodies inside the cosmic ship. However, the mutual attraction of these objects is insignificantly small relative to the earth's attraction. If, for example, two bodies each weighing 100 kilograms are placed one meter apart, then they attract each other with a force of approximately 1/40 milligram. Of course, this cannot exert a perceptible effect on the objects which will be practically under conditions of weightlessness until the cosmic ship approaches another planet, when that planet's attraction will begin to manifest itself.

How is the feeling of our own weight created in us?

At any position of a man on a supporting surface (standing, sitting, or lying down), the pressure on his body causes the same pressure from the support — the so-called force of reaction of the support. This brings about a certain temporary deformation of the tissues of the organism, primarily, at the points of contact of the body with the support. The nerve branches in the tissues receive the corresponding stimuli traveling to the brain, causing in the man the sensation of the weight of the body, his weight.

In everyday life there are several situations (short-lived ones, it is true) when a decrease occurs in a man's weight up to complete weightlessness. Our most familiar sensation of weightlessness is observed while descending in an elevator in a building or a mine shaft. In the first instant, when a man has not yet acquired the speed of the elevator, his body presses on the floor of the elevator considerably less than normal, especially if the motion begins quite rapidly. As a result, a sensation of weightlessness is created. But after a short interval of time, the man's body acquires the same speed as the elevator, and the weight of his body returns to normal. It is easy to visualize such a case when the acceleration of an elevator during its descent would be equal to the acceleration caused by the earth's attraction, that is, approximately 9.81 meters per second per second. Then the man in the elevator would become weightless.

An analogous phenomenon arises during a parachute jump. In the first seconds while the parachute is unopened and the air resistance is negligible (as a result of the small initial velocity of fall), the man has almost no weight. Of course, for this it is necessary to jump from a motionless apparatus, for example, from a balloon. In a jump from an airplane a man will fly at first with the speed of the latter; the air resistance here is sufficiently great and the force of weight sufficiently perceptible because of the mutual pressure of the parachutist on the air and of the air on the parachutist.

In all the cases described above, the action of weightlessness is felt very briefly. Man experiences a more protracted decrease in body weight while in water, especially in salt water. But even here, the decrease in weight is expressed insignificantly, although it is quite perceptible, especially at the moment of leaving the water.

Thus, people encounter the phenomena of change of body weight even on the earth.

Consequently, these phenomena and their influence on man can be studied, which is very important for solving a number of problems connected with cosmic flights.

Interplanetary communications will last many days, and sometimes even months. During this time man will be exposed to the action of a number of unusual factors, including weightlessness. How will it affect his vital activities and working capacity? What should be taken into account to ensure normal living conditions (including nutrition, clothing, sleep, locomotion inside the ship, etc.)? All such questions demand an answer in order to correctly organize and effectively ensure cosmic flights. It is necessary also to find out beforehand what organs will experience the greatest difficulties under the conditions of weightlessness; whether it is possible to adapt the organism to these conditions, and to develop ways and means of accelerating such adaptation.

At the outset, one should make the reservation that at present scientists still cannot study the influence of weightlessness for any protracted length of time. Such investigations will be conducted only after the creation of rockets performing flights with animals around the earth. Even now, however, there are certain data at the command of scientists, which make it possible to judge the effect of weightlessness on man.  Besides the reaction of an organism to jumps (for example, parachute jumps), to descent in elevators, etc., which were studied for a long time, special experiments were also carried out, in which the condition of weightlessness lasted for several seconds and even minutes.  Finally, for evaluating the influence of weightlessness, well-known scientific data on the degree of dependency of certain functions of the organism on the phenomena connected with weight will be utilized.  At the same time it will be determined what physiological processes take place with participation of the weight of the tissues and what processes do not depend on the latter.

As a result, important deductions are being made on the possibilities of a certain organ performing work under the condition of weightlessness.

Experiments studying the influence of weightlessness on animals were conducted by means of an insulated chamber located in a rocket of the V-2 type, or an improved model thereof.  In the ascent of the apparatus to the upper layers of the atmosphere, and on the attainment by it of a certain velocity, there appeared phenomena of weightlessness lasting several seconds.  As a result, it was found that no special changes in the functions took place.  The only exception was the blood pressure in the arteries which had an obvious tendency to decrease.  It is possible that this in some degree is explained by the exclusion of the hydrostatic blood pressure (because of its loss of weight), which participates in the regulation of blood circulation under the usual conditions of life.

The behavior of mice under the conditions of a more prolonged period of weightlessness (two to three minutes) was studied in other analogous experiments.  Previously the organs which signal the position of the body in space to the brain (the so-called vestibular apparatus located inside the temporal bones) had been removed from one of the mice.  Consequently, the normal life of this animal was disturbed with regard to its complete ability to orient itself in space.  After a certain time the mouse adapted itself to such orientation by using its sight.  In other words, if in normal animals control of the position of the body in space is realized to a large degree by signals coming from the vestibular apparatus, then, when this organ is removed, its role is compensated for, to a considerable degree, by signals coming from the other organs of the senses, in particular from the eyes.

Under the conditions of weightlessness, the mice behaved differently.  A normal mouse, having lost control of the vertical position of its body (because of the absence of signals from the vestibular apparatus which

arise under the action of the weight of its parts), exhibited the symp-
toms of lack of coordination of its movements.  It lay with its paws
up or on its side; it performed many movements with its extremities,
but without proper effect, since it could not set its body vertically.  On
the other hand, a mouse whose vestibular apparatus was destroyed
previously, behaved as if it were under ordinary conditions, that is,
it maintained its vertical position.

From these experiments one can deduce that if there are visual
orientations and if there is a possibility of utilizing the sense of touch,
it is quite feasible to maintain space orientation also under the condition of weightlessness when the signals from the vestibular apparatus
are not generated.

Experiments, similar to those described above, and with analogous
results, were also carried out on turtles in tanks filled with water.

Finally, there are described in the scientific literature observations
of a man under the conditions of weightlessness lasting 10 to 20 seconds.  These conditions were achieved in an airplane diving from a
great altitude and with anacceleration approximately equal to the
acceleration of the earth's force of gravity.  A task was set for the
man being tested: to write crosses in the squares on a sheet of paper.
On the ground and during ordinary flights, this assignment was carried out without errors.  Under the condition of weightlessness, however, the man being tested performed the assigned task with difficulty
and with large errors.  After several repetitions, however, the man
grew accustomed to coordinating his movements under the condition
of weightlessness, and the task was fulfilled quite successfully.

Therefore, even in this case training can help a great deal in the
normal functioning of the organism.

The experiments described above and other similar ones enable us
to assume that, even under the conditions of a prolonged period of
weightlessness, there is a possibility of maintaining a certain minimum
of man's working capacity.  Of course, for a direct proof of this, there
are needed suitable experiments on animals and preliminary observations on people.

The materials of a study of the various functions of man under normal living conditions yield an even greater assurance of the correctness of such an assumption.  As is known, most of these functions
are realized under the influence of osmotic processes, diffusion forces,
and even muscular contractions.  Evidently, the absence of weight
will have no effect whatever here, especially since many functions
of the organism take place when the body is in any position.

The problem of ensuring blood circulation requires a separate study. The point is that under normal conditions, the blood pressure in the vessels, which depends on its weight (the so-called hydrostatic pressure), also participates in regulating the blood circulation. During weightlessness, signals from the blood vessels caused by such pressure will not travel to the brain. Short-timed experiments and observations showed that no substantial violations were taking place. However, it is still not known how the system of blood circulation will cope with its function at the moment of return to normal conditions after a period of protracted weightlessness. There are observations on patients who spent long periods in bed. Their hydrostatic blood pressure in many blood vessels was considerably lowered and, therefore, participated in the regulation of the blood circulation to a lesser degree. In moving such people to the vertical position, disorders in their blood circulation were frequently observed. By analogy with this, one may expect similar phenomena also during a change from weightlessness to normal conditions.

Various measures are suggested for obviating the undesirable consequences in changing from weightlessness to normal conditions. Among them, special physical exercises during the period of weightlessness, utilization of special antioverloading suits, etc., deserve attention. Evidently, it will also be expedient to create periodic rotation of the space ship in order to produce an artificial force of gravity, as suggested originally by K. E. Tsiolkovskii. But the final solution of the problem will be found only after new investigations under the condition of more prolonged weightlessness than has been obtained up to the present time.

The above does not exhaust by far the range of problems pertaining to the phenomena of weightlessness. There is no doubt, however, that science will find a solution to all these problems.

An essential contribution will be made thereby toward ensuring the safety of cosmic flights. (*Nauka i Zhizn'*, December, 1955. The author is identified as "Candidate of Biological Sciences.")

# 12.  Biological Problems of Interplanetary Flights

*I. S. Balakhovskii and V. B. Malkin*

Not long ago flights into world space were only a dream.  Soon they will become a reality.  But before this happens, experiments and investigations are still necessary, part of which physicians and biologists must carry out.

The first step in the penetration of world space will be the creation and launching of an artificial earth satellite, aboard which, besides physical instruments, there will be laboratory animals whose physiological functions will be recorded and the records transmitted to the earth by an automatically operating apparatus.  The first steps in this direction have already been made: monkeys and white mice have been to a height of 57.5 kilometers for several seconds, hamsters and mice have lived for days in the gondola of an aerostat at a height of 25 kilometers.

One of the basic problems facing the new division of science — "cosmic medicine" — is connected with the change in the force of gravity: during the takeoff and the flight, while the engines are operating, a man's weight increases sharply for a short while, after which the stratonaut will pass over to a state of weightlessness.  The state of weightlessness can arise as a result of the fact that the body will pass beyond the limits of the earth's attraction.  It also arises under certain conditions of flight within the limits of the earth's stratosphere in those cases when the centrifugal force balances the force of gravity.

Another group of questions is connected with the harmful action of cosmic rays; a third, with providing for the stratonaut the vitally necessary conditions (the hygiene of the cabin of the interplanetary ship).  In addition there will have to be worked out means and equipment which permit a man to abandon the cabin in case of necessity and ensure the rescue of the crew when its safety is violated.

In order to leave the sphere of the earth's attraction, a body must move with ever-increasing velocity, that is, with a definite acceleration, as a result of which overloads arise — forces whose action on the organism leads to the same physiological effects as a sharp increase in body weight. The weight of a body under such conditions can increase ten times. Thus, according to computed data, if the stratonaut leaves the earth in four minutes, 45 seconds, then during this time he will be subject to the action of forces five times greater than his terrestrial weight; if he leaves in two minutes, then nine times; and if he leaves in 44 seconds, then his weight will increase thirty times.

It is interesting to note that at the end of the last century one of the founders of air navigation, K. E. Tsiolkovskii, considered that the action of acceleration during the start of the rocket could prove to be one of the obstacles for man's flight into cosmic space. Experiments which he conducted on the centrifuge, however, showed that insects and birds in this state endure considerable overloads.

The development of aviation has recently drawn the attention of many investigators to the problem of the effect of accelerations on the human organism. As a result of numerous experimental investigations conducted both in the USSR and abroad, it was established that the influence on the organism of mechanical forces that arise as a result of accelerations depends on the one hand on their magnitude, time of action, rate of accumulation, and direction with respect to the longitudinal axis of the body, and on the other hand on the functional state of the organism — that is, on the state the man's health.

In an airplane a man is most frequently subjected to the action of mechanical forces (overloads) directed along the axis of his body, that is, in the direction in which the force of the earth's attraction acts on it in a vertical position. In this connection most people are capable of enduring the action of accelerations not more than three to four times that of the earth without significant changes in their state of health. At larger accelerations the development of pathological phenomena is noted on the part of the cardiovascular system, which become apparent first of all in disturbances of the cerebral blood circulation. As a result of the inadequate blood supply to the brain and the retinas, and also for several other causes, impairments of vision develop — the appearance before the eyes of a grey and black shroud, and later even more serious disorders of the activity of the central nervous system, including loss of consciousness.

It was established that the disturbance of the blood circulation by the action of accelerations is caused by the displacement of a substantial mass of blood to the lower half of the body and by the exclusion of it from circulation, and also by the fact that when the body is in a vertical position the pressure of the column of blood proves to be so great that the heart is not capable of driving it into the overlying organs, particularly into the brain.

Moreover, as a result of the substantial increase in "weight" of the internal organs, their ligamentous apparatus is subjected to a great tension, and the irritation caused by this in the receptors of the internal organs can serve as a source of pathological reflexes. In order to increase a man's stability to the action of accelerations, recently investigators have begun to use an antioverload suit which is a system of rubber chambers interconnected by dense material (Figure 1). As the overloads arise, compressed air is automatically fed into the chambers of the suit. At the same time the suit squeezes the soft tissues, rich with blood vessels, of the lower half of the body, which to a certain degree wards off the accumulation of blood there and thereby contributes to the preservation of the brain blood circulation. The stability of the human organism can be raised also by means of systematic workouts. All these methods, however, yield comparatively limited results. Investigations conducted with people on centrifugal machines — centrifuges — showed that a man in a vertical position can endure, if only for a few minutes, accelerations four to five times greater than the terrestrial. Overloads are endured best of all when

Figure 1.
Antioverload suit.

they are directed perpendicularly to the longtitudinal axis of the body — that is, if in a rocket taking off vertically, the man is in a horizontal position. Experimental investigations have showed that under such conditions a man can endure for several minutes the action of forces that are 10 to 12 times greater than his "terrestrial" weight. Thus, one can now recommend that the stratonaut in the first few minutes of flight be in a horizontal — that is, prone — position. (It is interesting to note that this was already foreseen by K. E. Tsiolkovskii.)

The question of how the absence of the earth's gravity will affect a man is especially difficult in connection with the extreme complexity of reproducing in the experiment the conditions of weightlessness. The solution of this question is of great importance because shortly after the rocket takes off, immediately after the motors are shut off, the astronauts will find themselves under conditions of weightlessness in which they will have to be for a long time. What can happen to a man under these conditions? Many hypotheses have been made. On the basis of theoretical ideas, some physiologists doubted the possibility of human life under these conditions. Thus, the German cardiologist Langer expressed the opinion that under conditions of the complete absence of gravity, life can continue for only a few minutes since serious disorders will inevitably arise in the blood circulation because of the disturbance of its nervous regulation; the blood will lose weight and will not exert pressure on the walls of the vessels where special nerve endings (baroreceptors), sensitive to change in blood pressure, are located. At the same time, there will also be no blood pressure in the cavities of the heart during its relaxation, which can lead to a disturbance of normal heart activity.

Most investigators, however, consider that life is possible under conditions of weightlessness and that the organism is capable of adapting itself to new conditions of existence. In the adaptation process, however, disturbances can arise in the activity of the central nervous system connected with the fact that it will not receive signals from the nerve endings located in the skin and the muscles, and also in the special organ of balance — the labyrinth (located in the inner ear), which under normal conditions "reports" the position of the body and its separate parts. In this connection, disturbance in the regulation of muscle tone, upset of orientation in space, origin of the syndrome of "air sickness" — dizziness and nausea — and also disturbance of sleep are possible.

Under ordinary conditions the force of gravity limits the possibility of moving the torso by the contractions of the muscles. Without its action man will have to learn anew to perform target-directed motive acts.

Lately experimental rocket flights have been conducted during which the passengers — experimental animals — found themselves under the conditions of weightlessness for two to three minutes. By means of automatically operating instruments, a record was made of the breathing of the animals, an electro-cardiogram was taken, and the blood pressure was measured; filming permitted judging their behavior under the conditions of weightlessness. In one of these flights the experimental monkeys were for 20 seconds under conditions of weightlessness during which time, according to the data of the electro-cardiographic investigation, they showed no essential changes in heart activity and breathing, and their blood pressure fell insignificantly.

To study the influence of weightlessness on the ability of animals to orient themselves in space and to maintain normal posture, interesting experiments were conducted. On several experimental white mice the surgical destruction of the vestibular apparatus was performed; that is, the nerve receptor (sensory) device, which signals the position of the body in space to the central nervous system, was destroyed. In the first days after the operation the experimental animals were not capable of maintaining normal posture and periodically assumed an unnatural position. After some time, however, they adapted themselves and again began to orient themselves correctly in space. After this the animals that were operated on, together with the controls (the animals that were not operated on), were placed in a rocket during the flight of which they were for two to three minutes under the conditions of dynamic weightlessness. Data of the filming have shown that the behavior of the mice with destroyed vestibular apparatus was usual — they maintained normal posture, while the control animals assumed an unusual position, and their orientation was found to be sharply disturbed.

In 1951, in a special experimental flight in an F-80E jet airplane, the pilot found himself periodically for 15 to 20 seconds under conditions of weightlessness. In this connection he did not notice any disturbance in breathing and heart activity. Coordination of movement at first was disturbed, but after a few experiments the movements again became coordinated. Subjectively evaluating his state in these flights, the pilot noticed that he at first lost his ability to orient himself in space and later on could judge about his position in the airplane only by means of sight. By this it was established that the pilot during the repeated onset in flight of the state of weightlessness gradually became adapted to it, as a result of which after several such flights he maintained sufficiently good orientation in space. It is interesting that pilots who fly well under complex meteorological conditions, utilizing in flight only aircraft instrument readings, orient themselves better in space during the onset of weightlessness than pilots without instrument-flying experience. Thus, training for blind flight helps the development of correct orientation in space in the case of the onset of weightlessness.

The results of the above-mentioned experimental investigations indicate that man and animals can adapt themselves to a short stay under conditions of weightlessness. This gives a basis for hoping that adaptation is possible also for prolonged residence in space without gravity. But if this assumption proves to be incorrect, then an "artificial force" of gravity has to be created at the expense of centrifugal forces developed by the rotation of the interplanetary ship.

If the above facts and considerations permit us to conclude that man can without real danger to his life endure the transition from his usual terrestrial conditions to complete weightlessness, this still does not mean that the organism will be totally insensible to such a transition. Some changes will undoubtedly be observed in it; and in the first place one should expect a fall in the level of metabolic processes. This will have to be taken into account when working out food rations.

If one can speak today about the transition to the state of weightlessness from certain knowledge of the matter, then it is much more difficult to say anything about how the return from a long interplanetary voyage, that is, the transition from complete weightlessness to terrestrial conditions, can influence a man's physiological functions. As a rough analogy one can use the transition from a strict rest-cure to physical work. Obviously, some intermediate period of limitation of physical burden and of thorough medical control will be necessary.

Around the stratonaut there will be no terrestrial atmosphere that reliably protects him from the harmful action of cosmic rays and meteorites, and also from the corpuscular and electromagnetic radiation of the sun; the cabin itself must, therefore, protect him from the harmful action of these factors. Ordinary glass absorbs ultraviolet rays well. According to calculations, the statistical probability of an air ship three meters in diameter encountering a meteorite that is capable of piercing a layer of aluminum 0.32 meters thick corresponds to once in 2000 days.

It is more difficult to protect oneself against the harmful action of cosmic rays. Their intensity is not great — of the order of 5 to 15 milliroentgens per day; but they are composed of heavy particles with very great energy, which are capable of penetrating tissue deeply and of forming a large number of ions there (Figure 2).

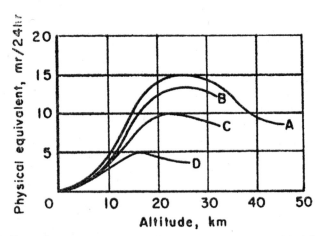

Figure 2. Dependence of cosmic radiation intensity on geographical latitude of terrain and height above sea level. A, B, C, and D correspond to 60°, 51°, 38°, and 3° North Latitude.

The basic difficulty in studying the biological action of cosmic rays is the impossibility of reproducing them completely under laboratory conditions; one can study only the biological actions of certain components on terrestrial equipment. Therefore the basic method of solving such problems is computing: the biological action of the particles is judged on the basis of their penetrating and ionizing capabilities which can be studied in purely physical experiments. Here it is assumed that if a particle of cosmic radiation forms on its path as many ions as, say, ten alpha-particles, which form as a result of radium disintegration, then its biological action is equivalent to the biological action of these ten alpha-particles.

If one assumes that the radiobiological equivalent (RBE) of cosmic particles is equal to ten—that is, that they, just like alpha-particles, cause a ten-times-larger biological effect than roentgen rays having the same ionizing capability — then a very simple calculation shows that irradiation of the astronaut amounts to 700 mr-RBE per week. This is considerably greater than the safe norm of 300 mr-RBE per week established by the international commission on radiological protection. Thus, from the point of view of these norms, an interplanetary ship must be equipped with a heavy protective screen. In a number of cases, however, such protection can have an opposite effect: as a result of these processes which take place during the interaction of cosmic rays with the nuclei of the atoms of the screen, their ionizing capability, and therefore their biological harmfulness, can increase. On the other hand, it is necessary to consider that the norms presented above have been worked out systematically for people exposed to the action of irradiation over a number of years, which, of course, will not be the case for the first stratonauts.

Regarding the biological action of cosmic rays, it is necessary to consider that some of the particles that have struck living tissues are capable of causing on limited areas the formation of such large quantities of ions as could be formed on such parts of tissue only by irradiation with hundreds or even thousands of roentgens. If in this process such vitally important tissues as nerve trunks or centers, and also certain endocrine glands or the building system of the heart, are affected, the changes can affect the functions of the entire organism.

It is necessary to consider also the change in hereditary properties of the organism under the influence of irradiation. The difficulty in studying this problem lies, in addition, in the fact that hereditary changes usually involve a recessive characteristic, that is, they become apparent only in case both the father and the mother of the child had such changes.

Recently a number of attempts were undertaken to study the biological action of cosmic rays by sending animals in balloons to altitudes where the intensity of primary cosmic radiation is sufficiently great. In these tests it was established that although the animals endured irradiation by primary cosmic rays for days without any visible harm for themselves, in their skin were found small areas with degenerate changes which can be connected with the intrusion of discrete particles of cosmic rays.

The most important problem is supplying the crew with oxygen. It is obvious that no compressor whatever can guarantee the constant pressure required inside the hermetic cabin of the cosmic ship; therefore the entire necessary supply of oxygen will have to be taken with it, and also the supply of material capable of absorbing the carbon dioxide exhaled by man. Such a cabin is said to be "regenerative." Construction of the cabin is simplified, and thus the reliability of its operation increases as the pressure within it decreases. The experience of living on high mountains, and also of flights in aircraft, indicates that healthy people can reside without harm to themselves for a long time at an atmospheric pressure of 500 millimeters of mercury which corresponds to an altitude of approximately 3.5 kilometers above sea level.  If the stratonaut breathes pure oxygen, however, this pressure can be lower still, at least 2.5 times, and the organism's supply of oxygen will only improve thereby.  Indeed, it has been known for a long time that the blood is completely saturated with oxygen if its partial pressure in alveolar air [1] reaches 100 millimeters. Since in the alveoli, besides oxygen there are still necessarily present carbon dioxide and water vapor, the total pressure there must be greater than 100 millimeters.  Usually the partial pressure of carbon dioxide amounts to 40 millimeters and the water-vapor tension at the body temperature is 47 millimeters; thus, altogether the pressure is 187 millimeters or, in round numbers, 200 millimeters, which are necessary for supporting human life inside the cabin.  If such a pressure is maintained not by pure oxygen, but, let us assume, by air, the crew of the interplanetary ship must wear oxygen masks all the time. Filling up the whole cabin with oxygen is considered dangerous in an incendiary respect — on earth in an atmosphere of this gas only, many organic substances easily burst into flame.  This obstacle can be overcome, however, by removing combustible organic substances from the cabin and by adding to the oxygen a small amount of inert gases which would play the role of "extinguishers."  To rid the crew of the cosmic ship of the oxygen mask is an important and completely feasible task. It is most economical to keep the supply of oxygen strongly cooled, in liquid form in special reservoirs.  This is facilitated by the fact that the outer medium of such a "thermos" can be airless space itself; it is necessary only to protect the reservoir from heating by the solar rays. An adult male consumes 400 to 500 grams of oxygen per day and generates approximately the same amount of carbon dioxide, which must be absorbed by a special absorbent.  Together with the necessary tare, these supplies appreciably increase the weight of the rocket; therefore it has been suggested that algae be utilized for the photosynthetic decomposition of carbon dioxide by means of sunlight. Special works have shown that this is the most economical method of obtaining oxygen under such conditions.

Passing through the earth's atmosphere, the interplanetary ship must overcome its resistance.  In this process the temperature of the walls increases sharply and can reach hundreds of degrees; thus, during the flight of a V-2 missile, the temperature of its walls reached 647 degrees.  For a rocket to overcome the force of the earth's gravity, it must move with a very great velocity and "slip through" the atmosphere in a few seconds, so that all the heat will be liberated in a very small interval of time.

If the external wall has a rather high heat capacity, then the layer of poor heat conductivity located under it will reliably ensure the necessary conditions inside the cabin.   Calculations show that in the vicinity of the earth a body receives from the sun almost as much heat as it radiates into world space, if its temperature approaches what foreign physiologists call the "comfort temperature."   The exact heat balance depends on the shape of the rocket, and also on the heat that will be generated inside it by man and at the expense of the operation of various aggregates.   Therefore, if a rocket escapes into free flight, its surfaces must be nonhomogeneous: the side facing the sun must reflect light better than the opposite side.   For artificial satellites that make a complete revolution in 1.5 to 2 hours, however, such a demand is not compulsory: the cabin will not have time to heat up in the 45 to 60 minutes for which this very short day will last.

But it is not enough to fly off into world space; it is still necessary to have the possibility of setting foot on a strange planet, and, in case of necessity, of helping a comrade who has come to grief.   For this, hermetic suits are necessary which protect man not only against the harmful action of oxygen starvation, but also against other effects connected with a sharp fall in barometric pressure.   In the blood and tissues of the human organism, primarily in the fatty tissue, dissolved nitrogen is always present, which during a fall in barometric pressure changes into the gaseous state with the formation of gas bubbles. Their appearance can lead to a number of painful disorders, primarily to strong, sometimes absolutely unbearable, so-called high-altitude pains in the region of the large joints.   One can combat this phenomenon not only by putting on a space suit, but also by purging the nitrogen from the organism by breathing pure oxygen (desaturation of nitrogen).

It is well known that when the atmospheric pressure decreases, the boiling point of liquids also decreases; evidently there exists a pressure at which the tissues and liquids of the human body "begin to boil." Special experiments, performed on rabbits and rats, showed that such a phenomenon actually takes place at pressures corresponding to altitudes of the order of 20 kilometers and more above sea level; it is expressed in the formation under the skin of massive gas bubbles, the so-called high-altitude gaseous emphysema.   Further analysis of these phenomena showed that not only water vapor but also carbon dioxide take part in their formation, which indicates the more complex nature of the process. The carbon dioxide here promotes the boiling of the liquid media of the organism at a much lower temperature. Made of fabric that is light but strong and impermeable to gas, the space suits must reliably protect man against the fatal action of airless space, ensuring at the same time sufficient freedom of movement. In it man must breathe air that is enriched with oxygen, while the carbon dioxide is absorbed by a special absorbent (regenerative type).

The supply of oxygen in the space suit can be in one of three forms: liquid, gaseous, or solid as a chemical compound. For the same tare volume, it will contain a greater amount of oxygen if it is in liquid form; but if a device (with liquid oxygen) is heated, its supply will not last long. In other instruments oxygen is formed as a result of some chemical reaction, the rate of which it is easy to regulate (the so-called instruments of the biscuit type); the Alpinists who conquered Everest made use of them. The advantage of instruments of this type lies in the fact that they are comparatively light; their supply of oxygen can be kept very long without losses. Finally, the most simply constructed, but also the most bulky, are those instruments in which oxygen is kept in the gaseous state at a pressure of 100 to 150 atmospheres. In such an instrument there can be only a limited supply of oxygen; otherwise the weight of the tank increases sharply. In working out the hermetic regenerative space suit it is most difficult to develop gloves in which one could perform rather delicate and accurate movements.

The problem of the safe landing of the interplanetary ship is rather complex; there are two methods, which differ in principle, of lowering the "cosmic velocity" to such a point that a safe landing at the aerodrome is possible. In the first method an engine is turned on, and braking is accomplished by means of the energy developed by it. Far more promising is the second method in which braking is accomplished by means of the earth's atmosphere. This is an aerodynamic method, for the realization of which the rocket must have wings, which guarantee flight along a gently sloping trajectory in the stratosphere. Calculations show that thanks to this, one can considerably reduce both the heating of the body of the rocket and the overload which can arise during the sharp braking of the interplanetary ship by the earth's atmosphere.

So we see, there are still many unsolved problems connected with the effect on the human organism of the different factors of interplanetary travel. The successes attained in this field in recent years, however, make us think that the human organism, reliably protected against the harmful action of factors unfavorable for it, will sustain interplanetary flight without injury to itself.   (*Priroda,* August, 1956.)

---

[1] By alveolar air is meant the air found in the pulmonary cells—the alveoli, in which specifically the blood is saturated with oxygen—that is, is oxygenated—and the carbon dioxide is extracted from the blood.

# 13.  Before Flight Into the Cosmos

*V. V. Rozenblat*

In view of the present state of science and technology one may dare assert that the first flights into world space will yet be accomplished in our century.  Of course, they will begin with the launching into the cosmos of automatic rocket ships guided from the earth.  But soon thereafter people will become direct participants in these flights. Hence it follows that besides the solution of many complex technical problems of interplanetary travels, scientists are also faced with the elucidation of such questions which are connected with the physiological state of the human organism under the unusual conditions of cosmic wanderings.  Therefore today not only physicists and mathematicians, astronomers and specialists in radio technology, and designers and engineers, but even biologists and physicians, and physiologists and biophysicists are taking part in the business of conquering world space.

One must say frankly that representatives of physiology and medicine, who are studying the problems of safeguarding the health of future astronauts, are running into very great difficulties.  Indeed not one living creature has yet found himself under the conditions of actual cosmic flight.  The means that scientists have no suitable experimental material on the basis of which one could draw definite thetoretical and practical conclusions.  But, nevertheless, enthusiasts of astronavigation are finding ways for overcoming this seemingly unavoidable obstacle.  The data of modern science permits presenting, if only approximately, the various factors under the action of which cosmic travellers will find themselves.  Making use of this information and also of the facts from adjacent fields (aviation medicine, for example), physiologists and physicians are working out measures which will prove to be indispensable for maintaining the health of the astronauts.

## ACCELERATIONS AND OVERLOADS

The faster a cosmic ship gathers the velocity required for overcoming the earth's attraction, the greater will be its fuel economy.  This means that smaller supplies of fuel will be required and that the dimensions of the rocket will be comparatively small.  Moreover, a smaller ship capable of high accelerations will be highly maneuverable, which will play no small role in the practice of cosmic flights.

But the rate of increase in a rocket's velocity is limited by the endurance of the human organism.  While the acceleration lasts, it experiences an overload, that is, its weight increases as many times as the given acceleration exceeds the earth's acceleration of gravity — 9.8 meters per second per second.  It is considered that a man can endure only a 4- to 5-fold overload, and that for only a short time.  This will permit a cosmic ship to gather speed with an acceleration not over 40 to 50 meters per second per second.  In that case almost five minutes will be needed to gain the cosmic velocity, and the weight of fuel must exceed (for vertical takeoff) 24.6 times the weight of the rocket plus the rest of the load.  In other words, the cosmic ship will turn out to be very bulky and unmaneuverable.  In this connection the question arises: Is it impossible to raise the limit of the permissible overload and at the same time secure the human organism against its undesirable consequences?  Some data say that this is a completely solvable task.

Scientists have ascertained that the influence of an overload on the organism is determined not only by the magnitude of the acceleration, but also by its direction relative to the longitudinal axis of the body.

During a positive acceleration (flight with increasing velocity with the head forward, or flight with decreasing velocity in the opposite direction) the overload acts from head to foot.  As a result the blood flows from the brain and accumulates in the lower parts of the body.  If the weight of the organism increases five times and more under these conditions, the heart is in no condition to raise the blood to the head, and loss of consciousness ensues.

True, in the case when a positive acceleration lasts a fraction of a second, it will not cause important changes in the distribution of the blood.  Thus, when jumping from a height of 120 centimeters a man experiences a 16-fold overload at the moment of contact with the earth.  And indeed athletes "land" safely from a height of more than two meters!  If the overload lasts several seconds, however, unpleasant phenomena already begin to be felt.  For example, a four- to five-fold increase in weight lasting more than three seconds leads to the first disturbances in vision, when a "grey shroud," as it were, arises before the eyes. During a six-fold overload of the same duration, loss of vision ("black shroud") can ensue, then syncope, convulsions, etc. Even though cessation of the overload quickly stops these phenomena which are well known to some fliers, it is nevertheless undesirable to tolerate them, especially as large accelerations will last, not for seconds, but for tens of seconds during cosmic travels.

Man endures even worse negative accelerations, when the overload acts from the feet to the head and as a result produces overfilling of the vessels of the brain and a sharp pressure increase in them. Under such conditions even for a two- to three-fold increase in weight with a duration of more than five to six seconds, disorders in vision ("red shroud") can appear, and in case of large overloads — hemorrhages and other serious consequences.

To a certain degree special antioverload suits help to avoid the harmful results of sizable accelerations. They consist of several bladders filled with water or compressed air, which squeeze the legs and abdomen and somewhat hold back the accumulation of blood which pours out of the upper half of the body into these regions of the organism. For all the discomfort of these suits, they make possible a certain increase in resistance to overloads. But their suitability is limited on the whole only by the conditions of positive accelerations; and, most important of all, antioverload suits do not provide the cardinal solution of the problem as it applies to cosmic flight.

Lately scientists have been paying attention to transverse accelerations during which the overload acts perpendicularly to the axis of the body (from the back to the chest, etc.). Such accelerations are endured much easier than positive or negative accelerations. This is clear because substantial displacements of blood, which hamper the feeding of vitally important organs, do not take place here. As a result, the resistance of the organism to overloads increases several times.

So far, unfortunately, transverse accelerations have been studied less than others. But even available data compel us to think that with the body in a suitable position astronauts will be able to endure considerable overloads. It has been established, for example, that a 15-fold transverse acceleration for five seconds causes only point superficial hemorrhages (evidently because of pressure against a hard support) and pain in the chest, and a 12-fold transverse acceleration is endured for one minute without unpleasant consequences. In experiments on a chimpanzee, even a 40-fold transverse overload for 15 seconds did not result in either loss of consciousness or other disturbances in the state of the animal. Evidently, a 10- to 12-fold acceleration is fully admissible for man; it is necessary only to consider that beginning with a six- to eight-fold acceleration, respiratory movements become difficult (the chest cavity becomes too "heavy" for the respiratory muscles); involuntary delay in breathing (in half-gasps) ensues. Apparently, it is precisely this in the main that limits the admissible time of action of an overload.

Thus, the utilization of transverse accelerations considerably increases resistance to overloads. But this is far from being the limit. K. E. Tsiolkovskii proposed softening the influence of accelerations by submersing the astronauts in a liquid of the same specific gravity as the human body. The scientist proceeded from a simple experiment. If one drops an egg into a glass with a salt solution of the same specific gravity, it will not only not break from sharp blows of the glass on the table, but it will not even move. K. E. Tsiolkovskii showed that precisely in such a way nature ensures the protection of our brain against many mechanical actions. Indeed, the brain, as is well known, is surrounded by a special fluid medium which fills in the space between its membranes and "absorbs" the force of various jolts and concussions.

While a man is immersed in a fluid of the same specific gravity, the overload will reduce to a uniform compression of the body on all sides, in contradistinction to its "flattening" by pressure in one direction only under ordinary conditions. It is precisely this that will permit raising the resistance of the organism to accelerations. True, in the given case the resistance will not be unlimited, since uniform compression, if it is very strong, is capable of causing adverse results. For example, the chest cavity, containing the lungs which are filled with air, remains a "soft spot." Here blood will begin to be "squeezed" out of the vessels of the torso and the extremities during very great overloads. This will hamper the functioning of the heart. Moreover, direct damage to the chest cavity may take place. In order to avoid this, one will have to suitably increase the pressure of the inhaled air and thus balance the forces which compress the chest from the outside. But then, if the overload is long, a new danger can arise. Increase in pressure within the pulmonary alveoli will cause increased solution of nitrogen in the blood. This gas, when the overload ceases and the pressure of the air inside the lungs becomes normal, will be discharged backwards, stopping up vitally important blood vessels and causing a number of unpleasant complications. In other words, the astronauts will become ill with something like the "aeroembolism" which arises during the rapid ascent of a diver from a depth, or they will experience the so-called decompression sickness which occurs during flight of jet aircraft with a nonpressurized cabin in the rarefied layers of the atmosphere.

Finally, one should consider that large overloads are dangerous not by themselves but because of displacements of blood and mechanical displacements analogous to them. Changes in weight of the various organs will result in the sharp irritation of the receptors (sensitive nerve endings) of these organs and of their ligamentous apparatus; this can cause a series of reflex disturbances, sometimes quite serious. One should also take into consideration that, for example, during a 50-fold overload, the contraction of the heart (which now weighs about 15 kilograms) will hardly be possible.

This means that even the application of the method proposed by K. E. Tsiolkovskii will not allow reaching any acceleration in a cosmic voyage. But it will undoubtedly play no small role. Indeed, if astronauts are given the opportunity of easily withstanding at least a 20-fold overload for a minute, this will be sufficient time for the rocket ship to gather the velocity that will allow it to escape from the earth.

It is necessary to assume that, while the rocket is accelerating, the passengers will not breathe normally under the influence of the overload. But after preliminary reinforced breathing (especially with pure oxygen), even a minute delay in ventilating the lungs will not present special difficulties. Pearl divers in southern countries, thanks to suitable training, after preliminary forced breathing can stay under water up to five minutes.

Of course, all the above data require more precise definition for which further experimental elaboration of the problem is required. In aviation medicine, necessary observations are conducted by means of large centrifuges which permit obtaining various overloads. Experiments with such instruments make it possible to establish precisely how much a man's resistance to accelerations will be raised while he is immersed in a fluid. But already today one can say that the problem of overloads will not be limited to a four- to five-fold acceleration; it is not at all possible to consider that the latter is the limit.

## WEIGHTLESSNESS

When a cosmic ship acquires the necessary velocity, its engine will be shut off and the rocket will continue its flight by inertia. The overload will change into complete weightlessness. Will this affect the vital activity of the organism?

Scientists today do not have a sufficient number of facts available which would permit answering this question exhaustively. There are only separate fragmentary observations on animals and people.[1] But certain conjectural judgments can be expressed even now.

First of all weightlessness essentially affects coordination of movement. Indeed all our movements are executed at the expense of the weight of the body or of its separate parts. When a man weighing 70 kilograms suddenly becomes lighter than a bit of fluff, his entire habitual coordination will be disturbed. For its restoration, special training is needed (both preceding flight into world space and during this flight). Then one will be able to achieve rebuilding the habits necessary for movements under the conditions of weightlessness.

Should astronauts find themselves in a world devoid of gravity for several months or years, they can incur considerable muscular atrophy in connection with the sharp decrease in loading. But so unpleasant a phenomenon is not at all inevitable. Special gymnastic exercises on spring and other devices, performed several times a day, will help in preventing it.

It is still difficult to say how the organs of blood circulation will behave under the conditions of weightlessness. The cardio-vascular system is "built" to function with blood possessing a known weight. Thus, the vessels of the lower part of the body differ more in significant tone than the vessels of the upper regions; thanks to this the blood does not "become stale" in the legs. If a man is bed-ridden for a long time by some sickness, then the usual "tuning" of the cardio-vascular system fails. Then when the man passes to a vertical position, the blood pours into the lower parts of the body, the brain receives little oxygen and as a result syncope (sudden faintness) sometimes arises. In connection with what was stated, it is difficult to say how weightlessness of the blood affects the operation of the cardio-vascular system. In experiments with animals the disappearance of gravity at once led to a lowering of blood pressure, although there were no sharp disturbances in cardio activity. But here the state of weightlessness lasted for a few seconds. As far as considerably longer periods are concerned, the question here still remains open.

It is possible that under conditions of weightlessness changes will arise in the operation of the gastro-intestinal track and of a number of other systems in which complications of a different kind can take place. On the other hand, there is no doubt that the human organism in the end will adapt itself to many unusual states characteristic of cosmic travel. Nevertheless, apparently it will be necessary to avoid prolonged weightlessness. Even if astronauts become accustomed to living in a world without gravity, on returning to earth they will find themselves in a very dangerous situation. Their reacquired weight can exert on them an influence equal to the action of a protracted overload.

How then will one be able to get rid of weightlessness? The answer to this question has already been found by K. E. Tsiolkovskii, who spoke about the necessity of creating artificial gravity on cosmic ships. For this it is necessary to rotate the rocket (or the cabin with passengers) around its longitudinal axis. Then as a result of the action of centrifugal force on the walls of the ship an artificial gravity will arise, it will be equal to the earth's if the velocity of rotation is in the necessary relation to the radius of the rocket. For example, a rocket four meters in diameter must make one revolution in three seconds; a rocket eight meters in diameter must make one revolution in four seconds, etc.

But here a new question arises: But will not the rotation of the cosmic ship cause dizziness, nausea, and asthenia, as it often does under analogous conditions on earth? This question can be answered with confidence in the negative. The fact is that dizziness and other unpleasant sensations arise only as a result of nonuniform rotation. Rotation by itself, if it is accomplished uniformly, does not influence the organism. The considerable resistance to rotation displayed by ballerinas, figure skaters and simply people who dance the waltz well depends not so much on training as on fluency of movement, on uniformity of rotation. Therefore artificial gravity in rockets (as well as in artificial satellites of the earth) will be harmless for astronauts under the indispensable condition of uniformity of rotation.

### FEEDING

During protracted cosmic trips (and a flight to Mars and back can at first take more than two years) a substantial supply of food, water and oxygen, necessary for the crew, will be required. We shall try to determine its magnitude.

In the course of the journey the astronauts in general will live a sedentary life. Only in the period of the brief "excursions" on the surface of the investigated planet will they have to perform moderate muscular work. Therefore the daily expenditure of energy for each man on the average, probably, will not exceed 2500 to 3000 calories.

How much food then is required for such an expenditure of energy? Theoretically, only about 650 grams: 100 grams of proteins, 75 grams of fats, 450 grams of carbohydrates and approximately 25 grams of mineral salts and vitamins. In practice, however, besides food substances proper, a man's daily ration must contain some palatable substances, and also "ballast" substances of the cellulose variety necessary for normal peristalsis (contraction) of the bowels. Taking all this into account, the minimum weight of "dry ration" will have to be raised to 800 grams; for a two-year voyage this will amount to about 600 kilograms per man.

The daily requirement for water amounts to about 2.5 liters. Of these 350 grams are generated in the organism itself (by the oxidation of proteins, fats and carbohydrates) and approximately one liter each is introduced by drinking and eating. Thus, for two years the necessary supply of water amounts to 1.5 tons per person.

Concerning oxygen one should say that associated with the energetic expenditures indicated above, each astronaut needs approximately 800 grams of it per day. A two-year supply of this gas then, just like the supply of food, will amount to 600 kilograms.

As a result, the weight of the food, water and oxygen required for a crew of four men will approach eleven tons. For a cosmic ship this is a very substantial amount. This is why scientists are searching for methods of diminishing it. What ways, then, can be outlined here?

One of these ways is the organization of the "rotation" of water and oxygen. Already this will effect a not inconsiderable economy.

Receiving two liters of water per day, the organism discharges all of it back, and what is more with an addition of 350 grams which are formed by the oxidation of food. About 1.5 liters are eliminated through the kidneys, about 0.5 liter through the skin and about 0.4 liter through the lungs. All this water can be caught and after suitable purification and treatment (distillation, addition of salts, etc.) used again. Then associated with the minimum general supplies of water there will be enough for washing, hygienic procedures, etc.

The problem of supplies of oxygen can be solved in an analogous manner. The human organism discharges daily about 950 grams of carbon dioxide and 350 grams of the "additional" water that was mentioned above. These substances contain about one kilogram of oxygen in chemically combined form, that is, more of it than is absorbed in the same time. Such an excess is again connected with the fact that oxygen is included in the composition of proteins, fats and carbohydrates of the food and escapes with the end products of their decomposition. Theoretically it is possible, by utilizing solar energy or some other energetic source, to obtain pure oxygen again from carbon dioxide and water (green plants — algae, for example — have been suggested for this). Therefore, the supplies of oxygen required for the crew can be reduced to a very insignificant amount.

Thus, thanks to the rational utilization of "wastes," the supplies required for the life of the astronauts will be limited in the main by food. For four men during a two-year voyage, about 2.5 tons of it are needed, of which about a third can be considered as a "potential" supply of water. And this under conditions of cosmic travel is a very substantial economy in weight (in comparison with eleven tons), which permits lowering the supplies of fuel many times.

Another way of solving the problem is possible. When atomic engines are utilized in rockets the fuel supply will be made up, first, of a small amount of nuclear fuel and, secondly, of a "working substance" (hydrogen, water, etc.) which forms the main load. The "slags" of metabolism (carbon dioxide, water, etc.) can be utilized as the latter. Their mass will be equal to the total mass of food, water and oxygen that have entered the organism. Therefore the entire eleven-ton "vital supply" may be regarded as fuel supply for the concluding part of the flight, for, having passed through the organism, it will then be utilized in the rocket engine.

\*     \*     \*

The first interplanetary travellers will have to overcome many difficulties and dangers. Many unstudied and still unsolved problems stand before physiologists and physicians who are called upon to provide safe conditions for the health of astronauts during cosmic flights. Are the powerful streams of cosmic rays which will have to be encountered in world space harmless? What is the best way to protect oneself against the powerful ultraviolet radiation of the sun? How will one be able to protect himself against collisions with meteorites? Scientists today are working persistently on the investigation of these and tens of other problems of cosmic travels, striving to pave mankind's way into the cosmos. And already the time is not far distant when manned rockets will escape into the vastness of the solar system, for, as K. E. Tsiolkovskii said, "The earth is the cradle of the mind, but one cannot live forever in a cradle." (*Nauka i Zhizn'*,

November, 1956.   The author is identified as "Candidate of Medical
Sciences, Sverdlovsk.")

[1] For details about this see the paper by P. K. Isakov, "Problems of Weightlessness," in *Nauka i Zhizn'*, No. 12, 1955. (See Chapter 11.)

# 14. Vital Activity of Animals During Rocket Flights Into the Upper Atmosphere

*A. V. Pokrovskii*

Rocket flight in the upper layers of the atmosphere poses a series of special problems of a technical and medico-biological nature. Safety of a flight of this kind can be guaranteed only if a number of complicated problems concerning the preservation of the vital activity of the organism at high altitudes and the development of a system necessary for man's survival at these altitudes have been solved beforehand. In the program for solving the problems raised, studies on animals have been included by a group of scientists. Dogs served as guinea pigs. Investigations were carried out in two stages.

In the first stage, the animals and the necessary apparatus were arranged in a hermetic compartment in the nose of a rocket. Two dogs were attached separately, by means of a suitable system of straps, to special frames. An air-regenerating system ensured the conditions necessary for the animals' life in this hermetic cabin. The equipment used allowed the air temperature and pressure in the cabin, and the respiration and pulse rates to be recorded automatically during flight. The behavior of the animals before and after the flight was studied; cardiographs and X-rays of the animals were made; the presence of the simplest alimentary conditioned reflexes was studied. The animals were filmed during flight.

As a rule of procedure the investigations in flight were preceded by experiments in a pressure chamber in an airplane and in the rocket itself on a test stand. During these preliminary experiments, the operation of the air-regenerating system and of the recording and cine-camera equipment was tested and the animals were accustomed to flight.

During the first stage, investigations were carried out on nine dogs, three of which were used twice in flight. The maximum altitude attained by the rocket was about 100 kilometers. The speed was about

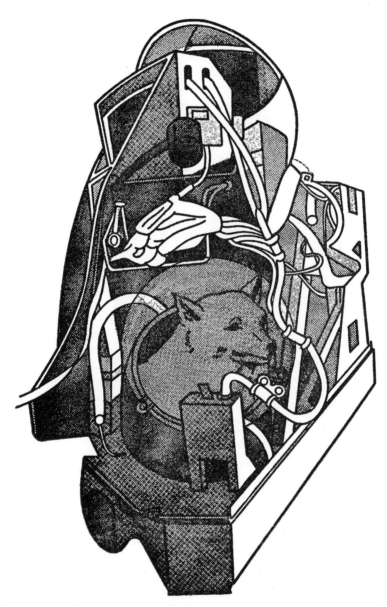

Catapultable chassis used in study
of canine behavior in rocket flight.

1170 meters per second (4212 kilometers per hour); the accelerations did not exceed 5.5 *g*.

The behavior of the animals and the state of their physiological functions during the flight did not change in any significant way. The disturbances in the pulse rate and in the character and rate of respiration were recorded only during the period of vibration which occurred during the free fall of the hermetic cabin of the rocket. The temperature of the animals remained practically constant. After the flight, conditioned alimentary reflexes were fully maintained. During the days following the flight the animals remained normal. After repeated rocket flights no changes were detected in the animals.

The records of the studies made permitted us to consider that during rocket flights to an altitude not exceeding 100 kilometers, a low-volume (0.28 cubic meters) hermetic cabin utilizing an air regenerating system ensures the conditions necessary for the life of two dogs for three hours; the complex of external factors, which arise during such flight, causes practically no important change in the behavior and in the state of the various physiological functions of the animal and is for this reason completely endurable. The parachute system ensures safe descent and landing of the animals in the sealed compartment of the rocket.

During the second stage of the investigations, the animals were placed in the nose of the rocket in a nonhermetic compartment with a volume of 0.28 cubic meters. Conditions necessary for life and rescue of the animals were ensured by means of special space suits equipped with removable helmets, without oxygen masks, and by means of an ejection chassis equipped with an oxygen supply system and a system of parachutes. Special attachments for securing the animals during flight were provided in the space unit. The ejection chassis was so constructed that the oxygen supply system, the parachute system, and all the equipment for recording physiological functions in flight could be fastened to it.

The oxygen supply system consisted of three two-liter bottles. The oxygen reserve of 900 liters was sufficient to keep the animal alive in the space suit for two hours. Thanks to a regulator valve, a pressure equal to 440 millimeters of mercury was maintained in the space suit during flight at altitudes above 4350 meters. An additional valve was provided in the helmet of the space suit. During the descent this valve opened automatically at an altitude of 4000 meters and allowed air to enter, in order to allow the animal to breathe after landing.

The parachute system was fastened on the side of the chassis and was designed to save the animal after ejection.

The equipment for recording the animal's physiological functions in flight was arranged on the back of the chassis. This equipment consisted of a special electronic amplifier, miniature signal transformers, a four-beam oscillograph, and an electric power source. The apparatus recorded the respiration and pulse rates, the systolic and diastolic blood pressure, and the temperature of the animal.

In addition to this equipment, an aerial cine-camera with lighting and two mirrors was fitted in the nonhermetic compartment.

The weight of the ejection chassis was 70 kilograms. The parachute ensured a vertical landing speed of about 6 meters per second.

The second-stage investigations were carried out with twelve dogs. The animals were subjected to preliminary training for their residence in the space suit, in a fixed position and with the signal transformers attached to them. Training was given to them daily for almost two months, with gradual increase in the duration of residence in the space suit. For the flight, only those animals which had calmly undergone a residence of three hours in the space suit during the last seven to ten days were used. Before the test the animals were on their normal diet of two meals per day.

On the day of the test, the animals were brought out to the starting point three to four hours before the rocket takeoff; all the work connected with the preparation of the animals for the flight was carried out here.

The takeoff of the rocket usually took place three to five minutes before sunrise. The altitude of the flight was between 100 and 110 kilometers. The nose section containing the animals separated from the body of the rocket at the vertex of the trajectory.

We were of the opinion that the evacuation of the rocket during the ascending part of its trajectory did not present any difficulty because under these conditions the flight of the rocket is stabilized. It was therefore considered necessary to study the possibility of evacuating the nose section of the rocket by ejection during the descending part of the flight trajectory, when the movement of the nose section is not stabilized.

Ejection of the animal in the right-hand chassis took place at an altitude of 80 to 90 kilometers during the period of unstable free fall. The speed at which the ejection of the chassis from the nose section of the rocket took place was approximately 700 meters per second. The system of escape parachutes for this animal operated three seconds after ejection: the animal descended to the ground from an altitude of 75 to 85 kilometers in 50 to 65 minutes and was subjected to the direct action of all the factors of the external medium in the upper layers of the atmosphere.

The nose section of the rocket which had been freed of the right-hand chassis continued to fall freely, turning. Ejection of the second animal in the left-hand chassis took place at an altitude of 35 to 50 kilometers at a speed of 1000 to 1150 meters per second. Then the left-hand ejected chassis containing the animal continued to fall freely to an altitude of 3.8 to 4 kilometers and only at this altitude did the automatic opening of the parachute take place.

The animals were filmed at all stages of the rocket flight, up to the moment the chassis was ejected from the compartment. To do this, the camera had been installed on the rear wall of the compartment, above and behind the ejection chassis containing the animals. This arrangement made filming necessary by means of mirrors coated with aluminum. The method of direct filming was prohibited because the construction and the dimensions of the compartment did not permit installation of the cine-camera equipment directly opposite the helmets of the space suits containing the animals.

Two dogs participated in each flight and some animals were used twice. None of the rocket flights during either the first or the second stage of the work resulted in the death of animals through lack of oxygen or because of the influence of external factors connected with flight in the upper layers of the atmosphere.

It is known that a complex group of factors acts on the animals during the flight of the rocket in the upper layers of the atmosphere. The character and the manner in which their influence made itself felt at the different stages of the flight present appreciable differences which require an analysis of the records of the experiment according to the peculiarities of the different parts of the flight. In this respect, it is rational to distinguish between the animal's flight during the powered motion of the rocket, its flight during the period of coasting in the ascending part of the trajectory, and the parachuting of the animal and its free fall in the nose section separated from the rocket.

Results of experiments performed have shown that during rocket flight the animals evidenced moderate changes in blood pressure and in respiration and pulse rate.

In the initial condition, before takeoff, the systolic blood pressure of the animals was usually equal to 120 to 135 millimeters of mercury and the diastolic pressure, 60 to 70 millimeters of mercury. During the powered part of the rocket flight a certain elevation in arterial pressure was observed in the animals and under these conditions its value never again reached the initial level.

In the period of free fall of the animals in the nose section of the rocket, up to the moment of their ejection, it was not possible to observe any regular character in the change in arterial pressure. In some animals the systolic and diastolic pressures rose slightly, and in other animals they fell.

Data on the change in frequency of contraction of the animals' hearts are of unquestionable interest. During the period preceding the takeoff, the pulse rate of the animals was equal to 110 to 170 pulsations per minute. During the powered part of the rocket flight, both an acceleration and a deceleration of the pulse rate was observed in the animals. In the majority of cases, the pulse rate increased 32 to 56 pulsations per minute.

The absence of a regular character in pulse rate change could not be explained by a difference in the strength and character of the stimulants acting externally during each flight. Thus, for example, for two animals having practically the same pulse rate before the flight, in the powered part of the flight a reduction of 25 pulsations per minute was noted in one of the dogs and an acceleration of 40 pulsations per minute in the other.

In connection with this fact it should be pointed out that one of the dogs, in both flights, reacted by a decrease in the rate of heart contractions and the other dog reacted by an acceleration. The circumstances indicated permit us to consider that the difference in the character of the change in pulse rates in the animals during the powered rocket flight is determined by the individual characteristics of each animal. It is important to note that in the powered part of the flight, in the majority of cases, the pulse rate changed in parallel with the change in arterial pressure.

In the coasting period of the rocket flight, no substantial changes were evident in the heart-contraction rate in the animals. Minute analysis of the data obtained shows that in this case only a certain tendency toward decrease in the pulse rate could be noted. In this period of flight, the rate fell 7 to 24 pulsations per minute in eight animals, and in two dogs only, the decrease in pulse rate amounted to 36 to 46 pulsations.

In nearly all of the animals the separation of the nose section did not cause any change in the heart-contraction rate, and in two dogs only, this separation was accompanied by a slight acceleration of short duration in the pulse rate. In the following period of the free fall of the animals the pulse rate usually decreased 8 to 24 pulsations. No change in the heart contraction rate was noted in the animals in the period of parachuting.

The respiration rate in the period preceding takeoff was 30 to 52 respirations per minute in the majority of the animals under normal conditions. During the powered part of the rocket flight the character and rate of respiration remained practically unchanged in the majority of the animals. In two dogs, however, a substantial decrease in respiration was observed. In one dog, the rate of respiratory movement changed from 156 respirations per minute to six per minute — and in another, a decrease between 52 and 28 respirations per minute was recorded. During the coasting period of the rocket, a decrease in respiration rate was noted in all of the animals. The decrease was moderate since it did not exceed 6 to 17 respirations per minute. During the period when the animals were parachuting, no changes of a regular character in the respiration rate were observed. The filmed data showed that in flight up to the moment of their ejection, the behavior of the animals changed very little with only one exception.

The experiments carried out show that the combination of factors acting during rocket flight in the upper layers of the atmosphere do not cause substantial changes in the cardio-vascular condition or the respiratory function of the animals. The functional changes observed do not have a pronounced character and are conspicuous by their short duration. Nor is any important change in the general behavior of the animals observed.

The experiments carried out have permitted the following to be established:

1. The space suits guarantee the creation and maintenance of conditions necessary for the animal's life during rocket flight up to an altitude of 110 kilometers — during the ejection, the descent by parachute from an altitude of 85 kilometers to the ground, and also during free fall from an altitude of 35 to 50 kilometers to an altitude of 4 kilometers.

2. The method of ejecting the animals from the rocket compartment at altitudes of 75 to 85 kilometers at a speed of the order of 700 meters per second, and at altitudes of 35 to 50 kilometers at a speed of 1000 to 1150 meters per second, ensures the recovery of the animals, the maintenance of their vital activity, and the absence of substantial changes in their various physiological functions.

3. The system of parachutes ensures complete safety of descent and landing of animals in the space suit, with parachuting carried out from an altitude of 75 to 85 kilometers.

4. A short flight of about one hour in the upper layers of the atmosphere does not cause any substantial sudden change in the behavior of the animals or in the state of the vital physiological functions of their organism.

There is no doubt that thanks to the collective efforts of the various branches of science, thanks to the efforts of scientists of all countries, it will be possible to realize manned rocket flight in view of the studies of the upper layers of the atmosphere. (Originally presented as a report at the Congrès International des Fusées et Engins Guidés, Paris, December 3-8, 1956. For the complete text in French see *Etudes Sovietiques* (Paris), January, 1957. The author is identified as "Director of Institute of Experimental Aviation Medicine, USSR Academy of Sciences.")

Part Four

# LUNAR AND COSMIC PROJECTS

# 15. Flight to the Moon

*M. K. Tikhonravov*

Is it possible in the near future to accomplish flight to the moon or even to the neighboring planets of the earth? Science and technology now answer this question affirmatively: Yes, such a voyage is already possible.

The famous Russian scientist Konstantin Eduardovich Tsiolkovskii, as far back as 1903, scientifically showed that people will be able to visit the other planets. He wrote: "The celestial ship must be like a rocket." But a rocket does not need the terrestrial atmosphere for flight; in airless space it moves even faster.

Half a century ago Tsiolkovskii could only dream about building a celestial rocket ship. At that time, the first airplane with puny motors had hardly begun to ascend above the earth. Today it is another matter. Science and technology, especially in our country, in the Soviet Union, have attained great successes. Powerful jet airplanes fly ever higher and farther. Engineers can show precisely how it is possible to accomplish flight to the moon and what is necessary for it.

Let us try to visualize what a celestial ship for interplanetary voyages will be like. Travelers will take seats in a spacious, comfortable cabin. The ship's strong metal walls will prevent the escape of the air and will protect the travelers against the cold of airless space. Also in the cabin will be a large number of the complicated precision instruments necessary for controlling the ship and determining its correct course in space, for conducting scientific observations, and for maintaining inside the ship conditions favorable for man's existence therein. A large part of the instruments will operate automatically. A powerful rocket motor with its complicated machinery will occupy the rear part of the ship, where much of the space will be used for the storage of liquid fuel and liquid oxygen.

The interplanetary ship will speed away into space with a tremendous velocity, one at which people have never traveled before. It is a long way to the moon and the planets — many hundred thousands of kilometers. And the main thing is that only with a very high speed is it possible to overcome the earth's attraction.

We do not have time to see in detail a jet airplane when it shoots by over our heads, when it shoots by with a speed of 250 meters per second or more. But for an interplanetary ship, even such a speed is inadequate.

Scientists have calculated exactly that if a rocket ship attains a speed of 8 kilometers per second, then the earth's attraction will still hold it back but will no longer be able to force it to come down. Such a ship will fly forever around the terrestrial globe at a great altitude. It will become a new satellite of the earth, a small moon. Tsiolkovskii proposed to create a large artificial satellite beyond the earth's atmosphere. On such a celestial island it will be possible to carry out very valuable observations, and interplanetary ships will be able to stop there.

For a journey to the moon an even greater speed is required — 11 kilometers per second. Only with such a velocity will a rocket completely overcome the earth's attraction. But if we want to set out for Mars, then the ship's velocity will have to be increased a little more.

Engineers have calculated that for a flight to the moon today it will be necessary to construct a ship weighing approximately 1000 tons. On such a ship, having a velocity of about 40,000 kilometers per hour, two men could be dispatched; they could reach the moon, circle around it without landing, and return to the earth. And if an artificial earth satellite is created, it will then be possible to send a much smaller space ship, weighing not more than 100 tons, from the satellite to the moon. To take off from such a satellite, a velocity of 3.5 kilometers per second will be sufficient.

Many scientists and specialists will work collectively in the preparation for the first interplanetary journeys. Metallurgists will prepare especially strong, but light, metals from which the rocket ship will be built. Chemists will create a fuel for the rocket, which will provide sufficient thrust; physicists will invent new instruments for the ship and together with astronomers will compute its precise path. Biologists and doctors will indicate what conditions will be necessary for the travelers in the ship so that they would not suffer in flight. It is still necessary to apply much work and knowledge in order to set out on such a long journey. But there is nothing impracticable in these plans, even today.

Interplanetary space will be mastered gradually. At first people will simply begin to ascend in rockets beyond the atmosphere, each time going higher and higher.   Later on, with the aid of rocket ships, an interplanetary station — an artificial earth satellite — will be erected.   Finally, from this satellite, or from the earth itself, the first travelers will be able to set out for the moon or for Mars.

On May 1, 1933, K. E. Tsiolkovskii in a holiday greeting to the pioneers said, "I believe that many of you will be witnesses to the first transatmospheric journey."

We do not have long to wait.   We can assume that the bold dream of the scientist will be realized within the next ten to fifteen years. All of you will become witnesses to this, and some of you may even be participants in as yet unprecedented journeys.   (*Pionerskaya Pravda,* October 2, 1951.   The author is identified as "Corresponding Member of the Academy of Artillery Sciences.")

# 16.  Moon Rocket Developments[1]

*Heinz H. Kölle*

In the Soviet newspaper *Krasnii Flot* (Red Fleet) for October 12, 1951, according to a German Press Agency report, it was asserted by V. Abiants that a moon rocket has already been worked out in the Soviet Union.  It is said to be 60 meters long, and to have a maximum diameter of 15 meters, a weight of 1000 tons, and 20 motors with a total power of 350 million horsepower.  In order for the alleged project to be judged and evaluated, the data are compared with various possibilities for a moon flight.

The following five cases have been investigated frequently as examples for flight to the moon and are discussed below.

1.  Takeoff from the earth — flight to the moon — no return (moon messenger);

2.  Takeoff from the earth — repeated revolution around the moon — return to the earth;

3.  Takeoff from the earth — single revolution around the moon — return to the earth;

4.  Takeoff from outer station — revolution around the moon — return to outer station;

5.  Takeoff from outer station — landing on the moon — return to outer station.

The last two plans assume the existence of an outer station.  They are thus out of the question for the following investigation.

The moon messenger requires for its single flight to the moon a characteristic velocity $u$ of 13.5 kilometers per second.[2]  From the fundamental rocket equation $u = c \ln R_i$ the required mass ratio $R_i$, which is equal to the product of the separate stage mass ratios,[3] can be calculated for a known exhaust velocity.  On the basis of an average exhaust velocity $c_m$ and an average cell factor $\varepsilon$ [ratio of net weight (empty weight without payload) to takeoff weight], the optimum number of stages $n$, the optimum construction number phi (ratio of net weight to payload of one stage), and the fundamental ratio $M$ (expenditure per ton of payload = a ratio of takeoff weight to payload of the first stage) can be ascertained. [4]   From the takeoff weight $G_{so}$ = 1000 tons and a fundamental ratio $M$, the feasible payload then results.   For the thrust of the primary stage, one can assume something between 2 and 2.5 times the takeoff weight.   The number of motors can be estimated when an agreement on the size and thrust of a single motor is found.   The comparative power in horsepower is obtained by multiplying the maximum velocity of each stage by the thrust, dividing by the conversion factor 75, and adding the results. The length and diameter can be estimated by assuming for the usual slenderness ratio for fluid rockets an average bulk density of 1 ton per cubic meter,[5] and for atomic rockets an average bulk density of 0.6 ton per cubic meter.[4]   These values depend to a large extent on the construction.

The computed values are compared in the numerical table.   It appears that the unmanned moon messenger with a payload of $G_5 = 300$ kilograms comes nearest to the data mentioned in the German Press Agency report.   The higher motor power of the Soviet project can be traced to the fact that a smaller number of stages was chosen, which raises the fundamental ratio and thereby reduces the payload.   For a revolution around the moon with a liquid rocket and otherwise equal conditions, the payload weight would reduce to only 15 kilograms. For the example of the atomic rocket an exhaust velocity of 10,000 kilometers per second is assumed, so that a payload of 3500 kilograms results.   In so assuming, however, it is necessary to take into consideration that at present no possibility is seen of giving a chosen direction to the particles released by nuclear disintegration.[4]   But as soon as a recoil mass heated by the heat of disintegration is taken into account, then the assumption of technically controllable gas temperatures leads to considerably less favorable results.   The atomic rocket in the last column of the table, therefore, is also eliminated as a possibility for the Soviet project.   There still remains the "optimale Mondumrundung" (optimum circumnavigation of the moon) for which by utilizing all theoretical possibilities (for example, aerodynamic braking for the return and landing on the earth), the necessary characteristic velocity would be decreased to 15 kilometers per second, so that a payload of 1500 kilograms would result.   With it the Soviet engineers could actually send several men on a trip around the moon, but the assumptions in this case were made so favorable that realization according to the present known state of development is unlikely.   A manned rocket for at best a two-man crew and a single circumnaviga-

TABLE 1

| Parameter | Symbols | Units | Project* | Moon messenger (unmanned) | Revolution around the moon | Optimum revolution around the moon | Revolution around the moon with atomic rocket |
|---|---|---|---|---|---|---|---|
| Characteristic velocity | $u$ | m/sec | ? | 13.5 | 18 | 15 | 18 |
| Mean exhaust velocity | $c_m$ | m/sec | ? | 2500 | 2500 | 2500 | 10,000 |
| Mass ratio | $R_1$ | .. | ? | 230 | 1450 | 400 | 6 |
| Mean cell factor | $\epsilon = G_N/G_X$ | .. | ? | 0.15 | 0.15 | 0.14 | 0.40 |
| Number of stages | $n$ | .. | ? | 6 | 8 | 6 | 3 |
| Takeoff weight | $G_{so}$ | ton | 1000 | 1000 | 1000 | 1000 | 1000 |
| Fundamental ratio | $M = G_{so}/G_{s(n)}$ | .. | ? | 3500 | 66,000 | 650 | 280 |
| Payload of last stage | $G_{s(n)}$ | ton | ? | 0.2–0.3 | 0.015 | 1.5 | 3.5 |
| Thrust of first stage | $P_1$ | ton | ? | 2500 | 2500 | 2000 | 3000 |
| Number of motors | $n_T$ | .. | 20 | 20–25 | 25–35 | 20–25 | 3 |
| Power of motors | $N$ | hp | $350 \times 10^6$ | $120 \times 10^6$ | $150 \times 10^6$ | $120 \times 10^6$ | $320 \times 10^6$ |
| Diameter | $d$ | m | 15 | 12 | 14 | 12 | 10 |
| Length | $l$ | m | 60 | 45 | 60 | 50 | 35 |

*Data are in accordance with DPA Reuter from *Krasnii Flot.*

172

tion of the moon with subsequent return to the earth lies as yet too close to the outermost limit of present attainments.

Even the unmanned moon messenger would require immense technical effort. The practical result would be trifling in comparison. On the other hand, the undertaking could be used psychologically and propaganda-wise, since by successful execution and the corresponding accompanying fanfare, it would represent a grandiose technical achievement and would obviously demonstrate that Soviet long-range rockets could just as well reach any point on the earth's surface. (*Weltraumfahrt*, January, 1952.)

---

[1] Original title of this article was "Is A Moon Rocket Being Developed in the Soviet Union?"

[2] By "characteristic velocity" ("idealer Antrieb" according to Oberth, also occasionally referred to in the literature as "ideale Brennschlussgeschwindigkeit," or ideal burnout velocity) is understood the velocity that a rocket will attain without the influence of outside force. Actual flight velocity is always smaller, since air resistance and the force of gravity, among other factors, act as outside forces.

[3] According to Oberth, $R_i$ is the "idealwert des Massenverhältnisses" (ideal value of the mass ratio).

[4] See H. Kölle, "Verfahren zur Bestimmung der minimalen Startgewichte und der güngstigsten Konstruktionswerte von Grossraketen" (Method of Determining the Minimum Takeoff Weight and the Most Favorable Construction Weight of Large Rockets), *Forschungsbericht der Gesellschaft für Weltraumforschung*, No. 5, Stuttgart, May, 1950.

[5] See E. Sänger, "Die konstruktiven Grundprobleme der Gasdruck-Raketenmotoren" (Fundamental Construction Problems of Gas Pressure Rocket Motors), *Weltraumfahrt*, No. 1, February 1950, pp. 2-8.

# 17.  Trip to the Moon: Fantasy and Reality

*Kirill Stanyukovich*

At the beginning of last month the *New York Times* (May 15, 1954), carried a report of a speech made by Mr. George Sutton, head of the aerophysics department of North American Aviation Company.  Mr. Sutton, the paper said, noted the Soviet Union's progress in the sphere of the rocket engine and in exploring the possibility of creating an artificial satellite of the earth.  The *New York Times* commented on the speech as follows: "The possibility that the Russians might be able to fire into the skies an artificial satellite of the earth that would appear as a 'red star' symbolic of Soviet superiority in the upper atmosphere was presented here today."

Since I have not seen the full text of Mr. Sutton's speech I cannot, of course, voice any opinion of his actual words and intentions.  But as an astronomer I cannot help taking objection to the *New York Times* irresponsible commentary, which is clearly intended to build up a false impression about the objectives pursued by Soviet astronomy, and at the same time to scare its readers with its idle talk about a Soviet artificial satellite of the earth and other space experiments for the purpose of attacking the United States.

What makes this sensation-mongering sleight of hand by the *New York Times* all the more absurd is the fact that many American political and adventure magazines regularly publish fantasies about the creation of such a satellite by the United States in order to gain world domination and attack the democratic countries of Europe and Asia.  The *New York Times* counts on gullible readers.  It is a plain case of the criminal shouting "stop thief!"

A trip to the moon and other planets and the creation of an artificial satellite of the earth are ideas that have long intrigued the minds of men.  During the past decade, newspapers and magazines have been writing about this problem more widely than ever.  Treatment of important aspects of interplanetary travel in nonscientific publications could be welcomed, were it not for the fact that certain publications in the West go in for the sensational, or, what is worse, for political and military speculations, relegating scientific problems to the background.

In a number of articles (in *Collier's* for one) fantasy goes hand in hand with a purely political and military interest in the problem of developing long-range rockets, for, their authors argue, rockets which can climb to a height of several hundred kilometers can cover tremendous distances and can be guided from any point of the globe to any other point. A rocket of that kind, the authors say, should have an A-bomb or H-bomb filling.

Let us examine this question of rockets and a trip to the moon to see just what is scientific and possible and what is superficial fantastic blather.

### WHAT PREVENTS A SPACE FLIGHT TODAY?

Although the basic features of an interplanetary rocket and the theory of its flight were formulated and worked out long ago by Konstantin Tsiolkovskii, the eminent Russian scientist, and by scientists of other countries, a trip into space has not yet been made. The explanation lies in the tremendous difficulties encountered even in building rockets intended for more modest purposes, such as taking soundings in the upper air.

To design an engine that will function for a long time at stable combustion regimens is an extremely complicated task. This partly explains the fact that we do not yet have an interplanetary rocket, although its principles are sufficiently well known. Konstantin Tsiolkovskii and Robert Goddard, the American physicist, were fully aware of these circumstances and each designed, independently, a composite rocket which, in his opinion, would solve the task of a flight into space.

The composite rocket consists of a number of separate rockets. After the fuel of each is exhausted, it drops off from the unused rockets. By that time the one or two remaining rockets have acquired a speed in the neighborhood of 10 to 15 kilometers per second in relation to the earth, the speed necessary for interplanetary travel. The engine of each of the rockets does not have to work a long time, and problems relating to its operation and cooling can be solved (and have already been solved in practice) much more simply than the problems raised by a single engine of a single large rocket.

Scientists and engineers are perfecting the design of such rockets, surmounting the numerous difficulties step by step. Apparently, after long rocket trips into the upper air, it will be possible to get down directly to building a rocket for a two-way trip to the vicinity of the moon, and only then to building a rocket for a flight to the moon with a landing there and subsequent return to earth.

Fuel would also have to be expended in slowing down the rocket for the landing on the moon and later for the takeoff, but that expenditure would be only 10 or 15% of the amount needed to overcome the earth's gravity.

Many people are interested in the question of the return from cosmic space to earth. The usual conjecture is that when the rocket entered the earth's atmosphere, wings would be spread out and it would be turned into an airplane or glider. Air resistance would quickly lower speed, and the craft would be able to land without any difficulty.

Hazards during interplanetary flights of long duration would be meteorites and cosmic dust. Every 24 hours, according to present-day data, not less than five tons of meteorites enter the earth's atmosphere. The possibility of a space rocket meeting a meteorite has been calculated as once in 5000 to 10,000 hours of flight. Yet even a meteorite weighing one gram is a menace, since it could tear as much as a whole kilogram of steel out of the shell of the craft, or pierce a shell scores of centimeters thick.

What seems most likely to me is that the first stage will be the sending of a rocket containing instruments to record the physical conditions in space and to take a sample of "moon ground." Flight by man into interplanetary space is theoretically possible, too, but it creates additional difficulties. For one thing, it is not known how the human body will withstand the absence of gravitational force while the rocket is flying by inertia. Evidently this will cause a sharp change in blood circulation. With the present-day achievements in the sphere of automatic control and radiolocation, the guiding of a pilotless rocket is fully feasible.

#### PROGRESS FOR PEACE, NOT WAR

In 1895, Tsiolkovskii thought and wrote about the possibility of creating an artificial satellite of the earth that would move in an orbit beyond the atmosphere and serve as a scientific and technical station for interplanetary rockets.

There can be no doubt that, if sponsored by peace-loving nations, an artificial satellite of the earth, as well as interplanetary travel in general, could and should serve mankind's further progress and prosperity and the broadening of human knowledge.

It should be noted, however, that *Collier's* and certain other American publications are inclined to view a solution of these problems only in terms of U. S. military potentialities, as a new weapon for forcing a definite system of political dictation upon the peoples of the world.

During World War II, we all saw the frightful consequences of rocket weapons used against the civilian population of Britain. It is the duty of every scientist working in the field of rocket techniques to prevent the achievements of human genius from ever being used for such purposes again.

I am deeply convinced that fantasy can be a powerful stimulus to the progress of scientific thought. The history of the science of interplanetary travel convincingly illustrates that. However, some of the articles of military-political fantasy in the field of astronautics and rocket techniques carried by *Collier's*, the *New York Times*, and other American publications can only harm science, and to no little degree, by compromising its peaceful aims in the eyes of scores of millions of people who sincerely believe that space travel will give man new knowledge, forces, and potentialities for his constructive labours on earth.

I think there is no doubt that if the scientists of different countries cooperate with one another, regardless of political views, if they really work together to solve the remaining problems of interplanetary travel for peaceful purposes, as is declared in the Charter of the International Astronautics Federation, then we shall be able within the next five to ten years to talk in practical terms about sending a guided missile to the moon for the benefit of international science. (*News: A Soviet Review of World Events*, English, June 1, 1954. The author is identified as "Professor" and "Doctor of Technical Sciences.")

# 18.  The Road Into the Cosmos

*Yu. S. Khlebtsevich*

A great many serious obstacles stand in the way of the realization of man's first flight into cosmic space, to the moon, and to the nearest planets — Mars and Venus.  We are far from knowing everything that astronauts will encounter during such flights, and, therefore, we cannot at present foresee everything required for normal vital activity of people during cosmic travels.  Also, we do not know all the dangers and surprises which await man during his flight in cosmic space and his stay on the other planets.  Consequently, we cannot at present foresee reliable ways and means of protecting the cosmic rocket and its crew.

Meanwhile, in spite of the serious difficulties, until quite recently the first interplanetary flights were thought of as flights of rockets with people inside a pressurized cabin.  Now, however, thanks to achievements in radio engineering, radar, automatics and telemechanics, electronics, television, technology of semiconductors and numerous branches of electrical engineering, and, finally, in the means of radio-telecontrol, it is possible to solve the problems of interplanetary flights rapidly and in a somewhat different way than was imagined previously. The present article discusses the prospects which are opening up in the investigation of cosmic space and the nearest planets.

### COSMIC LABORATORIES

The creation of radio-telecontrolled automatic rockets began with the very first stages of the jet engine.  Flights of such unmanned rockets have already taken place to an altitude of more than 400 kilometers.  This altitude, of course, is not the limit.  As jet technology develops, the ceiling of rocket flight will increase.  Simultaneously the scientific value of information received by radio from special instruments at higher and higher altitudes will also increase.

As a matter of fact, modern technology makes it possible not only to control flying devices by radio at a distance, but also to measure physical quantities of interest to scientists by means of instruments aboard them. For this purpose, the physical quantities are transformed into electrical ones, coded into various kinds of radio impulses, transmitted by radio, and recorded automatically on the earth by means of special registering devices. At the same time, the quantity and quality of such measurements and their records on the earth are such that for the ordinary realization of analogous work, the labor of several tens of men working under the most favorable conditions would be needed. At the same time, the use of television makes it possible to utilize completely new ways and means for studying at a distance from the earth the behavior of experimental animals during cosmic flight, for observing the surface of our planet from great altitudes, etc. Moreover, observations can be conducted also in those parts of the solar spectrum which are not perceived directly by the human eye (infrared and ultraviolet rays).

Thus, even a brief journey of unmanned radiotelecontrolled automatic rockets into the upper layers of the atmosphere and beyond its limits broadens our knowledge of nature and permits a more thorough study of the conditions and peculiarities of cosmic flight. But all this is already insufficient. For the further successful development of a number of sciences and primarily for new successes in solving the problem of interplanetary communications, it is necessary and possible to create a whole series of cosmic laboratories, which are, as it were, "artificial satellites" of the earth, revolving for a long time in different orbits around out planet.[1] This will open up new, unlimited horizons in the field of the most diverse scientific investigations and simultaneously will be the first stage in the conquest of cosmic space.

Cosmic laboratories, very compact and well equipped with instruments (again unmanned), can be taken by radiotelecontrolled rockets to different orbits and, subsequently, they will fly around our planet without expenditure of fuel. The program of scientific work for the laboratories will be assigned from the earth by radio. The instruments which carry out this program will record, in a definite order and at definite moments of time on magnetic tape, data on temperature and pressure in one region or another of cosmic space; on the intensity of solar radiation (over its entire spectrum), and also of cosmic radiation; on the strength and direction of the earth's magnetic field; on meteoric particles passing near the satellite, etc. All these data will be transmitted at high speed from the magnetic ribbon to the earth by special radiocommand and taken down by a suitable recording device during the flight of the cosmic laboratory over the control point. Then will follow the deciphering of the record and the

generalization of the results obtained. With such a method it is sufficient to have only one point for collecting data and controlling the
cosmic laboratories.

Of course, electrical energy will be needed for operating the radio
receiving-transmitting apparatus of the satellite, as well as for operating all its other instruments. It will be possible to obtain this
energy from a solar energy transformer, utilizing the technology of
semiconductors.[2] A photoelectronic following device can ensure constant setting of the surface of the transformer in the direction of the
sun during the motion of the cosmic laboratory in a circular or elliptic
orbit. When the laboratory falls into the region shaded by the earth,
however, feeding its apparatus will be accomplished by a special accumulator charged by the transformer. Special automatic instruments will ensure the necessary concentration of the electrolyte and
the control of the operation of the accumulator and transformer. The
influence of weightlessness on the operation of the accumulator can be
paralyzed artificially by pressure on the electrolyte created through
a flexible diaphragm. Such an arrangement of the power source will
guarantee normal operation of the cosmic laboratory apparatus for
several years.

Besides carrying out geophysical, astrophysical, and other observations, cosmic laboratories will be used also to study the changes that
take place in various construction and other materials under the conditions of cosmic space. This will help in the creation of materials
with improved properties and constructions necessary for successfully
building new rockets and cosmic laboratories.

Finally, monkeys and other experimental animals will be placed in
certain cosmic laboratories. Observing them will give much valuable
data to physicians concerned with the biological and physiological aspects of cosmic flight. Instruments will measure the temperature of
the body and the blood pressure of the animals, analyze the blood,
make cardiograms, and transmit the data obtained by radio. Television will permit seeing the behavior of the animals in flight. As a result, it will be possible to design successfully special cabin equipment
for the cosmic ship, to create special clothing for the interplanetary
travellers, and to develop a complex of necessary safety and training
procedures, thus facilitating the adaptation of the human organism to
the conditions of cosmic flight.

It will be very important to ascertain what factors can influence the
flight trajectory of the cosmic laboratory. This can be done by special
automatic training radar stations, which from the moment the satellite

flies into the zone of their operation will continuously measure its co-ordinates relative to the earth. The study of the results of these measurements will make it possible to reach definite conclusions about the causes of the change of the trajectory of the cosmic laboratory. Such conclusions will be very useful for developing interplanetary communications.

Other cosmic laboratories will be utilized also for the solution of a number of problems of the national economy. For example, a television station will make it possible to see and photograph on the earth the distribution of cloudiness and storm fronts over the entire territry of the Soviet Union and to determine the direction of their movement. This will make possible better long-range weather forecasts.

Utilization of the cosmic laboratory as a radio relay station transmitting the television programs of any town of our country over the entire territory of the USSR is envisioned.

### ROCKET ON THE MOON

The investigation of cosmic space, in spite of its great scientific importance, is not a goal in itself. It will serve as a preparation for the next stage in the development of interplanetary flights — the stage of studying the moon by means of radiotelecontrolled rockets equipped with suitable apparatus.

Before setting out for the moon, man must ascertain what he might encounter during his journey into a world completely unsuited for him. Only by knowing this, will it be possible to ensure passenger safety during takeoff, flight, and landing of the cosmic ship and to guarantee the return of the courageous investigators to their native planet. At the same time, it is still necessary to completely work out the landing of the rocket on the moon, its takeoff from the lunar surface, and its landing on the earth. It is also necessary to check the correctness of the calculations which determine the influence of the attraction of the sun and the other planets on the flight trajectory of the cosmic ship, and to ascertain the physical properties of the lunar atmosphere and the lunar surface, in order to take them into account in designing the rocket and implementing it with suitable equipment.

We shall recall further that the flight of a rocket to the moon and back with a crew is possible in the contemporary state of jet technology only if the route of this flight is divided into several intermediate stages with a guarantee of refueling the rocket at each stage. The use of atomic energy facilitates the solution of this task, but then introduces a number of additional conditions connected with ensuring the safety of the crew — primarily its protection against harmful radioactive radiations.

Flight to the moon demands, moreover, extremely high precision in maintaining the calculated trajectory and flight chart. Up to the present, almost no attention has been paid to these characteristics of cosmic flight. However, an error of only ±0.1% in the value of the vector of the initial takeoff velocity of a rocket heading for the moon will result in a "short" or an "over" of the order of ±12.5% of the general length of path, or several tens of thousands of kilometers. Consequently, the cosmic ship will still require an additional supply of fuel for maneuvering.

Finally, the real danger of meteorites hitting the rocket both in flight and on the moon greatly aggravates the difficulties of the original solution of all the problems of interplanetary travel involving direct participation of people.

All the above obstacles can be completely overcome in relatively short periods of time and without sacrifices, moreover, only in one case: if automatic radiotelecontrolled unmanned rockets are sent on the first flights to the moon.

A rocket controlled by radio from the earth will "land" on the moon, instead of a crew, a mobile laboratory which externally somewhat resembles a small tank. This "tankette-laboratory," as we shall call it, will also be controlled by radio from the earth. The transmitting television camera, mounted on a radiocontrolled boom having several degrees of freedom and fixed on the tankette-laboratory, will permit scientists on the earth to observe the lunar surface and the lunar sky with the disk of our planet visible on it (all this can be photographed on the earth), and to determine the safest path for the movement of the laboratory. Aboard it will be placed various automatic instruments transmitting to the earth their readings on the state and properties of the lunar atmosphere and the lunar surface. For moving the tankette and operating its equipment the necessary store of fuel and oxidant for the engine will be available. Utilization of other known sources of energy is also possible. Calculations show that for a tankette-laboratory with a total weight of not more than several hundred kilograms, serious initial investigations of the moon, sufficient for carrying out the next stage — the mastery of the moon by man — are possible in principle; and what is more, in case of necessity, it will be possible to "land" other tankettes, taking into account the results obtained earlier.

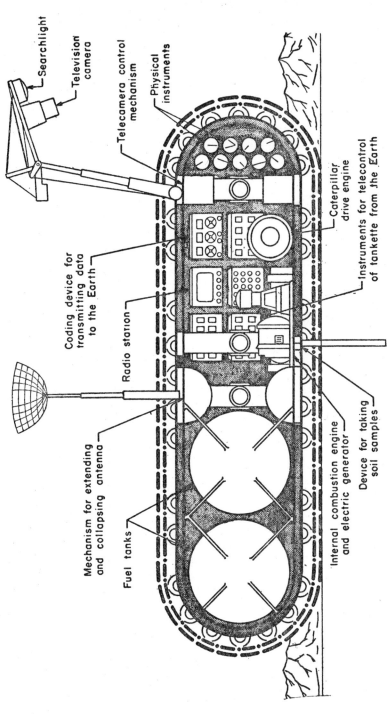

Searchlight

Television camera

Telecamera control mechanism

Physical instruments

Coding device for transmitting data to the Earth

Radio station

Caterpillar drive engine

Instruments for telecontrol of tankette from the Earth

Mechanism for extending and collapsing antenna

Fuel tanks

Internal combustion engine and electric generator

Device for taking soil samples

Tankette laboratory designed by Soviet astronauts for exploring the surface of the moon.

183

Together with the scientists, the television audience of the Soviet Union will also be able to "visit" the satellite of our planet; for the transmission of the image from the laboratory through the television center of any town to the screens of television sets will, to a certain degree, be analogous to an ordinary out-of-the-studio telecast.

The use of a radiotelecontrolled tankette as the first "investigator" of the moon also greatly simplifies the construction of the rocket that carries it. The special conditions, without which the departure of a crew is impossible, are not required for the tankette-laboratory. It and its apparatus can endure considerably greater accelerations and differences of temperature and pressure than can man. There will be no need to create means for protecting the rocket and the tankette from meteorites. On the contrary, each case of hitting by meteorites will permit making deductions that will be very valuable in designing cosmic ships intended for manned flights. Finally, it will also be possible to leave both the tankette and the rocket on the moon, without bringing them to the earth, as a result of which the flight route of the rocket is exactly halved, and takeoff from the moon and landing on the earth are obviated. All this will make it actually possible to substantially reduce the quantity of fuel that must be carried aboard the rocket, and will permit decreasing the weight of the payload. The latter, for launching the tankette, amounts to approximately 500 kilograms; and for sending a crew of three men with equipment, stores of provisions and protective clothing, armorplating of the most vulnerable spots of the cosmic ship against meteorites, and landing and takeoff mechanisms for the rocket when it reaches the moon, would amount to a minimum of 5 to 10 thousand kilograms. As a result, to launch a tankette-laboratory, a composite rocket with a gross weight of the order of several hundred tons will be necessary; but to send and bring back the above-mentioned crew, a multistage rocket with a gross weight of millions of tons would be required. Of course, the latter variant is hardly feasible in the contemporary state of technology.

Moreover, radiotelecontrol will permit in practice breaking up the flight route of the rocket to the moon and back into several stages and ensure refueling of the cosmic ship by means of automatic rocket-tankers (also controlled by radio) at every intermediate stage of the flight. How will all this take place?

The cosmic ship with a tankette-laboratory starts from the earth by means of a special winged rocket-carrier. Several types of jet engines are utilized in it for fuel economy. Flying in the direction of our planet's rotation, the rocket-carrier accelerates the cosmic ship to a velocity of 6 to 8 kilometers per second, after which the ship itself will increase its velocity to 10.3 kilometers per second and will begin to move without fuel expenditure in an elliptic orbit in the earth's gravitational field. Having performed one and a half revolutions in this orbit, the rocket will receive a radio command to switch on its engine at the upper point of the elliptic trajectory, and, having increased its velocity by 1.6 kilometers per second, it will fly out to the so-called stationary circular orbit with a radius of 42,180 kilometers (calculated from the center of the earth). This exit will take place at a point above the terrestrial radiotelecontrol station, and after an increase of 0.16 kilometer per second in velocity, the cosmic ship, moving in the stationary orbit, will hang in the sky in one spot, for the angular velocity of motion in the orbit will be equal to the angular velocity of the earth's rotation. Since at this moment the rocket will have almost completely spent its store of fuel, radiotelecontrolled automatic rocket-tankers will be sent to it by the same route. There, precise rapprochement with the cosmic ship will be carried out by means of radar control from the terrestrial station. During the approach of the tankers to the rocket at a distance of several tens of meters, television transmitting cameras will begin to operate, permitting visual control and guidance of the refuelling process from the earth. For this purpose methods already mastered in aviation will be utilized except that the "pilot" will be located at the terrestrial radiotelecontrol point.

After the refueling, the cosmic ship continues its flight to the moon. By suitable radio command, it will acquire an additional velocity of 1.02 kilometers per second and leave the stationary circular orbit in an elliptic trajectory to the satellite of the earth. Then, at a definite point on a command from the earth, the rocket, again having changed its velocity, will begin its motion in a circular orbit (that is, it will fly parallel to the lunar orbit), and under the action of the force of gravity, it will begin to fall gradually to the moon. The velocity of 2.3 kilometers per second which the cosmic ship would acquire at the end of its fall, will be cancelled by braking by means of the rocket's jet engine.

The most crucial moment — the automatic landing of the cosmic ship on the surface of the moon — will occur at this point. The antenna of the powerful earth radar station, aimed at our planet's satellite, will begin to operate. The impulses of this station, both the direct ones and those reflected from the lunar surface, will be received by the rocket's altimeters, which will determine the distance between it and the "landing area" in the central region of the moon previously selected by astronomers. The automatic landing device, utilizing the altimeter data, will turn the rocket at the proper time with its tail part to the moon and, in accordance with a special program, will carry out all the necessary operations of controlling the jet engines in the braking regime. Finally, the cosmic ship is on the lunar surface. The compact tankette-laboratory rolls off on caterpillar tracks and, obeying radio commands, begins its travel over the expanse of our planet's satellite.

Is it possible, however, to control the rocket by radio during its flight to the moon? Recent scientific data confirm this. In addition to the optical "window" into the universe which mankind has used for studying cosmic space, a "radio window" in the range of ultrashort waves was also discovered recently in the atmosphere. This discovery led to the creation of a new branch of science — radioastronomy. Radiolocation of the moon has already been achieved: a radio impulse has reached it, was reflected, and was again received on the earth.

By using this "window" we shall also be able to control cosmic rockets by radio.

Inasmuch as the path of the cosmic ship in interplanetary space will be sufficiently complex, its trajectory, as well as its entire plotted course, must be rigorously calculated in advance. These calculations will be "fed" into the input of a special electronic computer. After the start of the rocket, several automatic tracking radar stations will follow its flight. Working together with the apparatus aboard the cosmic ship, they will determine its coordinates with high precision. The corresponding data will enter the computer, which for a deviation of the rocket from the trajectory or from the plotted course will "compute" the necessary correcting radio commands. The control apparatus on board, having received these commands, will correct the deviation.

Such a system of radiotelecontrol of a cosmic ship, with its intermediate refueling in a stationary circular orbit, will require a composite rocket with a gross weight of the order of 100 tons, the construction of which is entirely possible in the contemporary state of jet technology. The use of radiotelecontrol will also facilitate considerably the utilization of atomic energy for interplanetary flights in the future.

MASTERY OF THE MOON BY MAN

After landing the first of such rockets on the moon and obtaining detailed data about the conditions existing there, the flight of man and the creation of a continuously operating scientific station on our planet's satellite will be possible. The most suitable spot for landing manned rockets and developing a scientific station will be selected by means of a tankette-laboratory on the moon. A number of similar rockets, guided by the same system of radiotelecontrol as the first cosmic ship, will deliver to the earth's satellite everything necessary for the life and scientific activity of the first astronauts: fuel for the needs of the station and for the return of the manned rocket to the earth; special and scientific equipment; stores of water, air, food — in a word, everything, including sectional pressurized houses with lighting and heating. There will also be delivered a special landing and takeoff device for the manned cosmic ship which will be assembled by special tankette-automats, guided by radio from the earth and controlled by means of television transmitting cameras. All these rockets will be landed on the selected spot in accordance with the signals of the tankette-laboratory radio station, which will serve as a "radio beacon." Altogether, only a little time will be required for the preparation and execution of all these operations after the landing of the first rocket on the moon. After this it will be possible to deliver the personnel for the scientific station to our planet's satellite by means of one of the rockets.

It should be emphasized that in such a variant of mastery of the moon by man, the construction of a rocket for manned flight then will no longer represent any difficulty. Such a cosmic ship will not need large quantities of fuel, for the stores of the latter can be replenished by rocket-tankers both while in flight (to the moon and back) and while on the moon. Moreover, the first astronauts will not be required to take with them too much foodstuff, water, etc., since all this will be stored in advance at the place of landing. The crew must be supplied with everything necessary only during the flight to the moon. As a result, the payload of the manned rocket will be a minimum, not exceeding 500 to 1000 kilograms, and the very flight of the cosmic ship will differ practically in no way from the flight of the first one-way rocket.

Having landed on the moon, its first investigators will be able to stay there as long as they want, for everything that they will still require during their stay on our planet's satellite will be delivered automatically by radiocontrolled rockets. At the same time, thanks to co-ordinated radio and television communication, the courageous astronauts not only will not feel isolated from the earth, but they will also be under the constant control of scientists of various specialties, including physicians. At any moment, in any unexpected event they will be given the necessary consultation and advice and will be rendered actual help by unmanned rockets. The clothing of the first investigators of the moon will be equipped with various instruments that describe their physiological condition. The readings of these instruments will be transmitted on a separate radio channel to the earth both during the flight and during their stay on the moon. Thus scientists will obtain the most complete data on the behavior of the human organism under conditions unusual for it, and physicians will be able to check the state of health of the first astronauts. Exchange of scientific personnel will be carried out according to the same scheme as its delivery.

Mastery of the moon by means of radiocontrolled rockets and tankette-laboratories will open up new possibilities and will not encounter fundamental difficulties from either jet or radiotelecontrol technology. This is why in the next five to ten years the conquest of our nearest celestial body can become a fact. Having started on the practical mastery of the moon and the utilization of everything that is useful there, man will be simultaneously preparing for flights to other planets of the solar system — Mars and Venus. Automatic radiocontrolled rockets will open up for him the road into the cosmos. (*Nauka i Zhizn'*, November, 1955. The author is identified as "Chairman of the Scientific-Technical Committee on Radiotelecontrol, Astronautics Section, V. P. Chkalov Central Aeroclub of the USSR.")

---

[1] The press has already reported the existence of a real basis in our country and in the US for the creation of "artificial satellites" in the next two years.

[2] For details about the transformation of solar energy into electrical energy by use of semiconductor elements, see the paper by M. S. Sominskii in *Nauka i Zhizn'*, No. 8, 1955.

# 19. Rendezvous With Mars

*Kirill Stanyukovich*

This September, Mars with its lurid reddish tint could be especially clearly observed. It is a planet that has fascinated man for centuries, ever since the Romans named it, for its sinister colour, after the God of War. Its resemblance to the earth, discovered as time went on, stirred the imagination of scientist and layman alike. In 1877, Schiaparelli saw on it canals of geometric regularity, and this led others to the belief that it must be inhabited by rational beings. H. G. Wells wrote a fascinating book about a Martian invasion of the earth, while the Russian writer Alexei Tolstoy in his novel *Aelita* painted a picture of social battles on Mars. And though the latest observations and studies have not borne out the thesis as to the geometrical regularity of the canals, the popular hypothesis that Mars is a life planet has not been refuted or even shaken. In short, the reddish planet is still a mystery.

This year has been a highly important one in man's attempts to solve its secrets. In September Mars stood at its minimum distance from the earth — 35 million miles. This happens only once in fifteen or seventeen years; for while oppositions between Mars and the earth occur every two years and some weeks, oppositions near the perihelion, when the distance is least, are — because of the elliptical, not circular, orbits — fifteen or seventeen years apart. Oppositions of this kind were recorded in 1877, 1892, 1909, 1924 and 1939.

Mars is a tremendously interesting planet. It has an atmosphere in which cloud formation takes place, and its poles are covered with "ice caps" which melt in the spring. According to the findings of many researchers, including G. A. Tikhov of the USSR, the founder of the new science of astrobotany, Mars can, and does, support plant life.

Certainly we should not regard our own planet as unique. In all likelihood, some form of life does exist on Mars, and probably on Venus. The other planets are totally unsuited to supporting it.

Even the best telescopic observations, however, cannot establish with sufficient veracity whether there are rational beings on Mars. For that matter, the existence of plant life too is still a matter of debate. In a year or two, when man-made satellites of the earth are launched, then instruments will give us more precise information. But conclusive answers to these and other questions can be obtained only when some spaceship or device lands on Mars, or at least approaches it.

The chief object of any such rendezvous with Mars would be to study its atmosphere and surface and to detect possible forms of organic life and resources of useful minerals. All this can be done by automatic instruments mounted in the space rocket. They will make photographs of Mars by light of different colours, and if the rocket lands, will take samples of the soil, chemically analyze it and transmit the results back to the earth. Things like these are now being done, without man's agency, in the interior of atomic reactors.

The dispatch to Mars of space rockets with instruments might be accomplished in the not-too-distant future, though manned flights are a considerably more remote prospect.

### THE TIME FOR A RENDEZVOUS

It is generally believed that the only good time for a rocket flight to Mars is during perihelion oppositions. But that is not so.

The difference in distance between aphelion opposition is some 28 million miles. Considering that the rocket would have to travel nearly 620 million miles in all, this can have no appreciable effect, and the differences in the initial speed to be imparted to the rocket is insignificant.

Calculations by many astronomers show that the most favourable orbit is when the rocket describes an elongated elliptical trajectory between the orbits of the earth and Mars.

The earth spins around the sun at 19 miles per second, and Mars at approximately 15 miles per second. If the rocket is launched along the shortest route, then as it approaches Mars, it must "level off" this difference, for otherwise, neglecting the Martian gravity, it would hit the planet with an additional velocity of four miles per second. In the course of the long route which it will, by the laws of celestial mechanics, cover, the rocket will do this automatically, and when it reaches the Martian orbit it will be travelling at the same speed as Mars. It will, accordingly, be able to land on the planet, cushioning the gravity attraction in the usual way; or it need not land on Mars at all, but simply travel round it and return to the earth by a similar route without additional expenditure of fuel.

As we have said, there is no need to wait until Mars swings its nearest to the earth.  That is important for telescopic observations; but for launching rockets there is absolutely no necessity to wait fifteen or seventeen years (in the present case, until 1971).  A flight can be launched within a year after the necessary technical equipment has been perfected.  Most scientists are of the opinion that everything needed for dispatching earth satellites will be available within one or two years, for a flight to the moon, within five or ten, and for a flight to Mars, within fifteen.  And in all likelihood it will be sooner still.

### ATOM POWER

Calculations suggest that interplanetary craft will be in the form of atomic rockets.  To overcome the pull of terrestrial gravity, the rocket must work up a speed of seven miles per second.  To attain this speed, a 100-ton rocket would need 96 tons of conventional fuel.  But since the tanks, the shell, and the control mechanism will obviously weigh more than four tons, this is not feasible.  Chemical fuels cannot do the job.

But nuclear fuels can: they can impart the required speed without involving such prohibitive loads.  Thus a 100-ton rocket will need from 70 to 80 tons of inert propulsion agent, leaving 20 to 30 tons for effective load.

The chief difficulty is that so far no atomic reactor has been devised that is capable of operating at the required high temperatures.  But reactor techniques are developing very fast, and it can safely be predicted that the necessary type will be produced within the coming few years, in a number of countries.

Manned flights present many formidable difficulties, at least during the initial stage of interplanetary exploration.  The human organism could not stand the collossal accelerations, nor the impact of meteorites on space craft, and the space travellers would not be able to direct and control their craft.

The instruments that man has devised in this age are much less fallible than he is.  They will be far more reliable pilots.  But they too have to be controlled and adjusted.  Just how is this to be done?  How will they react to the unexplored magnetic fields in cosmic space?  How will they be affected by the impact of meteorites?

These are all difficulties that must be overcome step by step — by dispatching first an earth satellite, then a rocket to the moon, and then a rocket to Mars.

### THE FINANCIAL ANGLE

The interplanetary rocket will require a mass of complex automatic equipment. The cost of its construction will run to tens of billions of dollars, more than any one country can afford. It will have to be an international undertaking.

The vast sums now being spent on bombers, atomic artillery and bomb stockpiles are simply wasted. All this money, and all the engineering ingenuity involved, is thrown down the drain by the cold war foisted on the world by the political unreasonableness and selfish aims of definite groups. If these resources and these efforts were addressed to producing atomic spaceships, all of mankind would stand to benefit. The investment would bring good dividends, not only in enriching our knowledge, but in enriching us materially; development of the natural resources of other planets is a very attractive prospect.

All of us today are anxious to eliminate the sinister symbol of Mars, the god of War, from the political horizons of the earth. And Mars the planet should become a planet of friendship, which the nations will cooperate in exploring. (*News: A Soviet Review of World Events,* October 16, 1956. The author is identified as "a noted physicist" associated with the Bauman Institute of Technology in Moscow. His article was subtitled "Must We Wait For 1971?")

# 20.   Cosmic Boomerang

*G. Chebotarev*

What is the basic practical difficulty preventing the realization of interplanetary flights today? It appears that by utilizing existing kinds of chemical fuel, it is possible to send an apparatus into cosmic space with the necessary speed only if the weight of this apparatus does not exceed a few kilograms!

Meanwhile if we want to send on a long journey a cosmic ship that could at our pleasure approach various celestial bodies, photograph them, and even make moving pictures of their surface, carry out astrophysical observations by means of automatic instruments, and then return to the earth, it is necessary to provide such a cosmic ship with sufficient stores of fuel for maneuvering. The total weight of this fuel (even if the rocket is unmanned) will amount to hundreds, and perhaps even thousands, and tens of thousands of tons, depending on the complexity of the chosen route. Contemporary technology is unable to send a cosmic ship of such weight into interplanetary space.

Thus, one would think, there is an unsolvable contradiction between the possibilities of technology and the necessary conditions of the task.

This, however, is not so. A way out can be found!

In Leningrad, on one of the quiet streets of the Vasil'evskii Island, in a small two-story building, is located the Institute of Theoretical Astronomy of the USSR Academy of Sciences. It is the world's only specialized institute whose task is the detailed study of the movements of celestial bodies.

By means of huge automatic computing machines the Institute carries out calculations of the movement in world space of the earth, the moon, and the other planets of our solar system, and also of the sun and the largest and brightest stars. And on the basis of these calculations, special astronomical calendars (called "astronomical ephemerides") are published, according to which one can easily determine the position of these celestial bodies on any day and hour of a given year.

But what does an interplanetary ship moving in cosmic space represent? From the point of view of astronomy, it is an ordinary celestial body, completely subordinate to the law of universal gravitation.

And here a new idea comes forth. Is it not possible by the methods of celestial mechanics to calculate such an interplanetary flight trajectory by moving along which a cosmic ship could approach the moon to a sufficiently close distance, round the moon, and then again return to the earth?

Since the motion of an interplanetary ship in this case takes place under the influence of the attraction of various celestial bodies, fuel is required only at the moment of takeoff in order to impart to the ship a cosmic velocity of 11 kilometers per second. As is known, this velocity is required to overcome the earth's attraction and to escape from the earth. And for this, according to the calculations carried out, only about sixteen tons of fuel are required. Calculations show that the rocket itself without fuel — that is, the apparatus and the instruments enclosed in the round shell — to all appearances, will weigh 50 to 100 kilograms.

The first trajectory of this type that was successfully computed in the Institute of Theoretical Astronomy allows the interplanetary ship after five days to approach the surface of the moon to a distance of less than 30,000 kilometers and then to return to the earth. The greatest distance of the rocket from the earth during the flight amounts to 416,000 kilometers. And the moon is 384,000 kilometers from the earth. This makes it possible for the rocket to round the moon, and since the speed of the ship at this time diminishes almost to zero, the rocket remains close to the moon for more than two days, investigating by means of automatic instruments the lunar hemisphere that is invisible from the earth.

The return flight to the earth also lasts about five days, during which time the ship's speed gradually increases under the influence of the earth's attraction and at the moment when the rocket falls into the region of the atmosphere, its speed again reaches eleven kilometers per second.

Safe landing on the earth's surface at such a speed represents a difficult technical problem. Since the density of the earth's atmosphere increases gradually, however, it is possible by means of a special parachute or glider device to safely land the rocket with its automatic instruments.

How can one clearly visualize the flight of a rocket without the expenditure of fuel on the way?

It is simplest to liken the rocket to a boomerang. It is known that this peculiar weapon has a habit of returning to the one who threw it.

Approximately the same thing happens with our rocket. "Thrown" with an enormous force into world space, it will fly up to the moon or, more correctly, it will cross the moon's orbit, round it and return to the earth. The resemblance of this rocket to a boomerang is, of course, purely superficial. It will move under the action of gravitational forces according to the laws of motion of a freely thrown body. And in this sense our rocket will resemble a stone thrown vertically upwards.

As is known, the initial velocity of a stone near the earth's surface diminishes as it ascends and at some point becomes equal to zero. Then the stone begins to fall, and near the earth's surface again it attains its greatest speed. But in this case only the earth's gravitational force acts on the stone. Indeed we cannot cast it very far. And on a rocket, which will move for an enormous distance in interplanetary space, the gravitational forces of the moon and of the sun will also exert an influence.

Manned flight in such a cosmic ship is impossible, of course, since in this case the necessary weight of the ship again greatly increases, even in the absence of fuel supplies. But it is completely possible to dispatch on this interplanetary voyage some living creature, a mouse or a guinea pig, for example.

The realization of the interplanetary flight of an unguided apparatus of small weight described here is in principle only a little more complicated than launching artificial earth satellites. Meanwhile it is known that such launching is proposed during the Geophysical Year. There is no doubt that immediately after the solution of the problem of creating artificial earth satellites, scientists of the whole world will proceed to the practical realization of the new grandiose jump into the cosmos. I think that flights of automatic unguided rockets to the moon and around the moon will be the next step in the conquest of interplanetary space. We have made a theoretical calculation of the flight trajectory of such a rocket. It is the business of engineers to make this project a reality. The level of development of modern technology fully allows this to be done.

It is perfectly evident at present that one can calculate the flight of an unguided interplanetary ship, also without the expenditure of fuel on the way, along a more complex trajectory — for example, to the planet Mars, with return to the earth. And we are already making calculations to determine the orbit of a rocket flight around Mars. Undoubtedly, however, this problem is more complicated. Indeed, in the flight to Mars not just the attraction of the earth, the moon, the sun, and Mars will have to be taken into consideration, but, possibly, that of Venus and of Mercury. And each new celestial body by far complicates the astronomical calculations. Landing on the surface of Mars is, of course, completely excluded, since descent on the planet and the return ascent would require the expenditures of an enormous quantity of fuel. (*Znanie-Sila*, February, 1957. The author is identified as "Professor" and "Doctor of Physico-Mathematical Sciences.")

# 21. Some Questions on The Dynamics of Flight to the Moon

*V. A. Egorov*

Associated with the contemporary development of rocket engineering is the attainment of velocities sufficient not only for the creation of an artificial earth satellite, but also for flight to the moon. But hitherto in the literature [1-5] no satisfactory solutions have been found for the fundamental questions of the theory of flight to the moon: the form and classification of unpowered trajectories, the possibility of circumflight of the moon with return to the earth, the possibility of periodic circumflight of the moon and the earth, the question of hitting the moon, and also the particularly important question of the effect of the dispersion of the initial data on the realization of hitting or circumflight. This is explained by the fundamental difficulties. Actually, in the simplest formulation, when considering only the main forces that act on the rocket, the task reduces to the unsolved circular restricted problems of three bodies (the earth $m_1$, the moon $m_2$, the rocket $m_0$). In 1953-1955 we undertook the attempt to systematically investigate the problem in the plane. For finding the trajectories of interest to us and for determining the effect of the dispersion of the initial data, the theoretical methods were supplemented with numerical methods by the use of electronic machines. Below are set forth the basic results of the solution of the problems indicated above.[a]

1. *The Problem of Hitting the Moon.* A method was found for determining the initial data that correspond to hits. It has been rigorously shown that the minimum distance of a rocket from the center of the moon is a quadratic function, not a linear function, of the errors in the initial data, so that an exact hit of the moon is a much easier task that hitting a nonattracting point moving just like the moon. For values of the angle $\alpha_1$ between the initial geocentric radius $r_1$ and velocity $V_1$, equal to $\pi/2$, dependencies on $V_1$ have been found: for time of flight, angular distance of point of start and point of hitting, and for the coefficients $k_i$ in the expressions $\varrho_i = K_i (\delta x_i)^2$ where

**197**

$\delta x_1$ is the variation of the ith initial datum) in the range $-0.1 < \Delta V_1$ $< 0.5$ kilometers per second, where $\Delta V_1 = V_1 - V_p$, and $V_p^2 = 2fm_1/r_1$. It turned out that minimum values of $\Delta V_1$, corresponding to a hit, belong to this range and that the course of relations for $\Delta V_1 > 0.5$ is asymptotic (to values corresponding to $\Delta V_1 = \infty$). It turned out also that discounting the attraction of the moon gives $\varrho \leqslant 1$ kilometer, if $\Delta V_1 \geqslant 0$. With decrease in $\Delta V_1$ the miss in $\varrho$ increases rapidly. In the sense of precision the least favorable velocities are those close to the minimum; the most favorable velocities are those slightly less than $V_p$. When $V_1 < V_p$ the moon can be hit by both the ascending and the descending branch of the trajectory, but the precision of a hit by the descending branch is two to five times poorer than the precision of a hit by the ascending branch for the same values of $\Delta V_1$. The effect of errors in the initial height for all cases turned out to be practically negligible.

*Example.* The errors $\delta V_1 = 10$ meters per second, $\delta\alpha_1 = 10^{-2}$, $\delta r_1 = 50$ kilometers cause, respectively, the following misses (in kilometers) in the ascending branch: (1) for $\Delta V_1 = -0.092828$: $\varrho_v = 11,184$, $\varrho_a = 1208$, $\varrho_r = 56$; (2) for $\Delta V_1 = 0$: $\varrho_v = 125$, $\varrho_a = 5159$, $\varrho_v = 43$; (3) $\Delta V_1 = +0.106093$: $\varrho_v = 318$, $\varrho_a = 6121$, $\varrho_r = 140$.

2. *The Problem of Circumflight of the Moon.* A method has been found for determining the initial data corresponding to circumflight of the moon with return to the point $m_1$. And here the miss during the return is a quadratic function of the errors in the initial data. Circumflight of the moon in the $\xi$, $\eta$ plane, which rotates with the straight line $m_1m_2$ (see Figure 1), is possible only in a clockwise direction, that is, in a direction opposite to the velocity of its rotation.

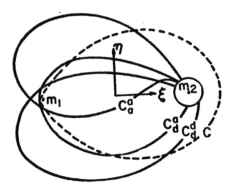

Figure 1.

Circumflight trajectories can be of two classes, depending on the character of the approach to $m_2$:

(1) A tight approach, which takes place for all values of $\alpha_1$ on an ascending (a) branch turning immediately into a descending (d) branch. (This class is designated $C_d^a$.)

(2) A weak approach, which takes place for all values of $\alpha_1 > 0$ on an ascending branch (subclass $C_a^a$) and for $\alpha_1 < 0$ on a descending branch (subclass $C_d^d$). The type of branch does not change after the approach. (The classes are schematically represented in Figure 1. All trajectories go clockwise around $m_2$.)

For large values of $\Delta V_1$ and $|\alpha_1| < \pi/2$ only circumflights $C_d^a$ exist. For decreasing $\Delta V_1$ circumflights of the subclass $C_a^a$ appear. When $\Delta V_1 = 0$, circumflights of subclass $C_d^d$ appear. For a sufficient decrease in $\Delta V_1$ circumflight becomes impossible. Circumflights first disappear for $\alpha_1 > 0$, then for $\alpha_1 < 0$. Solutions $C_a^a$ and $C_d^d$ occur for practically all values of $V_1$ beyond the moon's disk, and solutions $C_d^a$ only for values of $V_1$ close to the minimum.

Besides circumflights, there can be approach trajectories in the $\xi$, $\eta$ plane which does not encompass the moon but allow one to see everything on its opposite side and to return to $m_1$. They go around $m_2$ in a counterclockwise direction. We shall call them "afflights."

Afflight trajectories also fall into two classes analogous to circumflights:

(1) A tight approach, which takes place on the descending branch, immediately turning into an ascending branch, and only afterwards returning to the earth (class $D_a^d$).

(2) A weak approach, which takes place either on an ascending branch (subclass $D_a^a$) or on a descending branch (subclass $D_d^d$). The type of branch does not change after the approach.

The evolution of afflight trajectories is analogous to the evolution of circumflight trajectories.

3. *The Special Problem of Circumflight of the Moon.* This is the problem of finding circumflights in which the rocket returns obliquely into the earth's atmosphere. In practice such circumflights are of greatest interest. We shall apply the method of solving Problem 2 also to this problem. But in it the miss is merely a linear fuction of the errors of the initial data, which, together with the relatively small

thickness of the atmosphere, leads to much more rigid precision requirements. To each class of Problem 2 there correspond two classes of Problem 3, going round $m_2$ in the same direction, and $m_1$ in others. We shall call them $C^a_{d+}$ and $C^a_{d-}$ for the first class and $C^a_{a-}$ and $C^d_{d+}$ for the second class. Each pair limits in its class the circumflights of Problem 2 that correspond to the permissible dispersions of the initial data. At the same time there still exist trivial boundary solutions for the second class, not corresponding to an approach to the moon. Analogous facts also apply to afflight classes. The evolution of the classes of Problem 3 easily follows from the evolution of the corresponding classes of Problem 2.

The effect of dispersion in the initial data depends not only on the character of the passage of the trajectory relative to $m_1$, but also on $\varrho$. Dispersion manifests itself more strongly for small values of $\varrho$ than for large values.

*Example.* For a circumflight of type $C^a_{d+}$ with $\Delta V_1 = -0.083773$ kilometers per second and a flight time of 823,600 seconds, a value of $\varrho = 27,000$ kilometers was obtained. Errors in the initial data — $\delta V_1 = 2 \times 10^{-4}$ kilometers per second in velocity, $\delta \alpha_1 = 5 \times 10^{-3}$ in its direction — cause changes in altitude of 160 and 191 kilometers, respectively, on the return; that is, they are impermissible (changes in altitude must not exceed tens of kilometers). Decreasing $\varrho$ by an order of magnitude increases the effect of the errors by one to two orders.

4. *The Problem of Periodic Circumflight.* The simplest periodic solutions (solutions going to $m_1$ after the approach to $m_2$) are symmetrical and constitute two one-parameter families — circumflight and afflight. The circumflight solution, tangent to the atmosphere, was found by a method analogous to the method of the Copenhagen school [6], but it proved to occur inside the moon's disk and to be unstable. All solutions passing above the surface of the moon are at a distance of more than 94,800 kilometers from $m_1$ (see dotted line C in Figure 1) and are also unstable. For example, the solution with $r_1 = 82,824$ kilometers, $\varrho \approx 1500$ kilometers with an error of $\delta V_1 \approx 0.001$ meters per second in velocity goes off to infinity with the fourth revolution. Errors in the original data — $\delta V_1 = 10^{-4}$ kilometers per second in initial velocity, $\delta \alpha_1 = 10^{-4}$ in its direction and $\delta r_1 = 5$ kilometers in altitude — cause at the end of a revolution changes in altitude of 3,471, 5,252, and 262 kilometers, respectively.

5. *Classification of Trajectories in the Plane of the Moon's Orbit and the Problem of Rocket Acceleration.* Besides the hitting and circumflight trajectories of approach to $m_2$ that have been found, there are also trajectories of approach that correspond either to the rocket's acceleration after the approach or to its deceleration (relative to $m_1$), and no other trajectories of approach exist. Ascending trajectories of deceleration go around the moon clockwise, and accelerating trajectories counterclockwise. A trajectory tangent to the moon's disk corresponds to a maximum increment $\Delta V_{max}$ for any values of $V_1$ and $\alpha_1$ (compare (4) ). The maximum velocity can be obtained in any direction. Since the plane of the moon's orbit makes a small angle with the planes of the orbits of the other planets, acceleration without expenditure of fuel can be utilized for interplanetary flight. For the problem of acceleration, a method was created making it possible to obtain a trajectory with $\Delta V_{max}$ for any values of $V_1$ and $\alpha_1$. It is easy to see that the solution of the problem of any acceleration after replacing t by minus t always gives the solution of the problem of the same braking of the rocket when moving along a trajectory that is a mirror image of the accelerating trajectory. It can be used, for example, when the rocket is returning from an interplanetary flight.

*Remarks.* 1. The problem of minimum velocities $V_{min}$ is of fundamental significance (when $V_1 < V_{min}$ our problems have no solution). It was solved earlier in other problems. By examining a surface of zero velocity, passing through the libration point $L_1$, for the three-dimensional problem it was demonstrated that $V_{min}$ is the same in Problems 1 and 2 and equal to $V^*_{min} = 10.8315$ kilometers per second for practically all points of the sphere $r_1 = 6571.118$ kilometers. For values of $V_1$ close to $V_{min}$, however, the approach — that is, the entrance of the rocket into the sphere of action of $m_2$, $\varrho < \varrho^*$ — is possible only after a sufficient number of its revolutions (of the order of hundreds) around $m_1$. But for the approach to $m_2$ on the first revolution (which we assumed), the minimum velocities are different in Problems 1 to 5 and exceed 10.9052 kilometers per second.

Incidentally, the inaccuracy of a theorem of Martin [7] was revealed. If one puts $m_2 = \mu$, $m_1 = 1 - \mu$, then for distances $\varrho_1(\mu)$ and $\varrho_2(\mu)$ of the points $L_1$ and $L_2$ from $\mu$ when $0 < \mu < 1$, $\varrho_1(\mu)$ is always $< \varrho_2(\mu)$, and their equality is impossible when $0 < \mu < 1$, contrary to Martin's theorem.

2. The question of the possibility of the capture by the moon of a rocket released from the earth, obviously, is important for the solution of Problems 1 to 5. By a method analogous to that used by V. G. Fesenkov [8], it was shown for the three dimensional problem that capture is impossible regardless of the initial data. Incidentally, V. G. Fesenkov's criterion for the possibility of capture $1/a_2 + 2 \sqrt{p_2} \cos i_2 < \mu F$ was modified, and led to the criterion $\mu/a_2 + 2 \sqrt{\mu p_2} \cos i_2 < \mu F_1 + 10 (\mu/3)^{2/3}$, where $a_2$, $p_2$, $i_2$ are the elements of the $m_2$-centered orbit of the rocket, and $F$ and $F_1$ are finite.

3. The approximate theoretical methods used were based on the neglect of the perturbations of $m_1$ when $\varrho < p^* \sim 66{,}000$ kilometers and the perturbations of $m_2$ when $\varrho > \varrho^*$; several other secondary factors were also neglected. Almost all of the results, however, were verified and invariably confirmed by the more precise method — numerical integration. The integration was carried out for the regularized equations in Thiele variables on the STsM electronic machine [9] with 5 to 7 significant figures. Iteration methods were used for finding trajectories for a different purpose. In all, more than 600 trajectories were calculated. (*Doklady Akademii Nauk SSSR*, March 1, 1957. Paper presented to the USSR Academy of Sciences on September 27, 1956, by Academician M. V. Keldysh.)

---

[a] Obtained by the author at the Mathematics Institutes of the USSR Academy of Sciences and reported there in February, 1956.

[1] Bruno Thüring, *Weltraumfahrt*, Vol. 3, No. 4, 1952, p. 112.

[2] Bruno Thüring, *Weltraumfahrt*, Vol. 5, No. 3, 1954, p. 69.

[8] Bruno Thüring, *Weltraumfahrt*, Vol. 5, No. 4, 1954, p. 103.

[4] D. F. Lawden, *J. Brit. Interpl. Soc.*, Vol. 13, No. 6, 1954, p. 329.

[5] D. F. Lawden, *J. Brit. Interpl. Soc.*, Vol. 14, No. 4, 1955, p. 203.

[6] Elis Strömgren, *Publikationer og mindre Meddelelser fra Kobenhavns Observatorium*, No. 100, 1935, 44 pp.

[7] M. Martin, *Am. J. Math.*, Vol. 53, 1931, p. 167.

[8] V. G. Fesenkov, *Astronomicheskii Zhurnal*, Vol. 23, No. 1, 1946.

[9] V. A. Egorov, *Trudy konferentsii: Puti razvitiya otechestvennogo matematicheskogo mashinostroeniya i priborostroeniya*, 1956.

# Part Five

# ROCKET AND
# MISSILE DEVELOPMENTS

# 22.   Radio-Guided Rockets

*I. Kucherov*

Radio has found wide application for controlling at a distance the operation of various mechanisms and the movement of automobiles, tanks, airplanes, ships, etc.   The flight control of high-altitude rockets, designed for studying the physical condition of the terrestrial atmosphere and the properties of the ionosphere, for investigating cosmic rays at a great altitude, and for studying the sun's radiation, is achieved by radio.   Radio guidance will acquire a special role in the future, when interplanetary travels become possible.   The dream of creating a radio-guided rocket, capable of flying to the moon, is becoming more and more real.

Numerous works of scientists and investigators are devoted to the problem of interplanetary flight.   Among these works the investigations of the great Russian scientist K. E. Tsiolkovskii, the founder of cosmic rocket navigation, assume a special role.   He was the first in the world, more than 50 years ago, to scientifically found the possibility of interplanetary flight and to point out the technical means for its realization.   In particular, he showed that a rocket, equipped with a liquid rocket engine, can be utilized for cosmic flights.   Such an engine, developing a huge thrust, can operate in airless space.   Because of this the rocket will be able to overcome the earth's attraction and the resistance of the atmosphere, and, having torn away from the earth, to develop an enormous velocity.   There is no doubt that the first flight will be that of an unmanned "reconnaissance" rocket, which, having been equipped with suitable radiotelemetric apparatus, will permit investigating the unknown "path" to the moon, reporting continuously by radio all instrument readings and the operating condition of the aggregates of the rocket itself.   By transmitting suitable commands by radio, it will be possible to guide the flight of the rocket.   A television transmitter mounted in the rocket will be of invaluable service to investigators who will be able to observe the image of the moon's surface on a television screen on the earth.

The problem of the flight of a manned interplanetary ship to the moon, with its subsequent return to the earth, is undoubtedly more complicated. This is explained by the fact that for a nonstop flight directly from the earth to the moon, it is necessary to have a liquid-jet-engine rocket with a weight of about 1,000,000 tons and a length of about 400 meters. It is clear that it is almost impossible to build such a rocket today.

The solution of this task will become possible in principle by making use of special rocket engines that utilize such a powerful source of energy as the energy of the atomic nucleus.

It is possible to solve this task more simply by creating a special interplanetary transfer station. This station will represent an artificial satellite revolving around the earth at an altitude of several hundred kilometers. And to further facilitate the flight, two transfer stations can be created, one the satellite of the earth, and the other a satellite of the moon. The idea of creating interplanetary transfer stations is also due to K. E. Tsiolkovskii.

Flight control of rockets intended for building an artificial satellite and supplying cargo to the satellite is very complex. The fact is that here it is necessary to guarantee, not arbitrary flight of the rocket, but flight to a certain point at which the satellite and the rocket must meet. To guide such rockets from the earth it will be necessary, obviously, to have on the earth not only a simple rocket guidance station, but also a complicated computing device that guarantees working out navigational data for transmission to the rocket. It will also be possible to utilize the method of homing guidance (*samonavedenie*) of the rocket to the satellite, which is moving with a great velocity (of the order of 30,000 kilometers per hour).

In Figure 1 is presented a sketch of the flight of a rocket to the moon and its return to the interplanetary station. [Figure 1 is a diagram of a rocket's flight to and from the moon. It was ostensibly taken from *Conquest of the Moon*, C. Ryan (ed.), Viking Press, New York, 1953, p. 51.]

During the landing on the moon the engines must provide the braking of the rocket; and therefore the rocket, crossing the neutral line between the earth's and the moon's attraction, must turn around with its engine forward (Figure 2). The flight time of a rocket to the moon will be about five days. [Figure 2 is a diagram depicting the sequence of maneuvers to be carried out during the trip to the moon. Like Figure 1 it was taken from *Conquest of the Moon*, p. 61.]

A radio transmitting station on the earth satellite will send command signals to the rocket. A responder on the rocket will relay the transmitted signals back to the interplanetary station. This will make it possible to determine precisely the position and velocity of the interplanetary rocket.

Special computing devices located on the interplanetary station will calculate the necessary navigational data. If for some reason the rocket cannot continue its flight, then suitable navigational data, determining the rocket's return path, will also be transmitted by radio.

In military affairs radio-guided rockets and missiles were already used on a large scale at the end of the World War II.

Depending on their place of launching, guided missiles are classified as ground or aviation guided missiles. The former are launched from ground or ship launching installations. Such missiles include long-range rockets, flying bombs, and antiaircraft jet guided missiles. Aviation-guided missiles are launched from an airplane. They include guided bombs, guided aerial torpedoes, aviation flying bombs, and air combat missiles. The latter are designed for firing from aircraft to aircraft.

Let us examine the peculiarities of the radio-guidance systems of such missiles. Guidance of missiles can be carried out by means of inertial guidance (*avtonomnoe upravlenie*), homing guidance (*samonavedenie*), and remote control (*teleupravlenie*) systems. The latter also include automatic remote control systems. The inertial guidance system independently corrects the missile's motion during its flight according to a given program set by an operator before the missile is launched. The homing guidance system independently determines the necessary flight direction and in accordance with this, works out, itself, the commands fed to the controlling devices. In the remote control system, command signals are given by an operator from a control post and are received by a radio receiver mounted in the missile. Radio engineering methods of control have found wide application in the latter two systems.

Every remote control unit consists of a command-coding block, a control post transmitter, a receiver, and a decoding-executive block in the missile (Figure 3). The receivers can be built both as super-heterodyne and as direct amplifier circuits. Transmission of radio control signals is conducted on centimeter, decimeter and ultrashort (meter) waves. The command signal is given definite properties (code) by means of a modulator (coder), which also permits distinguishing one command from another.

The command signals sent from the control post are amplified in the receiver and then enter the demodulator (decoder). The demodulated signals control the operation of the executive circuits of the guidance organ instruments.  Electric motors, hydraulic and pneumatic motors, and electro-magnets can be used as instruments.  Amplification of the command signals can be accomplished by means of relay amplifiers, electronic amplifiers, pneumatic amplifiers, magnetic amplifiers, etc.

Recognition of guidance commands is called "selection" and is accomplished at the spot of reception by special selector instruments. In practice, distributing, qualitative, code, and combination selection are used.

Distributing selection is the simplest.  In this case the command signals have the form of successively sent impulses.  Each impulse that is received by the rocket actuates an electromagnet which by means of a pawl turns a ratchet wheel to a certain angle.  Depending on the number of impulses the ratchet wheel moves through a large or small angle.  At the same time, the commutating device, mounted on the same axle with the ratchet, will close the proper executive circuits.

In qualitative selection, the signal of one command can be distinguished from the signal of another in polarity (positive or negative sign), in phase, in frequency, and also in the number of impulses, their frequency of succession, duration and amplitude.  In practice, however, it is more expedient to make use of intermittent (length and frequency of repetition of impulses), frequency and quantitative (quantity of impulses) discrimination of signals.

Code selection provides for the transmission of several impulses differing among themselves in some signs, whereby this aggregate of impulses has a definite sequence.  Code ciphering of signals offers the possibility of making the system interference resistant, not only against natural, but also against special, artificially created interference.

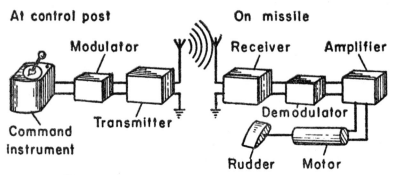

Figure 3. Block diagram of remote control system.

Combination selection guarantees the highest interference resistance of the system, since the executive mechanisms are actuated only by the simultaneous operation of two or three output elements of the selector unit. But the remote control system in which code and combination selection is used is more complex than the control system with distributing and qualitative selection.

The simplest method of remote control missile guidance is the method shown in Figure 4. The essence of the method consists in the fact that the missile must, during the entire time of flight, be on a straight line connecting the control point and the target. The deviation of the missile from this straight line is called the "guiding error."

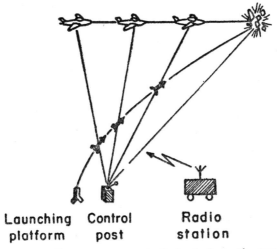

Launching   Control   Radio
platform      post    station

Figure 4. Guiding a remote controlled missile to the target.

The guiding error is determined at the control post by the operator who tracks the position of the target and the flight of the missile. He can accomplish this tracking visually, for example, by estimating the guiding error with the eye and turning the knob of the command instrument so as to reduce the guiding error to zero. But visual observation can be carried out only during good visibility of target and missile, which excludes the possibility of using missiles at night, in clouds, in fog, etc. It is possible to improve visual observation under conditions of poor visibility by installing tracers or powerful lamps on the missile.

A special radar station on the screen of which the mutual position of missile and target is registered can also be used for tracking the missile. In this case a radar responder is usually installed in the missile, which permits one to easily distinguish the blip of the missile on the radar screen.

When a television remote control system is used, a transmitting cathode-ray tube and a television radio transmitter are installed in the missile. The cathode-ray transmitting tube is mounted in the nose of the missile, and on its mosaic a map of the terrain or space that is in front of the missile will be reproduced. There is a televisor at the control post. The operator, watching the map of the area on the televisor screen, estimates the guiding error. Transmission of the commands to the missile is accomplished by radio, just as in the previously explained system. Television remote control systems guarantee very high precision of missile guidance. Such a guidance system, however, is more complex and has larger dimensions.

Several types of missiles (for example, long-range rockets, rocket-airplanes) are guided to the target by means of a narrow electromagnetic beam. The beam makes a trace of the missile's flight (radiotrope); its direction is assigned from the control post.

Automatic guidance systems, designed for direct guidance of a missile, are of great interest from a radiotechnical point of view. The so-called guide-beam system, for example, is used for correcting the course of a long-range rocket.

The control post equipment of such a system consists of two radar stations situated 20 to 30 kilometers apart. One of these stations is a control unit, the other a transmitting (guiding) unit. The latter has a radio transmitter with two antennas. The transmitting radio station, the launching platform from which the launching of the rocket is carried out, and the control station are all situated in the plane of the rocket's course (Figure 5). The transmitter operates on one of the operating frequencies in the range from 42 to 64 megacycles and has an output of 4 kilowatts.

The guidance equipment on the rocket consists of an antenna located in the tail section, a superheterodyne receiver tuned to one of ten possible operating frequencies of the transmitter, two resonance filters, one of which passes signals modulated at a frequency of 5,000 cycles per second and the other at 7,000 cycles per second, a control signal amplifier, and the rocket's steering gear.

By means of a special switch the transmitter of the guiding station is connected alternately for 0.01 second to one antenna (say, the left), the radiated signals of which are modulated with a frequency of 5,000 cycles per second, and for 0.01 second to the other antenna (the right), radiating a signal with a modulation frequency of 7,000 cycles per

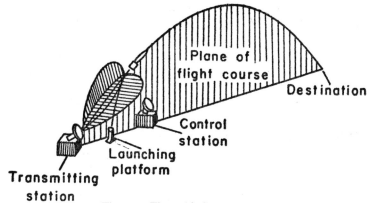

Figure 5. The guide-beam system.

second.  The axis of the radiation pattern of each antenna is set at an angle of 0.4 degrees to the axis of the equisignal zone (of the plane of the missile's course).

If the rocket flies on the correct course (is in the plane of the course), then the amplitudes of the control signals will be equal and, consequently, the summary command fed to the steering gear will be equal to zero.  Let us suppose that the rocket deviated from its assigned course to the left; then the amplitude of the control signal, corresponding to a frequency of 5,000 cycles per second, will be greater than the amplitude of the signal, corresponding to a frequency of 7,000 cycles per second.  As a result of this, the summary signal fed to the steering gear will be different from zero, and the rudder will deflect and thus turn the rocket in the plane of the assigned course.  As soon as the rocket returns to this plane, the summary command fed to the rudder again will become equal to zero and the rudder will assume a neutral position.  Guidance is produced in precisely the same way when the missile deviates in the other direction.

The automatic guidance system of antiaircraft missiles is constructed somewhat differently.

The complexity of firing at aircraft lies in the fact that the missile must be aimed, not at the point where the target is at a given moment, but at some anticipated point at which the missile must meet the aircraft.  Therefore two locators are used in the system: one ensures tracking the target and measuring the distance to the target, the other creates a radiozone for guiding the missile to the target.  Target location data are fed from the escort radar to a special computing device which computes the so-called angle of anticipation and in accordance with this angle gives the command to the power drive of the guiding radar so that the beam of the latter will be directed at the anticipated point.  As the missile approaches the target the axes of both beams converge.

*Homing Guidance Systems.*  For independent guidance of a missile to the target it must have, first of all, instruments that determine the position of the target relative to the missile.  The homing guidance device that solves this problem is usually called a "target coordinator."  A radar target coordinator consists of a directional antenna, more often of the parabolic, or rod type, a radar receiver of the superheterodyne type with automatic volume control and automatic frequency tuning, and an instrument for separating the signals received from the target through suitable control channels.

The target coordinator is mounted in the nose of the missile.  The magnitude of the guiding signal at the output of the coordinator will depend on the angle between the axis of the coordinator and the missile-to-target line.  These signals are amplified and they control the operation of the rudder gears.  The deflection of the missile's rudders changes its course.

A sectional drawing of a homing missile with a radar coordinator is shown in Figure 6.

Homing guidance systems that use the target's own radio emission are called "passive" homing guidance systems.  Such self-radiating targets include radar stations of various designations, aerodrome radio beacons, control posts of antiaircraft jet remote controlled missiles, and others.  The range of operation of such a system depends on meteorological conditions and the radiating power of the objective.

There also exist other homing guidance systems.  Target irradiation in these cases is accomplished either from the mother-aircraft or directly from the missile itself.  In the first case, the radar systems are called "semi-active," in the second case, "active."  A missile with active homing guidance contains, in addition to a radar receiver, a radar transmitter as well.  The same antenna device can be used for receiving and for transmitting signals.  The centimeter wave range is generally used for operation in such homing guidance systems.  The range of operation of these systems also depends on meteorological conditions and the power of the transmitter and can reach several tens of kilometers.

Radar homing guidance systems are subject to the effect of artificial radio interference.  In such systems, therefore, special methods are

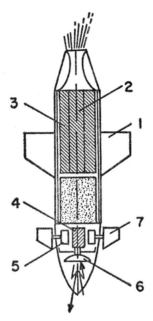

Figure 6. Homing missile with radar target coordinator.
1—wing; 2—fuel; 3—jet engine; 4—guiding signal amplifier;
5—rudder gear; 6—target coordinator; 7—rudder.

used for coding radio signals, allowing the creation of a guidance system sufficiently well protected against interference.

The pilotless rocket guidance apparatus must be compact. In the future, it seems, semiconductor instruments will be widely used.

The above-mentioned guidance systems have great prospects for development and will find wide use both in military affairs and in the national economy. (*Radio*, August, 1955. The author is identified as "Candidate of Technical Sciences.")

# 23. The Atomic Airplane of the Future

*G. Nesterenko*

The use of aviation is spreading every year in the socialist economy of our Soviet nation. It is already difficult to find a branch of economy that could manage without the airplane. The airplane has firmly entered Soviet man's mode of life.

At the same time the demands of aviation technology are growing. Jet engines are coming to replace piston engines. Thanks to this the speed and altitude of flight have increased fantastically. But designers never rest content with what has been achieved. Is it not possible to use nuclear fuel in an airplane? What does this new supreme achievement of human thought promise for aviation?

### PECULIARITIES OF ATOMIC ENERGY

There is a difference between the process of burning chemical fuel, at the expense of which is obtained the energy necessary for operating modern piston and jet aircraft engines, and the process of fission or synthesis of atomic nuclei by which atomic energy is obtained.

In the burning process, we obtain a certain quantity of energy in the form of heat as a result of the chemical interaction of atoms of fuel with atoms of oxidant. In this process changes take place only in the electronic shells of the atoms; the nuclei of the atoms undergo no changes whatever.

In the complete combustion of one kilgram of kerosene or benzine, 10 to 11 thousand calories of heat are released. If we consider that for flight beyond the limits of the atmosphere it is still necessary to have oxidant aboard the airplane (and four to five times more of it are necessary than of fuel), then it turns out that for one kilogram of fuel materials we can obtain only two to three thousand calories. This means that for flights over great distances, enormous fuel supplies will be required. It is possible, however, to take only a limited amount of fuel on the airplane. This amount, in practice, determines the duration and range of flight.

The tendency to increase the flight range leads to an increase in aircraft weight. At the same time an increase in fuel increases the total weight of the airplane. The greater the speed and flight range on which the airplane pays off, the greater its total weight.

In the nuclear processes used for obtaining atomic energy, there takes place the splitting of the atomic nuclei, the heaviest component parts of the atoms, containing enormous stores of energy. This is precisely why the atomic nuclear fission process yields millions of times more energy per kilogram of fissioning materials than the combustion process. On an airplane with an atomic engine the weight of nuclear fuel will represent an insignificant part of the total weight of the airplane. It has been calculated that about one gram of nuclear fuel is required for the operation of one engine with a power of 6000 horsepower for an hour, providing this engine has an efficiency of 20%. One kilogram of uranium (U-235) is theoretically sufficient for an airplane weighing 20 to 30 tons to circle the globe. More than 150 tons of chemical fuel would be required for this purpose.

The flight range of an airplane with an atomic engine is limited, not by the fuel supply, but by the operational capacity of the engine.

The prospects of unlimited flight range, naturally, are very alluring. The insignificant weight of nuclear fuel opens up great possibilities to designers in their constant striving to decrease the weight of the airplane and the engine. This is why many scientists and investigators are now directing their efforts to using nuclear fuel for aviation engines.

### SOME OF THE POSSIBLE SCHEMES OF ATOMIC AIRCRAFT ENGINES

The principal difference between atomic aircraft engines and existing jet aircraft engines will be the fact that the heat for raising the temperature of the air passing through the engine will be obtained, not at the expense of burning benzine or kerosene, but at the expense of a reaction taking place in a reactor. This atomic reactor, or atomic pile, has a structure similar in principle to that of the atomic pile which is supplying energy for operating the world's first Soviet atomic power station.

The turbojet atomic engine operating on nuclear fuel (Figure 1) may have all the basic parts of the conventional turbojet engine (TRD): diffuser, air compressor, turbine, and jet nozzle. But instead of a combustion chamber we see in it an atomic reactor and a heat exchanger.

An atomic nuclear fission chain reaction takes place in the reactor with the release of an enormous amount of heat; and a liquid, pumped through by a special pump, transfers this heat from the reactor to the stream of air passing through the engine.

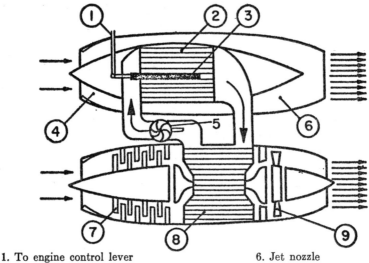

1. To engine control lever
2. Reactor
3. Control rod
4. Inlet diffuser
5. Pump

6. Jet nozzle
7. Compressor
8. Heat exchanger
9. Turbine

Figure 1. Diagram of nuclear fueled turbojet engine
coupled with ramjet engine.

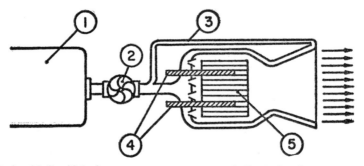

1. Tank with liquid hydrogen
2. Pump
3. By-pass duct for cooling the
   body of the engine

4. Control rods
5. Reactor

Figure 2. Diagram of nuclear fueled liquid rocket.

Air comes in from the atmosphere on the blades of the compressor, is adjusted to a certain pressure and, passing through the hot core of the heat exchanger, raises its own temperature considerably. Passing over the blades of the gas turbine, the air gives back a part of its acquired energy to the rotation of the compressor, and then, flowing out of the nozzle with enormous speed, it creates jet thrust. In order to additionally cool the reactor to more completely utilize its energy, the air fairings of the reactor can be converted into a ramjet engine (PVRD). At the expense of this improvement one will be able to obtain additional thrust, especially at supersonic speeds. It is proposed to use water, mercury, or sodium as a heat carrier in the heat exchanger. A cadmium control rod is used for controlling the chain reaction.

A turbojet engine makes it possible to perform flights only within the limits of the earth's atmosphere. Therefore, for flights beyond the atmosphere, that is, for interplanetary flights, another engine will be used — the liquid rocket engine (ZhRD).

A characteristic peculiarity of the ZhRD is the fact that not only fuel (hydrogen, for example) is fed from tanks into the combustion chamber, but also oxidant (oxygen), which too is stored in liquid form in special tanks in the airplane, and is not taken from the atmosphere.

The principle of operation of the ZhRD operating on nuclear fuel consists in the fact that a homogeneous working substance, hydrogen itself, for example, is used as the mass ejected by the engine. The hydrogen is forced from the tank into the chamber with the nuclear reactor (Figure 2). The hydrogen is heated on passing through the "core" of the reactor and, flowing with a speed of several thousand meters per second out of the jet nozzle, it creates a great thrust. The jet exhaust velocity of the hydrogen is assumed to amount to 10,000 meters per second and more. The thrust developed by the engine is, on the whole, determined by the gas jet exhaust velocity.

### DIFFICULTIES OF CREATING ATOMIC ENGINES

First of all, it is necessary to point to the relative lack of experience and the danger of working with fissioning materials. This to a considerable degree makes the creation of an atomic aircraft engine difficult.

A great difficulty is the creation of a reliable biological shield for the crew against the harmful radioactive radiation of the atomic reactor, against the so-called penetrating radiation. According to certain official information, the weight of the biological shield of an atomic passenger airplane with a payload capacity of 15 tons must amount to 100 tons, that is, more than the total weight of a modern transport airplane.

Of no less trouble to designers are the temperatures and pressures that are generated during the nuclear reaction. They are so high that it is difficult to select materials for guaranteeing engine stability and good heat transfer. The elaboration of reliable methods of heat exchange and the finding of suitable materials constitute one of the most difficult tasks.

Finally, the nuclear reactors themselves as yet are too bulky and heavy. Their weight, amounting to tens and even hundreds of tons, is caused entirely by the definite working volume that the active zone of the reactor must occupy in order that a chain reaction may take place in it. The creation of a compact nuclear reactor is one of the most important tasks of the general problem of using atomic energy for aircraft engines.

But this is not all. There are a number of less complex, but no less important, tasks that scientists and designers must solve.

For example, it is necessary to elaborate a reliable method of controlling the atomic engine and regulating it over the necessary regime of operation (for both large and small thrusts), to protect the uranium rods against the corrosive action of the gaseous working streams, etc.

### COSMIC FLIGHT

The creation of an atomic aircraft engine is a significant step toward the realization of interplanetary travels, mankind's cherished dream.

It is precisely in the field of achieving cosmic velocities, of creating an artificial earth satellite, and of realizing interplanetary flights that the question of the quantity of necessary fuel acquires a special acuteness. The use of atomic engines can present the problem of cosmic flights in a different light.

Let us try to glance into the future and imagine that there are at our disposal sufficiently light, compact, and reliably operating atomic turbojet and liquid jet engines. For a beginning let us build and equip with all necessary instruments a radio-guided "earth to moon" rocket plane (Figure 3) which has two atomic turbojet engines on the wing tips and one atomic liquid rocket engine in the tail part of the fuselage. Fully loaded with liquid hydrogen, the rocket plane will take off from a special launching installation and, gradually gathering speed along a gently sloping spiral at the expense of the thrust of the atomic turbo-

jet engines, will go out into the upper layers of the atmosphere.   During this period of acceleration the engines will make use of atmospheric

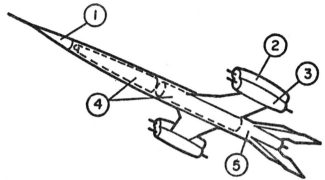

1. Control section
2. Ramjet engine                              4. Tanks with liquid hydrogen
3. Turbojet engine                            5. Liquid rocket engine

Figure 3. Rocket plane with atomic engines.

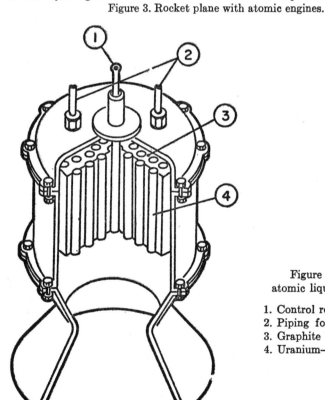

Figure 4. Diagram of
atomic liquid rocket engine.

1. Control rod
2. Piping for liquid hydrogen
3. Graphite block
4. Uranium—235 rods

air as the ejected mass, and fuel expenditure turns out to be a minimum; only the nuclear fuel is spent. The atomic liquid rocket engine will begin to operate in airless space; it will guarantee further increase in velocity up to 11.2 kilometers per second and the escape of the rocket plane to the assigned orbit for flight to the moon.

One can fly very far on the wings of fantasy, but what in reality is the matter with atomic engines for such purposes? How will the primary difficulties be successfully overcome during the calculations and designing of the first atomic engines?

### LIQUID ROCKET ENGINE OPERATING ON NUCLEAR FUEL

Our engine (Figure 4) is intended for installation in a large rocket for the purpose of achieving the first cosmic velocity, that is, the velocity necessary for the rocket plane to become an artificial earth satellite (8,270 meters per second). The atomic reactor is mounted in the combustion chamber of the engine. The active mass of the reactor is prepared from a mixture of U-235, U-238 and a graphite neutron moderator. Hydrogen, driven by pumps, flows through special channels in the porous active mass. The hydrogen, in cooling the reactor, receives enormous energy. Its temperature goes up to 3000 degrees, and the exhaust velocity at the nozzle outlet exceeds 7000 meters per second.

The quantity of heat that develops in the reactor is regulated by pulling out the control rods. These rods are prepared from porous cadmium and act like a fire extinguisher with respect to the chain reaction. They absorb neutrons and thereby lower the rate of the nuclear reaction. By pushing the rods into the reactor, we lower the heat formation or even stop the chain reaction entirely. So that the control rods will not melt in the reactor, their temperature is maintained sufficiently low by blowing cold hydrogen through them.

The use of porous material in the reactor considerably facilitates the solution of the problem of heat transmission, in view of the enormous contact surface of the hydrogen with it.

Let us now return to the determination of the size of the reactor. A chain, that is, nonattenuating, nuclear reaction can proceed in the reactor only when neutrons, flying out during the fissioning of the uranium nuclei, do not escape into the surrounding space, but, colliding with other uranium nuclei during their flight, cause them to split. Thus neutrons must travel a certain distance without leaving the limits of the active zone of the reactor. It is this condition that determines the smallest dimensions of the reactor and its so-called critical radius ($R_{cr}$).

If we take, for example, a cylindrical reactor whose length is equal to its radius, then we obtain $R_{cr} = 2.5$ meters — a reactor the size of a one-story house! The weight of such a reactor is about 32 tons. The rate of hydrogen consumption for an engine with such a reactor amounts to more than 3000 kilograms per second. In the not-unknown V-2 rocket the fuel consumption was only 125 kilograms per second. The thrust of an atomic liquid rocket engine turns out to be more than 2300 tons. The V-2 engine developed a thrust of 25 tons, that is, almost 100 times less. For a rocket with an atomic liquid rocket engine to develop a terminal velocity of 8270 meters per second during vertical takeoff, 1130 tons of liquid hydrogen, which the engine discharges in six minutes of operation, are necessary.

From the above examples it is clear that the dimensions and weight data which are obtained are better suited to a science-fiction novel than to a real engineering project. Therefore ways are being sought for reducing the size of the reactor.

The critical dimensions, it turns out, can be reduced by using enriched uranium containing a larger percentage of U-235, by installing special neutron reflectors, by using an improved fast neutron moderator instead of graphite, etc.

All these measures should decrease the weight of the rocket from 1000 to 100 tons. As is known, building an airplane or a rocket weighing 100 to 200 tons is no longer a fantasy in our time.

Such engines operating on nuclear fuel will be of special importance where great speed and flight range are necessary, that is, in modern aviation and rocket technology. In addition, powerful and highly economical atomic engines will make it possible to create a rocket that will overcome the earth's gravity. Mankind's dream of interplanetary flights will become a reality in the near future. (*Kryl'ya Rodiny*, January, 1956.)

# 24.  Atomic Engines

*R. G. Perel'man*

The people who first step on the moon's surface will, perhaps, be indebted for this to the creation of a rocket ship with an atomic engine.

The famous Russian scientist K. E. Tsiolkovskii, the founder of rocket technology, derived the equation that makes it possible to establish the ratio of rocket fuel weight to the structural and payload weight necessary for attaining a definite flight velocity. From this equation it follows that to attain a rocket velocity of 11.2 kilometers per second — the minimum velocity necessary to overcome the earth's attraction — the weight of its chemical fuel must be 20 times greater than that of the payload and structure.

Today, for single-stage rockets flying with a velocity of 2 kilometers per second, it turns out that the given fuel weighs approximately five times more than the structure and payload. Multistage rockets, "rocket trains," also first proposed by Tsiolkovskii, and the possibility of refueling rockets at intermediate stages, somewhat facilitate the solution of the task. By using chemical fuels, however, the takeoff weight and even the size of such a cosmic rocket are found to be very large. And although science and technology today are in a position to guarantee its creation, the use of atomic engines for cosmic flights seem to us more promising.

Let us dwell on the schemes of atomic rocket engines. One of them — "purely atomic" — proposes the direct utilization of the "recoil" of the gases that form during the chain reactions in the atomic fuel and are ejected from the nozzle. The theoretical velocity of the exhaust gases in this case can amount to 12 kilometers per second, which guarantees flights within the limits of the solar system. On this principle, however, it is possible to build an engine with a thrust of only a few kilograms. This engine can be used for driving the ship beyond the limits of the gravitational field of the earth and the planets. An attempt to build such an engine with a greater thrust would lead to the vaporization of the chamber under the action of the impact of particles moving with speeds of tens of thousands of kilometers per second. Also unsolved is the problem of the directed flow of the

222

products of reaction. A rocket with such an engine is therefore called a "pseudorocket."

The so-called thermal atomic rocket engine, which makes use of a working substance heated in a reactor, is feasible. In this case there is no need of an oxidizer whose volume is usually several times greater than that of the fuel. Substances with low molecular weight and rather high density may be used as working substances (exhaust velocity increases with decrease in molecular weight). Especially expedient is the use of substances that decompose into simpler ones at high temperatures. Preheated in the "jacket" of the engine, the working substance is fed through the injectors into the reactor, where it is heated and then, flowing through the nozzle, creates thrust. The need for transmitting huge quantities of heat to the working substances, however, leads either to an excessive increase in the temperature difference between the working substance and the elements of the reactor (at great absolute values of temperature), or to the excessive growth of the heat exchanger surfaces, and consequently also of their weight. Even if one assumes that the reactor can operate at 3500 degrees, all this will substantially lower the advantages of the scheme under consideration in comparison with future rocket engines operating on possible new chemical fuels.

The best prospect is an atomic rocket engine in which an enriched nuclear fuel and a working substance are fed into a chamber with walls that reflect neutrons well and have special film cooling, for example. It is in this chamber that the chain reaction takes place. This makes it possible to obviate several difficulties connected with the creation of super-heat-resistant reactors with large heat exchange surfaces. If a gas temperature of 4000 degrees to 5000 degrees is obtained in the chamber, its exhaust velocity will increase to 8 or 9 kilometers per second, and it will be possible to achieve "escape velocities" at a practicable mass ratio. It is supposed that such a "lunar" rocket will be equipped with several hundred tons of hydrogen and will be about 12 meters in diameter and 120 meters long.

It is advantageous to separate the atomic engine from the crew cabin, using the fuel tanks and structural elements as a biological shield. In the composition of a cosmic rocket it is desirable, therefore, to make use of the atomic stage as one of the intermediate stages. The first stage may have an air jet engine, the second a ramjet, and the third an atomic engine that will begin to operate at a great altitude where the ejected gases are not dangerous. At the same time the spent stages can be returned to earth by means of parachutes

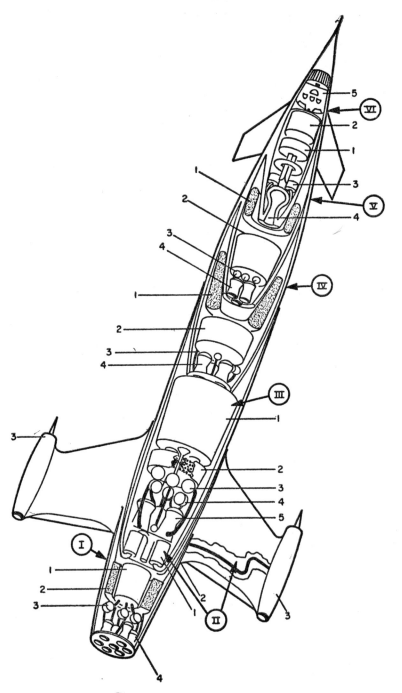

Figure 1. Cosmic Rocket.

to be used again. The use of atomic engines opens up unlimited prospects for rocket technology. (See Figure 1.) (*Nauka i Zhizn'*, January, 1956. The author is identified as "Candidate of Technical Sciences.")

Notes For Figure 1

I.  Booster stage with liquid rocket engine: 1—Fuel tank. 2—Oxidizer tank. 3—Turbopump assembly. 4—Combustion chamber.
II.  Ramjet stage: 1—Compressed air tank. 2—Fuel tank. 3—Ramjet engine.
III.  Atomic engine stage: 1—Working fluid tank. 2—Nuclear fuel. 3—Turbopump assembly. 4—Nuclear fuel feed units. 5—Combustion chambers.
IV.  Liquid rocket engine stage: 1—Fuel tank. 2—Oxidant tank. 3—Turbopump assembly. 4—Combustion chambers.
V.  Liquid rocket engine stage: 1—Fuel tank. 2—Oxidant tank. 3—Turbopump assembly. 4—Combustion chambers.
VI.  Liquid rocket engine stage: 1—Fuel. 2—Oxidant. 3—Turbopump assembly. 4—Combustion chamber. 5—Crew's cabin.

# 25.   Combustion, Applied Mechanics and Space Travel

*L. I. Sedov*

A delegation of the USSR Academy of Sciences, which in addition to myself included Academician V. N. Kondratyev and Corresponding Member L. N. Khitrin, was invited to attend the Sixth International Symposium on Combustion at Yale University in New Haven, U. S. Besides being one of the oldest of America's universities, Yale is also an important center of research.

Combustion research has long acquired great practical significance, and it plays a very big part in the development of internal-combustion, jet and rocket engines and in every industry in one way or another connected with thermal power.   Research in combustion techniques is closely associated with research in chemistry, physics, and aerodynamics.

These symposiums on combustion are held regularly in the United States once every two years and in recent years they have attracted quite a number of foreign scientists.   In 1954 the Americans set up a special Combustion Institute whose director, Dr. Bernard Lewis, was chairman of the New Haven Symposium.   The interest displayed by industry in this new branch of research was evident from the large number of practical engineers who took part in the proceedings.

Unlike ordinary scientific conferences, the Symposium began with a round-table discussion which concentrated chiefly on experimentation. One of the most interesting problems examined was reaction of gases under high temperatures and pressures.

Though there were only three of us in the Soviet delegation, we made a significant contribution to the discussion.   In addition to our own papers, we reported on the work of some of our colleagues (there were 17 Soviet communications out of a total of 116) and also took part in informal discussions.   We established personal contact with such distinguished American researchers as Doctors Lewis, Elbe, Kistiakowsky and Wohl, and were invited to visit various laboratories. Arrangements were made for exchange of research reports.

Our American colleagues had a high opinion of Soviet research. At the Massachusetts Institute of Technology we found that experimentation in flameless combustion was being conducted by methods first applied in the USSR. Other places visited included Dr. Kistiakowsky's laboratory of physical chemistry and Dr. Purcell's laboratory of nuclear magnetism and radio-frequency spectroscopy at Harvard, Dr. Wohl's combustion laboratory at Delaware University, and the gas turbine laboratory at the Massachusetts Institute of Technology.

Much of American research is concetrated in the universities and colleges, where physical experimentation, in particular, is conducted on a wide scale. The laboratories are all excellently equipped and offer a wide variety of facilities to undergraduates and graduate students, and also to specialists, many of them from other countries. This system enables laboratory directors to advance young talent and give the student the knowledge and practical know-how necessary for independent research.

Our discussions in New Haven centered around special problems, but the next conference I attended, the Ninth International Congress of Applied Mechanics in Brussels, covered a very wide area and was attended by practically every leading expert in the field.

The Soviet Union sent a rather large group, and the papers read by one of its members, Dr. E. A. Krasilshchikova, on supersonic aerodynamics were one of the highlights of the discussion. Dr. Krasilshchikova has found a solution to the basic problem of supersonic aerodynamics of a thin wing. Besides her two papers, a communication on the results of her investigations took up much of the general survey made by Dr. Germain of France. My own paper was devoted to the unsteady motion of gases with reference to the problem of variable stars.

As in New Haven, our delegation was given a cordial welcome. We were invited to inspect the durability laboratory and Professor Jaumotte's very interesting gas-turbine laboratory at the University of Brussels. The president of the Congress, Professor van den Dungen, took us through his acoustics laboratory. Everywhere we found that scientific research in Belgium was of a high order.

The last stage in my itinerary was Rome, where I was to attend the Seventh International Astronautical Congress. We often speak of the "science of the future," and this term, I think, eminently suits astronautics, which deals with the problems of space travel. It is a science that will bring to realization one of the oldest dreams of mankind. True, even today there is a good deal of daydreaming in this field of research, but in many respects astronautics is firmly based on realistic and tested data.

With the foundation of the International Astronautical Federation a few years ago, these congresses have been held regularly every year. The fact that this one brought together 350 delegates from 23 countries is proof that astronautics is making rapid progress.

The Congress was welcomed by the Mayor of Rome and representatives of the Italian government. The President of the International Federation, Dr. F. C. Durant of the United States, said in his opening speech that man would set foot on the moon before the close of this century. He predicted that within twelve years manned satellites would be travelling around the earth, and within 25 years rockets would be circling the moon.

However, the Congress dealt chiefly with a more realistic project, namely, the launching of small satellites for automatic observation during the forthcoming International Geophysical Year. There have been several detailed reports of such projects in America, and a bulky volume on the subject has been published there. In Rome we were given additional information on the American studies of how rarefied atmosphere would affect the trajectory of a satellite.

Dr. Joseph Kaplan, Chairman of the American International Geophysical Year Committee, announced that lay observers would be enlisted to follow the flight of the satellite. Their work would be coordinated by Professor Whipple. Dr. Kaplan suggested a conference to arrange for international observation and joint observation stations.

The Soviet Union, as already reported in the press, is to launch a satellite too.

There were papers on the legal and political problems that might arise in connection with the launching of these satellites. I might add that some foreign publications suggest that the satellites could be used for military purposes.

Other papers dealt with rocket techniques and the theoretical aspects of physical and chemical processes in rocket engines, also with projects for space ships, flights around the moon, and even the use of photon rockets for space travel. Some of these papers were of undoubted theoretical interest, but others were based on fantasy rather than on sound scientific investigation.

It was decided to hold the 1957 Congress in Barcelona. Professor

Shepherd of Britain was elected president of the Federation and I was made one of the vice-presidents.

The three conferences demonstrated anew the respect that Soviet science commands abroad. (*New Times,* English periodical published in Moscow, November 15, 1956. The author is identified as "Academician.")

# 26.  Table of Soviet Missiles

*Alfred J. Zaehringer*

The following table brings up to date Soviet missile development. New developments include medium range and intercontinental ballistic missiles, (T-2 and T-3), the I-2 rocket interceptor, and J-3 submarine-launched cruise missile, and the T-7A ballistic rocket. Also of interest is the deployment of barrage and guided rockets around key Soviet centers.  These weapons, in conjunction with a well-developed radar warning network, are mainly intended for defense against B-36, B-47, and B-52 type targets.  It also appears that conventional jet interceptors are being readied for the use of heavier guided aircraft rockets.  The T-2 missile has been vertically fired in animal-carrying experiments, and has reached altitudes of about 250 miles.  The T-2, which is now in production, is to be coupled with another stage to form the T-3 intercontinental ballistic missile.  An alternate version of the T-3 may be the satellite vehicle which the USSR will fire during the IGY.  Pending the development of the T-3 ICBM, existing missiles have ranges to place most of Europe under fire.  In addition, the growing Russian submarine fleet would allow most of the United States and Canada to be hit with existing cruise or ballistic missiles. Rockets are a standard defense weapon of the Red Air Force.  The Red Army has been completely overhauled with highly mobile rockets capable of delivering nuclear warheads.  The apparent attitude of USSR rocket philosophy is to have them ready in large numbers, make them extremely simple and reliable, and not worry about cost. As the newer types of weapons come off the assembly lines, older types are being used for training purposes, and for use in the Soviet satellite nations.

### SYMBOLS

| | | | |
|---|---|---|---|
| SA | — Surface-to-Air | HE — High Explosive | in — Inches |
| SS | — Surface-to-Surface | Lox — Liquid oxygen | wt — Weight |
| AA | — Antiaircraft | Max — Maximum | lb — Pounds |
| AP | — Armor-piercing | Mod — Modified | alt — Altitude |
| AT | — Antitank | dia — Diameter | |
| VTO | — Vertical Takeoff | ft — Feet | |

| MODEL | TYPE | CHARACTERISTICS |
|---|---|---|
| T-1 (M-101) | SS: Medium-range Ballistic Missile | Single-stage improved A4 (V-2). Lox-kerosene motor of 77,000 lb thrust. Range of 400 mi. Total impulse: 4.6 million lb-sec. |
| T-2 (M-103) | SS: Long-range Ballistic Missile | Two-stage modified A4-A9, total wt: 75-85 tons. Stage 1, lox-kerosene rocket motor of 254,000 lb thrust. Stage 2 is T-1. Total impulse: 20.4 million lb-sec. Range: 1,800 mi. In production. |
| T-3 | SS: Intercontinental Ballistic Missile | Three stages. Stages 1 and 2 may use components of T-1 and T-2. Launching wt: 125 to 250 tons. Length: 100-160 ft. Range: 5,000 mi. |
| T-3A | Satellite Vehicle | Three or four stages. Payload c. 1 ton. Product of T-3 development. Orbits at 125-1000 miles up. Last stage in development. |
| T-4 (M-102) | Supersonic Glide Missile | Winged T-1. Length 50 ft; dia 5½ ft. Range 500-1000 mi. In production. |
| T-4A | Manned Rocket Bomber | Two stages, track launched. Launching wt: 100 tons. Total impulse: 60.74 million lb-sec. Range: 4,000-10,000 miles. In development. |
| T-5 | Standard RATO | Thrust: 2500-3000 lb for 8-15 sec. Double-base and composite solid propellant. |
| T-5A | Ballistic Rocket | Modified T-5 for SS and AT use. Composite solid propellant. In production and field use. |
| T-6 | Barrage Rocket | SS version of RS-132A. Dougle-base solid propellant. Projector guidance. |
| T-7 | Guided AA Rocket | SA: mod. German "Wasserfall." Launching wt of 3-4 tons. Acid-amine rocket of 17,000 lb thrust with liquid or solid booster. Max alt of 50,000-70,000 ft. Speed unknown. For B-47 type targets. In production. |
| T-7A | SS: Ballistic Rocket | Solid propellant version of T-7. Length of 23-25 ft, dia of 31 in. Total wt of 8,800 lb. 17,600 lb thrust for 30-60 sec. Composite, smokeless propellant with range of 30-60 mi. Standard artillery rocket, launched from standard army truck. HE or nuclear warhead. |
| I-1 | Manned Rocket Plane | All rocket power. Speed 200 mph; alt: 100,000 ft. Research craft only. |
| I-2 | Rocket Interceptor | Manned. Max speed of 700-800 mph. Endurance of 7-10 min. Armed with cannon and/or rockets. VTO. In production and deployed |

| MODEL | TYPE | CHARACTERISTICS |
|-------|------|-----------------|
| | | around key centers. To be used for B-36 and B-47 type targets. |
| J-1 | Subsonic Cruise Missile | SS: modified German V-1. Pulse-jet powerplant. Range of 300 miles. |
| J-2 | SS: Cruise Missile | Turbojet or ramjet. Ground or submarine launch. Range of 700 mi. Speed not known. In production. |
| J-3 | SS: Cruise Missile | Turbojet or ramjet. Ground or submarine launch. Speed not known. Range of 1,500-1,800 mi. In or near production. |
| M-1 | Guided AA Rocket | Two-stage SA missile for B-36 type targets. Speed: Mach 0.9-1.3. Solid propellant booster, peroxide sustainer. Wt: 3,300 lb; diam: 22 in; length: 14.7 ft. Max alt of 50,000 ft. In use but probably being replaced by T-7 or T-7A type AA rockets. |
| M-100 | Guided Aircraft Rocket | For air-to-air use. Diam. of 10 in., wt about 1000 lb. Composite propellant. For B-47 or B-52 type targets. In development or near production. |
| RS-82 | Ballistic Aircraft Rocket | Developed from German R4M. Dia of 3.2 in. Wt 15 lb. Double-base solid propellant. Standard aircraft rocket in production. |
| RS-132 | Ballistic Aircraft Rocket | Improved RS-82. Dia of 5.2 in, wt of 51 lb. For air-to-air and air-to-ground use. Double-base solid propellant in use. |
| RS-132A | Ballistic Aircraft Rocket | Improved RS-132. Dia of 5.2 in, and wt of 93 lb. Double-base solid propellant. In use. Later models may be guided. |
| 25KgAT | Aircraft-launched AT Rocket | 55 lb AP warhead. Solid propellant. |
| GVAI | Barrage Rocket | Surface-to-air (AA), for low-altitude defense. Double-base solid propellant. |
| Yak-21 | Manned Rocket Plane | Auxiliary rocket power. Span: 31 ft; length 21 ft; wt: 12,000 lb. Test models only. |
| La-17 | Manned Rocket Plane | Auxiliary rocket power. Span: 36 ft; length: 36 ft; wt: 16,000 lbs. Test models only. |

*(Journal of Space Flight, May, 1956)*

# 27.  Report on Intercontinental Ballistic Rocket

*Tass*

Successful tests of an intercontinental ballistic rocket and also explosions of nuclear and thermonuclear weapons have been carried out in conformity with the plan of scientific research work in the USSR.

### I

A few days ago a super-long-range, intercontinental multistage ballistic rocket was launched.

The tests of the rocket were successful; they fully confirmed the correctness of the calculations and the selected design. The flight of the rocket took place at a very great, hitherto unattained, altitude. Covering an enormous distance in a short time, the rocket hit the assigned region.

The results obtained show that there is a possibility of launching rockets into any region of the terrestrial globe. The solution of the problem of creating intercontinental ballistic rockets will make it possible to reach remote regions without resorting to strategic aviation, which at the present time is vulnerable to modern means of antiaircraft defense.

Taking into consideration the tremendous contribution to the development of science and the great importance of this scientific-technical achievement for strengthening the defensive capacity of the Soviet Union, the Soviet Government expressed its gratitude to the large collective of workers who have taken part in the development and manufacture of intercontinental ballistic rockets and of the complex of facilities that assure their launching.

### II

Recently a series of explosions of nuclear and thermonuclear (hydrogen) weapons has been carried out in the USSR. In order to assure the safety of the population the explosions were set off at great altitudes. The tests were successful.

In connection with the above-mentioned tests, Tass has been authorized to state the following:

The problem of disarmament, including the question of banning atomic and hydrogen weapons and the question of stopping their tests, has been discussed for many years in the United Nations Organization without result.

The Soviet Government, steadfastly conducting a policy of peace, has more than once submitted concrete proposals concerning a substantial reduction of the armed forces and the armaments of states, concerning the prohibition of atomic and hydrogen weapons, concerning the stopping of tests of these kinds of weapons, and concerning other measures connected with the problem of disarmament. The Western powers, however, have not yet taken any positive steps in the field of disarmament. On the contrary, they have put all kinds of obstacles in the way of reaching agreements on this most important problem of our time.

It is well known that the United States and its partners not only reject the prohibition of atomic and hydrogen weapons, but in fact also do not want an agreement on the unconditional and immediate cessation of tests of nuclear weapons, meanwhile conducting a large series of tests of these weapons.

Encountering such an obviously negative attitude on the part of the Western powers—primarily the United States—toward a positive solution of the disarmament problem, the Soviet Government has been forced to take all necessary measures for the purpose of safeguarding the security of the Soviet Union.

At the same time the Soviet Government will continue persistently to strive for agreement on the cessation of tests and the prohibition of atomic weapons and on the problem of disarmament as a whole, in a positive solution of which, all the peoples of the world are interested. *Pravda,* August 27, 1957.)

# Part Six

# SATELLITE PLANS

# 28. Artificial Earth Satellite Principles

*K. Stanyukovich*

Officers V. G. Andreev, N. V. Denisov, and P. D. Blokhin ask the editor the question: What is an artificial satellite of the earth and for what purposes can it be created?

The successes of modern science and technology, and particularly of jet technology, have made completely real the problem of launching into cosmic space a so-called artificial satellite of the earth. Such a satellite, revolving around the earth, would automatically communicate to it the readings of the instruments installed in the satellite.

Artificial satellites of the earth can be utilized for very diverse scientific investigations, the conducting of which from the earth is hindered by the air envelope of the atmosphere. They will permit the solution of important problems of the physics of the sun and solar phenomena which influence the earth, then will make possible meteorological observations of the cloud cover of the earth and other investigations. With the aid of an earth satellite, a more detailed study of cosmic radiation will also become possible. Finally, satellites can play an important role as space stations for man's further penetration into universal space.

The possibility of launching an artificial satellite is based on precise calculations. The fact is that a rocket, having taken off at a tangent to the earth's surface and attained a velocity of about 8 kilometers per second, can fly around the globe along the equator. If the flight of such a rocket takes place beyond the limits of any dense atmosphere, that is, at a height of more than 200 kilometers, it will not fall to the earth, but will circle around it and turn into a satellite of the earth. The force of gravity, which acts on the rocket, will in this case be compensated by the centrifugal force.

Recently, there appeared in the press reports that American scientists propose to launch in the coming International Geophysical Year, which will extend from July, 1957, through December, 1958, several extra-high-altitude missiles — satellites of the earth intended for scientific observations in the upper layers of the atmosphere. Just what can such missiles be and how can they be launched?

Today there are a great number of projects for building satellites, quite different in their designs and weight. A small missile, the creation of which is the least complicated, will probably be launched first. Such a satellite will have the shape of a hollow sphere, the size of a basketball, in which instruments will be placed. The protective shell of the sphere must shield it from the action of the explosion during the launching.

The satellite can attain the necessary velocity with the aid of a two-stage rocket which contains the satellite sphere. It is launched at an angle of 45 degrees. When the rocket attains an altitude of 300 to 500 kilometers, at the highest point of its trajectory, an explosion must take place which will eject the sphere in a direction parallel to the circumference of the earth with a velocity of 8 kilometers per second and thereby convert it into a satellite. Calculations of Soviet scientists, and in particular of Professor G. I. Pokrovskii, show that in order to impart the necessary velocity to the sphere, the weight of the explosive charge must be ten times as great as the weight of the satellite itself. Between the satellite and the explosive there must be some inert mass which protects the satellite from the action of the explosion. This mass can be a compressed gas. Undoubtedly, there can be also another, better version of launching the satellite.

The movement of artificial earth satellites is subject to the same laws of celestial mechanics as the movement of other celestial bodies. Therefore, the distance of an artificial satellite from the center of the earth determines its velocity and period of revolution around it. A missile launched at a height of 350 to 500 kilometers with a velocity of about 30,000 kilometers per hour will revolve around the earth for several days. The flight of the missile will be retarded by the small amount of atmosphere which still exists at this altitude, and it will begin to move in a spiral. At an altitude of the order of 100 kilometers it will begin to shine and gradually vaporize. This vaporization, apparently, can be observed even with the naked eye, as we observe, for example, the flight of a meteor.

It should be pointed out that the possibility of launching a satellite into interplanetary space does not appear as a great surprise today, as this could have been assumed. The state of scientific thought has led mankind to such discoveries that the launching of a satellite has become a completely real and feasible matter. This has become possible, thanks to the contributions to the development of science of the scientists of many countries of the world — the most outstanding foreign theoreticians Friedrichs, Taylor, Karman, as well as the well-known Soviet scientists Khrestianovich, Sedov, Fesenkov, and many others.

In the Soviet Union preparations are being made at the present time for launching a satellite and for carrying out observations from it. The realization of the Soviet project can be expected in the comparatively near future. The level of technology in the given field is, as a matter of fact, identical to that of most of the great countries. Soviet scientists are glad to welcome the initiative of their American colleagues and to contribute their share of the work in realizing the launching of a satellite, provided, of course, this will be directed to the good of mankind, for the progress of science. (*Krasnaya Zvezda*, August 7, 1955. The author is identified as "Professor" and "Doctor of Technical Sciences.")

# 29.  Cosmic Laboratory*

*A. G. Karpenko*

Many of the most prominent specialists in the fields of mechanics, astronomy, physics, and thermotechnology participate in the work of our commission.  Personnel of a number of research institutes of the USSR Academy of Sciences, of the academies of sciences of the Union Republics, and of some branch institutes are occupied with the solution of the problems connected with interplanetary communications.

Today the efforts of scientists, designers, and engineers are directed first to solving the problems of creating the so-called artificial earth satellite.  I refer to the creation of an automatically operating laboratory which could stay in cosmic space a long time.

It should be noted that the idea of such a cosmic station is not new. Serious works in this direction began to appear with the publication in 1903 of the paper "Investigation of World Spaces by Reactive Instruments" by the famous Russian scientist K. E. Tsiolkovskii.

Last week the International Astronautical Congress ended in Copenhagen.  Most of the papers read at the congress were devoted to plans for creating an artificial earth satellite.  The report by Soviet scien-

---

* This statement appeared in *Moskovskaya Pravda*, August 14, 1955, after the following remarks:

Never before has any, even the most daring, dream of man been so close to realization as in our days of atomic and jet technology. The investigations of scientists, the inventions of designers, the bold searches of the creative mind unveil before us still unprecedented horizons. While only yesterday the conquest of cosmic space was only a beautiful, fantastic dream, today we speak of the rocket ship as something real which will in the near future leave the earth and go off on its first interplanetary voyage.

Lately, in the Soviet Union much consideration is being given to research problems connected with the realization of interplanetary communications. The first steps in the creation of an "artificial earth satellite" have been taken.

In order to coordinate research work in the field of interplanetary communications, the USSR Academy of Sciences formed an interdepartmental commission. A *Moskovskaya Pravda* correspondent requested the scientific secretary of this commission, Comrade A. G. Karpenko, to tell about the work of Soviet scientists in the field of astronautics.

tist Academician L. I. Sedov on the availability today of a real basis for creating artificial satellites was received with exceptional interest.

What possibilities will open up to investigators when such a cosmic laboratory is at their command?

One can name a whole series of physical, geophysical, and astrophysical investigations which it would be desirable to conduct by means of an artificial earth satellite in the upper layers of the atmosphere. Today the rich and multiform "life" of the atmosphere is being studied only in the layers nearest the earth. This is explained by the fact that neither airplanes, nor weather balloons, nor radiosondes, which are sent daily into the stratosphere from different points of the earth's surface, are able to penetrate to a great altitude. Meanwhile, the phenomena which occur at an altitude of several hundred kilometers are of great importance for life on the earth.

Consider even such processes as the formation by the action of cosmic rays of the ionosphere, which plays an important role in short-wave communication. Observations of the propagation of radio waves can make an invaluable contribution to the development of future communication with cosmic ships, and also, possibly, will help solve the problem of relaying television broadcasts over long distances.

Delayed filming, carried out under the conditions of the transatmospheric station, would make it possible to investigate later the complex dynamics of the surface phenomena on the sun and to more precisely establish the connection between these changes and the phenomena which take place on the earth.

The accessibility for observation of the ultraviolet and roentgen radiations of the sun and the stars is an especially remarkable possibility which will open up to investigators beyond the limits of the atmosphere. Such observations would permit the study of many new phenomena that take place in distant worlds and the observation of the origin and decay of different chemical elements under conditions of exceptionally high temperatures and pressures.

Until recently, the phenomena in the upper layers of the atmosphere were arrived at only by conjectures or else by some indirect observations, since there was no means which would permit the attainment of great altitudes.

What altitude have modern cosmic rockets attained?

Cosmic rockets radio-guided from the earth have already reached an altitude of almost 500 kilometers. Sensitive instruments automatically recorded the pressure and the temperature and determined the composition of the air.

And some animals have also been sent up to this altitude in special cabins. Their state and behavior under such unusual conditions were observed from the earth.

If we can obtain information of interest to us by means of cosmic rockets, what role will be assigned to the artificial earth satellite? The fact is that in spite of the rich results obtained by means of high-altitude rockets, their utilization for scientific research purposes is very limited. A rocket flight usually lasts a total of only a few tens of seconds. Besides that, a rocket stays at a given altitude for only an instant. Therefore, the main shortcoming of observations thus obtained is their brevity. It is not difficult to imagine how much of this very interesting information on cosmic phenomena could be obtained if it were possible to linger at the attained altitude for several hours or days. An artificial earth satellite, on which stationary observations will be made, will replace reconnaissance rockets.

What kind of artificial earth satellite projects are there today and how real are they?

At present there are many projects for creating artificial satellites of various sizes and weights, from a few kilograms to several tons. The reality of such projects is well known to engineers, designers, and scientific workers engaged in and interested in rocket technology.

According to these projects the satellite must revolve around the earth at such an altitude at which the air resistance is quite weak. It is possible that for the first satellites this altitude will be from 200 to 1000 kilometers and for the subsequent ones from 1500 to 2000 kilometers.

It has been calculated that at an altitude of 2000 kilometers the velocity of the satellite must be about 8 kilometers per second, that is, the velocity must be such that the force of gravity on the flying laboratory will be neutralized by its centrifugal force. The "artificial earth satellite," apparently, will not revolve in the plane of the equator, but in a plane passing through the polar axis. In view of the daily rotation of the earth this will make it possible to conduct observations over all parts of the terrestrial globe.

Results of investigations carried out in our country give a basis for thinking that the project of creating an artificial earth satellite will be realized in the comparatively near future. (*Moskovskaya Pravda*, August 14, 1955.)

# 30. Artificial Earth Satellite Problems*

*G. I. Pokrovskii*

The launching into cosmic space of an artificial earth satellite is entirely feasible at the present time. The achievements of science and technology at the contemporary stage permit the transition to the practical realization of this idea.

The first task is to escape from the dense layers of the earth's atmosphere, to go out into cosmic space where there is no air. This means that it is necessary to raise a suitable device — say, a rocket, essentially above the dense layers of the atmosphere to a height of 300 to 400 kilometers above the surface of the earth. Ascent to such a height is necessary; otherwise, the air, even though it has a very low density, will hinder movement — the satellite will gradually descend and will fall to the earth or burn up like a meteorite.

Science has completely solved the problem of escaping from the atmosphere into cosmic space. Cosmic rockets radio-guided from the earth have already attained a height of almost 500 kilometers. Some animals were raised in special cabins to cosmic height and they safely descended to the earth.

The second task is that of casting a suitable body with a speed of the order of eight kilometers per second in an orbit around the terrestrial globe. The traveling speed of the earth satellite must be such

* This statement appeared in *Izvestiya,* August 19, 1955, after the following remarks:

Recently the American and European press has been animatedly discussing the report that the United States intends, during the coming International Geophysical Year, which will extend from July, 1957, through December, 1958, to launch into cosmic space artificial satellites of the earth which will revolve around it.

According to reports of foreign newspapers, American scientists think of the artificial satellies as being in the form of small spheres that are launched to a considerable height by means of rockets. These spheres will make one revolution around the earth every 90 minutes with a speed of 18,000 miles per hour, moving at an altitude of from 200 to 300 miles above the surface of the earth.

The editorial office of the newspaper *Izvestiya* requested the well-known scientist in the field of technical physics, Doctor of Technical Sciences G. I. Pokrovskii, to speak on this question.

that it could cover the distance from Moscow to Leningrad in approximately 1 minute. This task has been successfully solved by scientists for the time being only under laboratory conditions. In 1944, I personally obtained a speed of 25 kilometers per second, that is three times as great as that required for an earth satellite.

My work was published in the *Doklady Akademii Nauk SSSR* in 1945. The American scientists W. S. Koski, F. A. Lucy, R. G. Shreffler, and F. J. Willig achieved speeds up to 90 kilometers per second in 1952. Their work was published in the American publication, *Journal of Applied Physics,* in December, 1952.

Laboratory experiments conducted by both Soviet and American scientists yielded velocities considerably greater than that required for an artificial satellite. Now the whole matter consists in raising those means which were created in the laboratories (shaped charges of ordinary explosives) to a height of 300 to 400 kilometers by means of rockets and produce the explosion there. Thus an artificial satellite of small dimensions can be created which does not carry any instruments but is intended for observations of its motion by means of telescopes or, perhaps, by radar.

For such a satellite to be as visible by telescope as, say, the most distant planet of the solar system (Pluto), it is sufficient that the artificial satellite have a diameter of only a few centimeters; that is, it should be the size of a billiard ball. But in practice it is expedient to make the first satellite several decimeters in diameter.

The next step in this direction is the creation of earth satellites which carry various instruments. But it is impossible to project such satellites with the necessary velocity by means of an explosion. Here one must use a multistage rocket which utilizes the long-known idea of K. E. Tsiolkovskii. Motion in different directions can be imparted to the new satellites of the earth. This will allow their movement to be observed from all parts of the terrestrial globe.

The purpose of such earth satellites is to secure physical, geographical, and astrophysical observations in the upper layers of the atmosphere, as yet inaccessible to investigators. It will be interesting to become acquainted with the phenomena which take place at an altitude of several hundred kilometers, for the solution of the tasks of the peaceful development of science and technology for the good of all nations.

Later on it will be possible to send rockets without people to the moon. An atomic or hydrogen explosion could serve as a signal of its arrival on the surface of the moon.  The flash of light caused by such an explosion could be photographed through a telescope.

Scientists of the Soviet Union are following with great interest the reports concerning the proposed launching by the Americans of several cosmic projectiles as satellites of the earth and designed for various scientific observations.

Preparation for the launching of an artificial earth satellite is also being conducted in the USSR.  Our country has made important achievements in the field of ballistics, gas dynamics, technology of propulsion, and directed explosions.  The preparatory stages of scientific investigations concerning the creation of artificial earth satellites have already been conducted.  All research works in the field of interplanetary communications are coordinated by the interdepartmental commission specially created by the Academy of Science of the USSR and made up of scientists of diverse specialties.

We now have serious reasons for saying that the time is not far off when a cherished dream of mankind will be realized; cosmic ships will regularly leave the earth on interplanetary voyages.  (*Izvestiya*, August 19, 1955.)

# 31.  Television of the Future*

*V. Petrov*

Enormous and extremely varied technical difficulties have to be solved before the first flying apparatus starting from the surface of the terrestrial globe will overcome the force of the earth's gravity. At present we have available a whole complex of scientific and technical knowledge which will permit us to realize building such a flying apparatus within the next two years.  It will be an artificial satellite of the earth (ASE).

Even twenty years ago there were few persons who believed in the practical possibility of utilizing atomic energy for obtaining electrical energy.  Today, however, through the efforts of Soviet scientists this grandiose problem has not only been solved, but has also occupied an important place in the directives of the 20th Congress of the CPSU in the sixth five-year plan for the development of the national economy of the USSR for 1956-1960.

The program for organizing interplanetary flight, widely discussed today in the world's scientific literature, is divided into four stages: the building and launching of an automatic rocket — an unmanned satellite; the building of a cosmic station or artificial satellite of the stationary type; the realization of regular manned flights in an orbit around the earth, and also of several flights of cosmic rocket-automats around the moon; and the first interplanetary voyage with landing on the moon, and later on the other planets within the limits of the solar system.

The scientific and technical problems connected with the organization of flight into cosmic space can be successfully solved only with the wide cooperation of all the branches of science and technology: physics and chemistry, astronomy and mathematics, mechanics and astronavigation, mechanical engineering and metallurgy, radio and electronics, biology and medicine.

---

*Subtitled "Utilization of Artificial Earth Satellite for Worldwide Television Broadcasting."

The basic condition ensuring the possibility of overcoming the force of the earth's gravity is the creation of an engine capable of imparting to the rocket a velocity by which it, overcoming the force of gravity, either becomes a satellite of the earth or goes off into interplanetary space.

It is known that the velocity of a body moving in a circular orbit near the surface of the earth is equal to 7.9 kilometers per second.

A rocket engine is the only one that can at present guarantee the achievement of such velocities.

German military rockets of the V-2 type weighing 12.9 tons have already developed a velocity of 1.6 kilometers per second and have attained a maximum altitude of 80 kilometers. The time of operation of the rocket motor was 60 seconds, and the entire flight lasted five minutes. During this time the rockets covered a distance of 270 to 320 kilometers.

Since 1946 in a number of countries intensive work has been developed concerned with the creation of improved types of rockets to be used for studying the upper layers of the atmosphere.

The tendency to increase the maximum altitude has led to the creation of composite rockets. Already the first tests in this direction have shown that by means of multistaged rockets with existing chemical fuel it is possible to achieve greater altitudes and velocities.

Beginning in 1954, reports began to appear about a two-stage rocket project worked out in the U. S. The proposed range of flight of the rocket was 8000 kilometers, the altitude of the highest point of the trajectory was 1280 kilometers, and the velocity at the end of the active section was 6.7 kilometers per second.

The information presented about existing or under-construction types of rockets indicates that the velocities necessary for the creation of an artificial satellite are completely feasible even today.

### AN AUTOMATIC ARTIFICIAL SATELLITE OF THE EARTH

The idea of creating an artificial satellite and utilizing it for the realization of interplanetary flights had already been expressed by the great Russian investigator Tsiolkovskii. According to his project the altitude of the artificial satellite's orbit (35,800 kilometers) is so calculated that the satellite's period of rotation around the earth would be equal to 24 hours. As a result of its fixed position such a satellite could serve as an original launching platform for interplanetary rockets. Projects of such satellites can be realized only at the later stages of interplanetary flight. In the early stages, obviously, automatic artificial satellites will have to be of small dimensions.

Professor S. Singer (U. S.) has proposed a project of a small orbital unmanned artificial satellite of the earth (MOUSE).

The purpose of creating the projected satellite is the investigation of solar and cosmic radiation, the accumulation of data for long-range weather forecasting, and the study of disturbances in long-distance radio communication.

The satellite, according to his (Singer's) project, is a rotating hollow aluminum sphere 600 millimeters in diameter and 45 kilograms in weight. The proposed orbit is 320 kilometers above the surface of the earth. Inside the satellite are the automatic apparatus necessary for the observations, a storage battery, and a radio transmitter.

It is proposed to put the artificial satellite into a circular orbit by means of a three-stage rocket.

### AN ARTIFICIAL SATELLITE OF THE STATIONARY TYPE

After building automatic artificial satellites of various sizes, it will be possible to turn to the creation of artificial satellites of the stationary type — intermediate stations from which in the future it will be possible to dispatch rockets to other planets. These same stations will serve as scientific research laboratories.

The artificial satellite project proposed by Von Braun has received the greatest attention for some time past.

Von Braun proposed erecting an artificial satellite at a distance of 1730 kilometers from the surface of the earth. For this, a gigantic three-stage rocket [1] with a total weight of some 7000 tons, of which 90% is fuel, will be launched from the earth. After the fuel has burned out in the first stage, the latter separates automatically. The rocket receives a new impulse as a result of the combustion of the fuel in the second stage. The period of operation of the rocket engines is 300 seconds. The entire journey lasts 1 hour. The maximum acceleration amounts to 9 $g$. Only the third stage with a total weight of 220 tons, part of which also is fuel, reaches the circular orbit. The payload of the rocket amounts to 36 tons. This load represents the prefabricated parts for the future artificial satellite. Having become free of the load, the third rocket returns to the earth.

It will be necessary to build several such rockets. They will have to deliver in turn their load to the circular orbit. After all the materials have been delivered to the orbit, men will be sent there on a similar three-stage rocket to assemble the artificial satellite.

The satellite is a large wheel-like, three-decked structure, 80 meters in diameter, divided into compartments.

The speed of the satellite is 7.07 kilometers per second, and its period of revolution around the earth is two hours.

### THE SIGNIFICANCE OF AN ARTIFICIAL SATELLITE

The creation of an artificial satellite will be of extremely great scientific importance. The investigations which will be carried out with its help will permit widening our knowledge in all fields of science. The satellite can be utilized as a vacuum, chemical, and biological laboratory for research in the fields of electronics, of chemical reactions in vacuo and in the absence of an effective gravity, and of the observation of the growth and division of cells experiencing the effect of irradiation in a medium without gravity; for astronomical and astrophysical observations outside the earth's atmosphere, particularly for a detailed study of the unknown portions of the spectrum of the radiation of the sun and the stars, and for observation beyond the cloud cover of the earth for the purpose of weather forecasting; and for setting up on it a relaying television station. It can also be used for military purposes.

The original uses of such a satellite for military purposes, according to Von Braun, are reconnaissance and photography with the aid of 254-centimeter reflector telescopes freely flying in space around the satellite, and also observation by means of radar devices. Besides the reconnaissance purposes, it is proposed to use the artificial satellite as a launching platform for winged rockets with an atomic charge which can be accurately aimed at a target.

True, many authors point to the great vulnerability of a satellite which, while moving with astronomical precision in its orbit, can serve as a target for attacking rockets. But only a cosmic missile can reach it.

### THE LAUNCHING OF A SATELLITE

For a cosmic ship flying into the cosmos and returning to the earth it is very important that, having freed itself from the earth's attraction, the ship preserves as great a store of fuel as possible for its interplanetary travels and return to the earth. For rockets which carry earth satellites to their orbit it isn't obligatory to strive to fly farther away from the earth. It is important that they develop the necessary velocity, not less than the so-called characteristic one (what this velocity is we shall explain below).

It is necessary to consider that the process of delivering the satellite to its orbit takes place in time and not merely in space; that is, a rocket starting from the earth vertically and carrying a satellite does not acquire velocity at once, instantaneously, but gradually (for example, for an artificial earth satellite orbit 300 kilometers above the earth, this time amounts to six to eight minutes). The force of the earth's gravity, however, during this time causes the so-called reverse gravitational drift to the center of the earth which, for example, in 100 seconds develops a velocity of 1 kilometer per second, and in 800 seconds creates a reverse velocity of 8 kilometers per second imparted to the rocket and directed toward the earth. Thus, if the rocket after its vertical start would move upward all the time along a radius of the earth, without changing the position of its longitudinal axis relative to the normal, then the force of the earth's gravity after a certain time would absorb the force of thrust of its jet reactive engines; and the rocket, having stopped at some point and having spent its store of fuel, would then begin to fall back to the earth (just as happens with contemporary high-altitude geophysical rockets).

Consequently, it is necessary to launch an artificial earth satellite by means of a rocket in the following manner. The rocket is launched vertically, but as soon as it pierces the armor of the troposphere, its longitudinal axis, by means of guiding devices, gradually turns along a rigorously calculated optimal curve which directs the rocket into the circular orbit; and when the rocket that carries the satellite reaches the flight trajectory parallel to the earth's surface, its next-to-last stage will separate, and, having attained the circular velocity, it will obtain a new acceleration. This circular velocity of the rocket will impart to it centrifugal forces that will counterbalance its centripetal forces.

It is natural that in order to obtain the necessary centrifugal force, it is necessary to select a suitable velocity for the rocket flight. This velocity is called the characteristic velocity.

This velocity varies with the distance of the satellite's orbit from the surface of the earth. Calculations show that the smallest value of the characteristic velocity is 7912 meters per second near the surface of the earth. Such a velocity is called the "first cosmic velocity." With further removal of the satellite's orbit from the earth this velocity increases to a value of 11,190 meters per second. Such velocity is attained by moving the artificial earth satellite's orbit to infinity and is called the "second cosmic velocity." The intermediate values of the characteristic velocity can be quite different, depending on the altitude of the orbit to which satellite is launched. Thus, for example, at an altitude of 1730 kilometers it amounts to 8716 meters per second, and at an altitude of 35,800 kilometers it reaches 10,709 meters per second. In order that the force of the earth's gravity will not absorb the force of thrust of reactive engines, it is necessary to add to the characteristic velocity a certain magnitude of velocity which takes into account the loss of reactive impulse in overcoming the force of the air resistance and the earth's force of gravity during the rocket's acceleration. In order to overcome the earth's attraction, it is necessary to perform an enormous amount of work. This work is equal to 6,378,000 kilogram-meters for each kilogram of the rocket-carrier's takeoff weight. In order to clearly visualize the meaning of these figures we say that in order to lift one kilogram of the weight of the satellite and its apparatus, it is necessary to perform work equivalent to two hours' work of the Dnieper Hydroelectric Power Station! The task of engineers who compute the takeoff program of the satellite carrier-rocket to the orbit, is in addition, to make sure that losses of velocity from air resistance and the earth's gravitational force are minimum — 10 to 15% of the value of the characteristic velocity. Thus, to the above values of the satellite rocket-carrier characteristic velocities equal to 8716 and 10,709 meters per second at altitudes of 1730 and 35,800 kilometers, to obtain the orbital velocity — that is, the velocity of the rocket of the satellite with a calculation of the mentioned losses — it is necessary to augment their magnitude by about 15%. In this case their orbital velocities for altitudes of 1730 kilometers and 35,800 kilometers will be 10,012 meters per second and 12,305 meters per second, respectively. The formula for computing this orbital velocity was first derived by K. E. Tsiolkovskii and, in the literature, therefore, this velocity is called the "Tsiolkovskii velocity." According to this formula the Tsiolkovskii velocity is equal to the product of the velocity of the exhaust gases of the rocket engine and the logarithm of the Tsiolkovskii number. The Tsiolkovskii number expresses the ratio of the initial mass of the rocket at the start to the mass of the rocket after expending all the fuel stored in the tanks of the rocket engine. A velocity of 10,012 meters per second will correspond to a Tsiolkovskii number equal to 46. Whence, the idea of multistage rockets. It is not possible to realize such a high weight ratio in a one-stage rocket. From these reasonings, it is obvious that in order to attain an orbital velocity for the smallest weight of the earth satellite's carrier-rocket, the greatest velocities of the exhaust gases of a rocket engine at the smallest volume of fuel are necessary. It is precisely for this that contemporary jet technology is striving.

It is advantageous to launch satellite carrier-rockets in the direction of the earth's rotation since this permits obtaining additional velocity equal, for example (when launching a rocket at the equator), to 405 meters per second, that is, velocity greater than the velocity of any contemporary jet fighter.

The utilization of an artificial earth satellite will permit solving a problem exciting in its technical conception and possibilities — this is the realization of worldwide television broadcasting by means of artificial earth satellites.

In order to visualize how this can be done we shall first talk about satellite orbits and about the demands imposed on them, which proceed from the practical realization of this grandiose task.

We have already talked about the altitudes of the orbits of artificial earth satellites. We shall mention only that the position of a satellite relative to the earth's coordinates can change in time, depending on the altitude of the satellite's rotation above the earth. Thus, for example, a satellite launched to an altitude of 320 kilometers makes a complete revolution around the earth in 90 minutes, that is, revolves around it 16 times per day. During each such revolution the earth will turn 22.5 degrees around its axis. Thus the satellite, having made one revolution, cannot appear over the same terrestrial geographical coordinates; with each new revolution it will fly over a new latitude and longitude. The only exception is an orbit whose plane coincides with the equatorial plane. In this case the satellite will always fly over the same countries of the world.

But if the satellite is launched to an altitude of 1730 kilometers, it will fly around the globe in 2 hours, or will complete 12 revolutions around it in 24 hours. The earth, then, in this case, during each revolution of the satellite will have time to turn 30 degrees around its axis.

When it is necessary to obtain the same angular velocity of rotation of the earth and of the satellite — for communication from it to earth or for the purpose of worldwide television retransmission, for instance — the satellite must be launched from the equator to an altitude of 35,800 kilometers.

Astronomical investigations show that when a satellite is launched from the equator, the plane of its orbit will be fixed with respect to the plane of the equator — that is, it will not rotate relative to world space. Instead, under the influence of uneven distribution of the earth's masses at the equator (because of the compression of the earth), the plane of the satellite's orbit in this case will slowly rotate in world space around the earth's axis in a direction opposite to the earth's rotation with an angular velocity of 20 seconds of arc per hour. When an artificial satellite is launched over the poles, however, the plane of its orbit will be fixed in world space; but if the satellite is launched so that the plane of its orbit passes in any intermediate position between the poles and the equator, then it will rotate in world space relative to the plane of the equator with a velocity up to 3 degrees per day.

Consequently, for worldwide retransmission of television programs by means of three artificial earth satellites, the following requirements must be made regarding their launching: to insure the immobility of the ASE with respect to the surface of the earth, the launching of a satellite must be made in the plane of the equator with a 24-hour period of revolution around the earth. As a result of the velocity of the earth, the motion of the ASE's orbit in this case will be maximum (20 seconds of arc per hour), and it will be the same for all three satellites. This will not change their mutual disposition. Each satellite will be located above the same point of the earth (with a drift of 20 seconds per hour); launching a satellite over the poles to accomplish the circular retransmission of television programs makes no sense.

One must bear in mind that in the course of time the mutual disposition of ASE's with respect to the earth may change; this will make suitable corrections necessary.

Also, in our discussions, the influence of the action of the moon and the sun on the motion of the ASE was not taken into consideration.

### BASIC PRINCIPLES OF REALIZING WORLDWIDE TELEVISION BROADCASTING BY MEANS OF THREE SATELLITES

Let us imagine three satellites launched from a point on the equator (Figure 1). To accomplish circular retransmission of television broadcasting, the satellites must be launched to an altitude of 35,800 kilograms at intervals of exactly 8 hours. In this way, all three satellites delivered into the orbit will be placed 120 degrees from each other in the orbit, and their distance from each other will be 72,660 kilometers. In this case all three satellites will be fixed relative to each other and to the earth, since their angular velocity is the same and is equal to the angular velocity of the earth.

All three satellites are launched so that the plane of their orbit coincides with the plane of the equator. In this case, the movement of the orbit, although a maximum (20 seconds of arc per hour), will be the same for all three satellites, and therefore will have no influence on the change of their mutual disposition. This movement is so insignificant that it will not affect the quality of the television broadcasting.

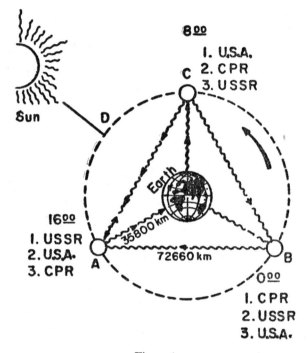

Figure 1.

Thus, each of the three satellites will be located over the same terrestrial television center (with a drift of 0.3 minutes of arc per hour). At the same time all three satellites will move relative to universal space with a circular velocity of 3,076 kilometers per hour.

It is precisely this fact that will determine the schedule of operation of the worldwide television broadcasting system.

Bearing in mind the annual rotation of the earth with its satellite relative to the sun and the equatorial disposition of the earth's satellites, each of them can carry out the reception of television programs from the earth through the western satellite and simultaneously transmit this program to its terrestrial central television stations. At the same time, one must bear in mind that the direction of the sun's radiation should never coincide with the direction of the line of communication, since this can create serious communication disturbances.

Let us assume that one of the satellites is located over the USSR, the second over the Chinese People's Republic, and the third over the United States of America.

Let us see how circular retransmission will be carried out in this case.

The transmitting television center operates from 0:00 hours until 8:00 (local time) and this ensures the reception from the western satellite from 16:00 to 24:00 hours. According to such a disposition of the stations, the USSR can operate on the U. S., the U. S. on the CPR and the CPR on the USSR.

In order to utilize the three other combinations of transmission by television at the same intervals of reception (from 16:00 to 24:00) each of the television centers must operate from 8:00 to 16:00 hours.

With such a selection of time and scheme of transmission, the direction of the solar radiation will never coincide with the directions of the lines of communication. An exception is the moments of transition from transmission to reception at the point A, when the direction of solar radiation coincides with the line of communication E-B, but in this instance the ASE, located at the point B, is screened by the earth.

The second case of coincidence of the directions of solar radiation and the line of communication takes place when the ASE reaches the point D; in this case, however, the radiation of the sun is directed to meet the transmitting waves directed from the earth. Thus, the sun will not irradiate the receiving antenna on the satellite.

Everything described above permits one to assume that in directed antenna systems the interference from solar radiation will not be of great significance for the quality of television transmissions.

Taking into account the small weights and sizes of equipment installed in the satellite, the described method of circular retransmission requires a compromise in the choice of wave lengths. From the point of view of the small dimensions and weight of the equipment, it is desirable to operate on the very short waves right up to millimeter wave lengths; in this way a considerable gain can be obtained at the expense of narrowing the antenna radiation patterns; realization of this gain, however, is possible only by an extremely precise stabilization of the mutual disposition of the coordinate axes of the satellites relative to each other. Stabilization relative to the earth does not require such precision of the fixed position in view of the fact that in this case wider antenna radiation patterns must be utilized. In the described scheme the direction from the sun to each of the satellites does not coincide with the direction from satellite to satellite, which also excludes the possibility of interferences during television transmission.

Moreover the efficiencies and the capacities of modern instruments of this range at present do not permit utilizing the indicated advantages to a sufficiently complete extent. One should remember also that beyond the limits of the atmosphere, interference from the sun and the stars during television transmission is much greater than it is on earth.

Among many other scientific observations, the first satellites launched within the next two to three years to an altitude of 300 to 2000 kilometers will have to study the dispersion of waves in the ultra-short-wave range under conditions of cosmic space. But even now one may say that reception of programs televised from the earth to a satellite will be realized most probably in the meter wave range, and from the satellite to the earth — from the standpoint of minimum weights and sizes of the equipment — on the waves of the decimeter, the centimeter, or even the millimeter range.

One should bear in mind that narrowing of the antenna radiation pattern even for very short waves, evidently has a limit. This limit depends on the dissipation of electromagnetic energy for various reasons as yet unknown.

It is obvious that at such enormous heights above the earth, forces of mutual attraction provoking electrostatic fields, changes of temperature gradient, etc., will be manifested. But communication between the satellites for the purpose of retransmission under the conditions of cosmic space, where there is practically no atmosphere and where almost "eternal day" reigns, will most probably be realized on the waves of the centimeter or millimeter range, depending on the weight and dimensions of the equipment and the direction of antenna.

Attenuation of radio waves determines everything. At present it is difficult to say what it is at an altitude of 35,000 kilometers. Consequently the choice of a working range of waves, considering the conditions of propagation, so far presents difficulties.

The basic weight of radio equipment will be related to the source of power. Therefore the transformation of atomic energy into electricity is the most important problem of the circular television.

The power in the antenna of such a television station probably will be within the limits of 10 kilowatts minimum, and the source of power will be 100 kilowatts. It is possible that television transmission in the future can be accomplished, not in a continuous regime of radiation, but in a pulsed regime, where the power required will be one hundred times less.   In any case, the rate at which peaceful uses of atomic energy are developing permits us to assume that lightened atomic sources of power will be realized much earlier than will the launching of a satellite to an altitude of 35,800 kilometers.   (*Radio*, June, 1956.)

---

[1] A figure shown but not reproduced here is a sketch of the three-stage rocket ship depicted on page 24 of the book *Across the Space Frontier,* Cornelius Ryan (ed.), Viking Press, New York, 1952, xiv + 147 pp.

## 32. Experimental Verification of the General Theory of Relativity and Artificial Earth Satellites

*V. L. Ginzburg*

As is known from press reports, artificial satellites of the earth will be created for the first time in 1957-1958 during the International Geophysical Year.

The first artificial satellites will move at comparatively low altitudes of 300 to 500 kilometers above the earth (Figure 1) and will have rather modest dimensions. But with the course of time it will undoubtedly become possible to dispatch to any altitude large satellites capable of carrying complicated equipment. As the design of the satellites and the technology of their launching improves, the possibilities of making various physical, geophysical, and astrophysical investigations by means of them will be widened all the more. Here one can point to the study of the earth's ionosphere, primary cosmic rays, ultraviolet and roentgen radiation of the sun, etc. Artificial satellites of the earth will be able to be used also for the further veri-

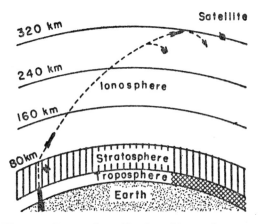

Figure 1. Proposed satellite launching trajectory.

fication of the general theory of relativity. Our main task is precisely to talk about this latter possibility. In this connection, however, in order to correctly understand the possible role of the artificial satellites, it is necessary at the beginning to touch upon the contemporary state of the question of the experimental verification of the general theory of relativity without the use of artificial satellites.[1]

## THE GENERAL THEORY OF RELATIVITY

The general theory of relativity, one of the greatest scientific achievements, was created about 40 years ago by the great physicist Albert Einstein (1879-1955). It is difficult to overestimate the influence shown by the general theory of relativity on the development of physics, geometry, and cosmology.

Within the limits of the present paper, however, it seems impossible to dwell both on an exposition of the general theory of relativity and on an expatiation of its scientific importance. We shall limit ourselves therefore only to certain remarks that are essential for the following.

The general theory of relativity is in the first place the theory of gravitation or, somewhat more precisely, the theory of the gravitational field,[2] which generalizes the well-known Newtonian theory of universal gravitation. According to Newton, all bodies are attracted to each other by the forces of universal gravitation which are inversely proportional to the square of the distance $r$ between the bodies. Specifically, the force between two bodies with masses $m$ and $M$ is equal to

$$F = kmM/r^2, \tag{1}$$

where $k = 6.67 \times 10^{-8}$ dyne cm$^2$/g$^2$ is the constant of universal gravitation or, as it is often called, the gravitational constant. Here the force $F$, acting on the mass $m$, is directed toward the mass $M$ along a line connecting both masses, and the force, acting on the mass $M$, is equal to $F$, but has an opposite direction. Thus, the forces of universal gravitation are central forces and satisfy the law of equality of action and counteraction. The magnitude of these forces at a given moment of time is completely determined by the position of the masses at the same moment of time. In other words, gravitational action according to Newton's theory is transmitted instantaneously: If the mass is displaced and its distance from mass $M$ changes, then the force between the bodies will also change instantaneously. For example, if our sun were to divide into two parts (there is no reason whatever to expect this and we say this only for illustration), then this would manifest itself instantaneously in the motion of the earth, according to the law of universal gravitation. Meanwhile light from the sun reaches the earth not instantaneously, but after eight minutes; the velocity of light in a vacuum — $c = 3 \times 10^{10}$ centimeters per second $= 300,000$ kilometers per second — is the greatest velocity known in nature of the propagation of signals which can produce any action.

It was natural therefore to think that the Newtonian theory of universal gravitation is inaccurate and only approximately corresponds to reality, that it is correct when one can neglect the time of propagation of gravitational effects. This approximation must be very good within the limits of our solar system, inasmuch as all the planets move very slowly in comparison with the velocity of light (thus, the rate of motion of the earth in its orbit is $v = 3 \times 10^6$ centimeters per second and, consequently, $v/c = 10^{-4}$).[3]

Similar assumptions about the approximate character of the Newtonian theory of gravitation changed into certainty after the formulation and brilliant success of the special (particular) theory of relativity, created by Einstein in 1905. The fact is that on the basis of the special theory of relativity precisely the principle of the finiteness of the velocity of propagation of any signals is assumed, and the light signal is considered to be ultimately fast. And so, after the formulation of the special theory of relativity, the necessity arose for generalizing the Newtonian theory of gravitation, for creating a theory of gravitation which is in accord with the special theory of relativity and, in particular, with the principle of the finiteness of the propagation of gravitational effects. This problem is also solved by the general theory of relativity. In this theory the concept of gravitational field is introduced, in a sense analogous to that of the electromagnetic field. At the same time the Newtonian theory of gravitation plays approximately the same role as electrostatics with its Coulomb law plays in the general theory of electromagnetic phenomena. Thus, in the case of two rather slowly moving charges $e_1$ and $e_2$, the Coulomb forces $F = e_1 e_2 / r^2$ are greatest (largest), just as the analogous forces of universal gravitation, Eq. (1), are fundamental in the case of the motion of a planet around the sun. But moving charges create, besides an electrical field, a magnetic field also, which results in a change in their interaction. Moreover, a change in the motion of one charge manifests itself in the motion of the other charge not instantaneously, but after the time required by the electromagnetic waves to pass through the space between these charges.[4] Precisely in the same way, according to the general theory of relativity, the forces between moving masses are not exactly the same as between masses at rest, and gravitational effects, as already mentioned, are propagated with ultimate velocity.

To what must the inaccuracy of the Newtonian theory of gravitation lead? Evidently, in the first place, it is necessary for this reason to expect the well-known changes in the motion of the celestial bodies, particularly in the motion of the planets around the sun. This assumption is confirmed, and at the same time there are other effects connected with the general theory of relativity which also admit of experimental verification.

EXPERIMENTAL VERIFICATION OF THE

GENERAL THEORY OF RELATIVITY

In the classical Newtonian theory of gravitation, a planet moves in an ellipse in one focus of which is the sun (Figure 2). According to the general theory of relativity, the motion will be different even in the absence of any perturbations from the other planets, which we now assume. Here the change in a planet's motion is best visualized thus: It moves in a classical ellipse which, however, itself rotates very slowly in its own plane in the direction of the planet's motion (Figure 3). As a result the vertex of the ellipse nearest the sun, which is called the perihelion, moves in space, and after one revolution of the planet the deflection angle of the perihelion is equal to

$$\delta\psi = \frac{24\pi^3 a^2}{c^2 T^2 (1-e^2)} = \frac{6\pi k M}{c^2 a (1-e^2)} \tag{2}$$

where $a$ is the major semiaxis of the ellipse, $e = (a^2 - b^2)^{\frac{1}{2}}/a$ is its eccentricity, $b$ is the minor semiaxis (see Figure 2), $T$ is the period of rotation of the planet around the sun, $M$ is the mass of the sun, and $k$ is the gravitational constant (1). In passing from the first expression in (2) to the second, one takes into account that in the classical theory $a^3 = (kM/4\pi^2) T^2$ (this is Kepler's third law).

The presence of the speed of light, $c = 3 \times 10^{10}$ centimeters per second, in expression (2) in the denominator is, of course, no mere chance, but, on the contrary, occurs for all effects connected with the theory of relativity. In fact, if one imagines that the velocity of light c could change, then as it tends toward infinity, the perturbations would be propagated instantaneously, and therefore the effects of relativity would vanish. In accordance with this in (2) as $c$ approaches $\infty$, the deflection $\delta\psi$ approaches 0.

It can be shown that for small eccentricity $e$, the relative angular

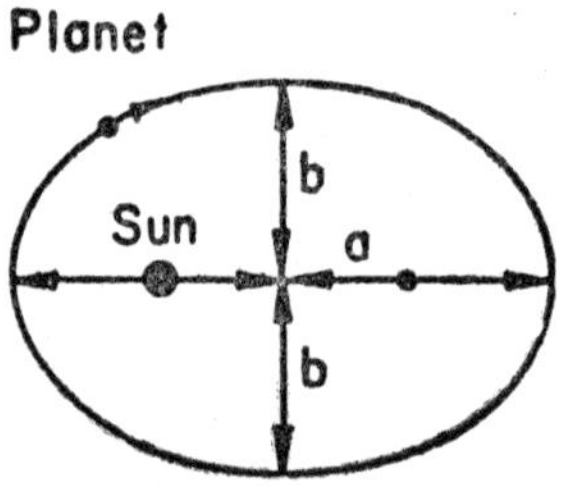

Planet

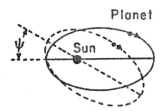

Figure 2. Schematic representation of trajectory of planet moving around the sun, proceeding from the classical (Newtonian) theory.

Figure 3. Schematic representation of trajectory of planet moving around the sun according to the general theory of relativity. ψ is the angle of rotation of the perihelion.

displacement[5] $\delta\psi/2\pi$ according to (2) is simply equal to $3v^2/c^2$, where $v$ is the rate of movement of the planet in the orbit. This result also is not accidental, inasmuch as the effects of the theory of relativity are characterized precisely by the parameter $v^2/c^2$. For our solar system this parameter is very small and, for example, for the earth it is equal to $10^{-8}$. This explains the insignificant smallness of the corrections (or perturbations, as they are called) connected with the theory of relativity associated with the motion of planets. Therefore it is convenient to refer the deflection angle of the perihelion, not to one revolution, but to a century. This angle, measured in seconds of arc per century, according to (2), is equal to
$$\psi = \frac{8.35 \times 10^{-19}a^2}{T^3(1-e^2)}, \qquad (3)$$
where the major semiaxis of the ellipse $a$ is measured in centimeters (for the earth, $a = 1.4964 \times 10^{13}$ centimeters) and the period of rotation $T$, in days. Let us note that the mass of the central body does not enter into expression (3) and therefore it is applicable not only to the planets of the solar system, but also in other similar cases. The value of ψ for a number of planets is presented in Table 1.

TABLE 1

| Planet | ψ according to formula (3) | eψ | ψ from observation |
|---|---|---|---|
| Mercury | 40".03 | 8".847 | 42".56 ± 0".94 |
| Venus | 8".63 | 0".059 | ------- |
| Earth | 3".8 | 0".064 | 4".6 ± 2".7 |
| Mars | 1".35 | 0".126 | ------- |
| Jupiter | 0".06 | 0".003 | ------- |

It should be noted that the accuracy of measurement of the discussed effect of the displacement of the perihelion is determined not only by the quantity $\psi$, but that it depends also on the eccentricity of the orbit, $e$. Indeed, it is evident that it is more difficult to observe the displacement of the perihelion for an orbit that is very nearly circular than for an orbit with a large eccentricity. In this connection Table 1 also presents values of the quantity $e\psi$ which characterizes the experimental possibilities better than $\psi$. From the table it is clear that both the quantity $\psi$ and $e\psi$ are especially large for Mercury, which is situated nearest the sun and has, therefore, the greatest velocity, and for which, by happy coincidence, the eccentricity of orbit also is the greatest. For all other plants the value of $e\psi$ is very small. Therefore, taking into account the attained accuracy of astronomical measurements, it appears that theory and experiment can be compared in practice only for Mercury. And this comparison shows that experimental data completely verify the conclusion drawn from the general theory of relativity (see first line of Table 1). Thereby, incidentally, an old problem has been solved, since in the middle of the last century Leverrier had already detected some rotation of the perihelion of Mercury not explainable by the perturbation of the other planets.[6] In the course of a number of decades scientists tried in various ways to explain this rotation, but only Einstein in 1915 gave a satisfactory and complete solution to this problem, by deriving formulas (2) and (3) and thereby at once explaining the nature of the effect observed by Leverrier. Further, more precise definition of the experimental value led to still more complete agreement of the theory with experiment (see first line of Table 1).

Let us pass over to the other effects of the general theory of relativity.

One of the most remarkable consequences of the special theory of relativity is the law of the equivalence of mass and energy, according to which any form of energy $E$ has a mass $m = E/c^2$. In particular, light also has a certain mass, and we refer now to inertial mass — the mass which appears in the well-known Newton's law of motion: $mu = F$, where $m$ is the inertial mass, $u$ is the acceleration, and $F$ is the force. In the law of universal gravitation (1) there also appears the mass of a body $m$ which in this case is called ponderable of gravitational mass. "Gravitational mass" is, as it were, the gravitational charge of the body, analogous to the electric charge in Coulomb's law. Inertial and gravitational masses are strictly equal to one another, which leads, in particular, to the fact that the velocity of fall to the earth of all bodies is independent of the mass of these bodies.[7] The equality of inertial and gravitational masses has been demonstrated with extreme accuracy by the experiments of the Hungarian physicist Eötvös, and is the foundation stone assumed by Einstein as a basis for the general theory of relativity. On the strength of the above, it is natural that from the point of view of the theory of relativity, light has not only an inertial mass $m = E/c^2$, but also the same gravitational mass; and therefore light rays must deflect when they pass near heavy bodies. A calculation, made by Einstein in 1915, led to the following expression for this deflection:

$$\alpha = \frac{4km}{c^2 r} \quad ,$$

(4)

where $\alpha$ is the angle of deflection of a ray which passes at a distance $r$ from a body with mass $M$ (see Figure 4). At the same time, in accord with the physical essence of the effect, the deflection of the rays corresponds to their attraction to the corresponding mass.

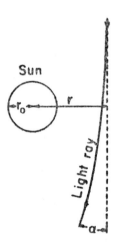

Figure 4. Schematic representation of deflection of ray of light as it passes near the sun. $\alpha$ is the ray's angle of deflection.

If $\alpha$ is measured in seconds of arc, then in the case of rays passing near the sun

$$\alpha = 1''.75 \, r_0/r,$$

(5)

where $r_0 = 6.963 \times 10^5$ km is the radius of the sun. Thus, even for a ray passing near the very edge of the sun's disk, when $r = r_0$, the angle $\alpha = 1''.75$. For comparison we may point out that the same angle is subtended by a matchbox at a distance of about five kilometers. Nevertheless, the precision of astronomical observations is so great that this effect can be detected. It will become apparent in the fact that in a photograph of a part of the sky, the stars which are situated

near the sun (that is, those stars from which the light rays, going towards the observer, pass near the edge of the sun) will be slightly displaced from their true positions, and just "moved aside" from the sun
in accordance with the law of Eqs. (4) and (5), that is, inversely proportional to the "distance" of their rays from the center of the sun.
How then does one recognize the true position of the stars? For this
it is necessary to photograph a given section of the sky for a certain
time when the sun has already "left" this region.

But, unfortunately another really essential difficulty stands in the
way of the investigation of the effect of the deflection of light rays
by the sun. It lies in the fact that it does not seem possible to photograph stars near the sun under ordinary conditions because the photographic film is illuminated by the far brighter radiation of the sun.
Therefore detection of the effect under discussion is possible only during total solar eclipses when the sun is covered by the moon and one
can photograph even stars situated very closely to it. Such observations were first made in 1919, and their success caused a genuine sensation which attracted universal attention to the general theory of
relativity. Observations during total solar eclipses are very rarely
successful (bad weather interferes; the band of the eclipse often passes
over the ocean, where it is not possible to conduct astronomical measurements, etc.). Therefore up to the present time Einstein's effect
has been observed only eight times. The mean value of these measurements, referred to the edge of the sun, is $\alpha = 1''.98$ with a precision
of the order of 10 to 15 per cent. Thus the effect of deflection has
been found with certainty, and the magnitude of the deflection is in
agreement with theory; but, for the reason indicated, the precision is
still comparatively low and, chiefly, resulting from Eqs. (4) and (5),
the dependence of $\alpha$ on $r$ still cannot be considered verified.

The third conclusion of the general theory of relativity which ad-
mits of experimental verification is the gravitational displacement of
spectral lines. This effect lies in the fact that the frequency of the
light emitted by the atoms in the sun or in the stars, when the radiation is received on the earth, differs from the frequency radiated by the
same atoms on the earth (this is why it is said that the spectral lines
shift; that is, the wave length $\lambda$ or the radiation frequency $v = c/\lambda$
changes). In a quantitative relation the matter is as follows: The
change in frequency $\Delta v$ or the change in wave length $\Delta \lambda$ is equal to:

$$\frac{\Delta v}{v} = -\frac{\Delta \lambda}{\lambda} = \frac{\phi_1 - \phi_2}{c^2}, \qquad (6)$$

where $\phi_1$ and $\phi_2$ are the so-called potential forces of gravitation at the points of emission and reception of the radiation, respectively. The potential difference $\phi_1 - \phi_2$ is, by definition, the work performed by the force of gravity on a body of unit mass when it is displaced from point 1 to point 2. Taking this circumstance into account, it is easy to understand the meaning of expression (6).

In fact, light, which possesses gravitational mass, must perform work during its propagation in a field of gravity (this work can have a negative sign — in which case the field performs work "on" the light).

In order to compute this work, let us recall that from the quantum point of view, light consists of corpuscles (photons or quanta) with energy $E = h\upsilon$, where $h$ is Planck's constant and $\upsilon$ is the frequency. The mass of a photon is therefore equal to $m = E/c^2 = h\upsilon/c^2$, and the work of the force of gravity on the photon is equal to $\frac{h\upsilon}{c^2}(\phi_1 - \phi_2)$. But the only thing that can change in a photon is its frequency $\upsilon$, and a change in frequency of $\Delta\upsilon$ corresponds to a change in energy of the photon of $h\Delta\upsilon$. On equating the two expressions $\frac{h\upsilon}{c^2}(\phi_1 - \phi_2)$ $= h\Delta\upsilon$, we obtain formula (6) after cancelling $h$. This formula, of course, can be derived also without any consideration of quantum ideas,[8] directly from the general theory of relativity.

If the spectrum emitted by the atoms in the sun or in the stars is observed on the earth, then the earth's potential $\phi_2$ may be neglected and formula (6) assumes the form

$$\frac{\Delta\upsilon}{\upsilon} = -\frac{\Delta\lambda}{\lambda} = \frac{\phi_1}{c^2} = -\frac{kM}{c^2r}, \qquad (7)$$

where $r$ is the radius of the star, and $M$ is its mass. In the case of the sun, $\Delta\upsilon/\upsilon = -2.12 \times 10^{-6}$; that is, the displacement of the lines of the solar spectrum when they are being observed from the earth is very small (when $\lambda = 5000$ A, $\Delta\lambda \simeq 0.01$ A $= 10^{-10}$ centimeters). The negative sign of the displacement of frequency means that the spectral lines are displaced to the red side of the spectrum ($\Delta\upsilon<0$; $\Delta\lambda>0$), by virtue of which the effect under consideration is often called the "effect of the red displacement of spectral lines." This designation, however, is not especially apt because, for example, during the observation of terrestrial lines from the sun, the effect would be violet.

In spite of the smallness of the displacement of the lines in the solar spectrum, this displacement can be observed and in fact is observed. Besides the gravitational displacement of frequency, however, there are also other reasons leading to its change. Therefore the use of solar data for the quantitative verification of the theory has not yet been found to be sufficiently conclusive. Another possibility consists in studying the spectra of a special class of stars — the so-called white dwarfs. The radius of these stars is tens of times smaller than the radius of the sun, but their mass is comparable with that of the sun. Therefore, as is clear from (7), the gravitational displacement of the lines in the spectra of the white dwarfs will be considerably greater than for the sun. Such a displacement to the "red" side, coinciding in order of magnitude with the theoretical, is actually observed. But even in this case the situation is not especially favorable for quantitative verification of the theory, since the radii of the white dwarfs are known only very approximately.

As a result, it can be said that the existence of the gravitational displacement of spectral lines has been demonstrated by experiment, but formulas (6) and (7) still cannot be considered strictly verified.

### WHY FURTHER VERIFICATION OF THE GENERAL THEORY OF RELATIVITY IS IMPORTANT

As we have seen, all three effects predicted by the general theory of relativity are very small. For this reason, experimental verification of the theory with the attainment of high precision is naturally difficult. In spite of this, in the case of the precession of the perihelion of Mercury the coincidence of theory with experiment is very good, the measured deflection of light rays in the field of the sun agrees with the theoretical value within the limits of an attained accuracy of the order of 10 to 15% and, finally, the effect of the gravitational displacement of frequency has been revealed and its magnitude does not contradict the theoretical value. Therefore the question arises about how important is further verification of the general theory of relativity. The nonspecialist may also doubt the importance of the general theory of relativity itself, inasmuch as the effects connected with it which were discussed are so insignificant.

In this connection it is necessary here first of all to point out that the significance of the general theory of relativity to no extent whatever can be "measured" by the magnitude of the deflection of rays in the sun's field or by the other effects to which reference was made. The general theory of relativity is, first, the only consistent theory of gravitation; it reveals the deep connection between space, time, and matter, and it belongs to the number of fundamental physical theories. Secondly, the effects of the general theory of relativity are small only within the limits of our solar system, and our galaxy. But in passing to larger space distances the situation changes, and in cosmology, which studies the properties of the universe on a large scale, the general theory of relativity comes completely into its own.[9]   Therefore in cosmology the general theory of relativity serves as the leading method of research and has already made substantial advances, although in this field there is still much that is not clear.

After what has been said, as one might expect, no doubts will arise as to how important is the most accurate possible experimental verification of the general theory of relativity, as well as that of any other fundamentally significant theory.   And the fact that the effects accessible for the quantitative verification of the theory are very small changes nothing here.   Having verified the theory in these examples with the greatest possible precision, it will be possible to apply the general theory of relativity to other phenomena and processes with still greater confidence.

And what is the possibility of further verification of the general theory of relativity?

In the case of the displacement of the perihelion of Mercury the agreement of theory with experiment is already very good today, but it would be desirable to make a comparison with other objects also, since, in principle, one coincidence could be accidental.   In this regard the astronomical possibilities are very limited.   As is clear from Table 1, for the earth it is necessary to raise the precision of the measurements at least one order of magnitude; the possibilities of observing the effect in the case of Venus and Mars are also small.   The case is somewhat better with the small planet Icarus, for which, apparently, a precision can be attained even several times greater than for Mercury.   To obtain the required material, however, tens of years of astronomical observations are needed in this case.   In regard to measurements of the deflection of light rays near the sun and the gravitational displacement of the spectral lines as a result of the use of astronomical data (observations during eclipses, observations of the spectra of the sun and of the stars), only very slow progress can also be expected, and agreement of theory with experiment with a precision of more than a few per cent appears scarcely possible in the foreseeable future.   Therefore, the question naturally arises whether there are no new ways for verifying the general theory of relativity, since the history of science testifies to the fact that precisely the application of new methods and new methodics generally results in a rapid movement forward.

Such new ways of verifying the general theory of relativity are now indeed being outlined and are connected primarily with the use of artificial satellites of the earth.

If various perturbations are not taken into consideration (the influence of the moon, the nonsphericity of the earth's surface, the resistance of the remnants of air, the effect of the general theory of relativity), artificial satellites, as well as all other bodies, will move around the earth in elliptical orbits. Here the period of rotation $T$ of the satellite is

$$T = 2\pi a \sqrt{a/kM_{\delta}} = 3.14 \text{ x } 10^{-10} \text{ x } a^{3/2}, \qquad (8)$$

where $M_{\delta} = 5.98$ x $10^{27}$ grams is the mass of the earth, the major semiaxis $a$ is measured in centimeters, and $T$, in seconds. A satellite moving very close to the earth — which, of course, is unreal because of the air resistance — would make one revolution in 1.41 hours $= 84$ minutes. At a height of 400 kilometers above the earth, the satellite will make one revolution in 1.54 hours. The speed of such a satellite is $v = 7.7$ kilometers per second, or approximately 28,000 kilometers per second. For comparison we note that the speed of sound in air is 0.33 kilometers per second, or 1200 kilometers per hour.

We shall point out, finally, that a satellite moving in a circle with a radius of 6.6 earth radii (the mean radius of the earth is 6367 kilometers, and the distance from the earth to the moon is equal to 384,400 meters) will make one revolution in 24 hours. Such a satellite, if its orbit coincides with the plane of the earth's equator, will be stationary relative to the earth's surface, which rotates with the same angular velocity.

How then will the displacement of the perigee of a satellite (in the case of satellites the perihelion is called the perigee) be connected with the general theory of relativity (Figure 5)?

At first glance it seems that this effect must be even less than for the earth itself during its motion around the sun. Indeed in this last case $v^2/c^2 = 10^{-8}$, while for a satellite at a height of 400 kilometers $v^2/c^2 \simeq 6.5$ x $10^{-10}$. Therefore, as is clear from what was said above, the displacement of the perigee of a satellite for one revolution is actually less than for the earth. But if we refer to the displacement for a certain period of time, then the situation changes, inasmuch as the earth makes a revolution around the sun in a year, and the satellite under consideration turns around the earth in 1.54 hours. But one can make certain of what was said at once by means of formula (3) which is applicable to satellites with the same success as to planets.

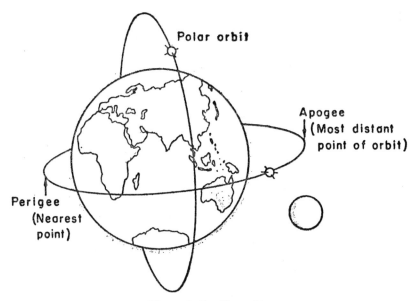

Figure 5. Satellite orbits.

The corresponding values of $\psi$ (in seconds of arc per century) are presented for a number of satellites [10] in Table 2. From Table 2, it is seen that the precession of the perigees of satellites can be 30 times

TABLE 2

| Satellite | Mean distance to center of earth in km | Eccentricity e | $\psi$ | $e\psi$ |
|---|---|---|---|---|
| SI | 6,770 | 0.01 | 1450" | 15" |
| SII | 17,000 | 0.06 | 146" | 9" |
| SIII | 17,000 | 0.40 | 196" | 78" |
| SIV | 7,200 | 0.02 | 1250" | 25" |
| SV | 10,000 | 0.25 | 587" | 147" |

greater than the similar effect of the general theory of relativity for Mercury; the values of $e\psi$ for satellites also can be about 20 times larger than for Mercury. A more detailed consideration shows that the possible precision of determining the displacement of the perigee by astronomical methods will still be considerably greater for satellites than for Mercury. As a result, a year of satellite observations can be the equivalent (in the sense of precision attained) to a century of observations of Mercury. The utilization of radio methods will perhaps make it possible, as in a number of analogous cases, to increase even more the precision of the measurements.

Thereby the tempting possibility opens up also of observing still another (the fourth) effect of the general theory of relativity, the observance of which, in the case of the solar system (for Mercury, for example), seems perfectly hopeless. This effect is the additional displacement of the perigee of a satellite (or of the perihelion of a planet) caused by the rotation of the central body — the earth (or the sun in the case of the planets).

In the classical, Newtonian theory of gravitation the motion of a body around a stationary or a rotating sphere is entirely identical. Not so is the case in the general theory of relativity — here the forces which act, even though very weakly, on a planet or a satellite, depend on the speed of rotation of the sun or the earth, respectively, around their axes. In order to understand this, use can be made of the already-mentioned analogy with electrodynamics.

If we have a stationary charged sphere, then it will create only an electrical field which will act on a charge located nearby. But if this sphere is rotating, then this means that there exists a certain current which, as is well known, will create a magnetic field. At the same time there will act on the moving charge, besides the electrostatic force, still another force which is proportional to the ratio of the rate of motion of the charge to the speed of light (this force, moreover, is proportional to the magnitude of the charge on which it acts and also to the intensity of the magnetic field). Precisely the same type of additional force (analogous to the magnetic force) acts on a satellite as a result of the rotation of a heavy sphere — the earth. Calculation shows that this additional displacement of the perigee of the satellite, caused by the rotation of the earth, can amount to 50 seconds of arc per century — that is, it is approximately the same as the entire effect of the general theory of relativity for Mercury. In the case of the planets there exists a similar effect connected with the rotation of the sun, which makes one revolution in approximately 25 days, but it is very small and even for Mercury amounts to only 0.01 seconds of arc per century! Therefore, as we have already said, it is obviously impossible to observe the "effect of rotation" on the planets. But in the case of satellites, when the effect is approximately 5000 times greater,[11] its observation represents a task that one can hope to solve. Nevertheless, one should not underestimate the difficulties that stand in the way of observing the influence of the effects of the general theory of relativity on the motion of satellites, since for this purpose it is necessary to take into detailed account all the other possibilities (see above) and to determine the trajectory of the satellite with very great precision. Very close satellites (400 to 600 kilometers high) in this connection will, generally speaking, probably be found useless because of their powerful braking by the remnants of atmospheric gases. Nevertheless, a number of estimates (see, in particular, the above) and the rapid development of technology, which have made it possible to proceed to the solution of the very task of building satellites, give every basis to look optimistically at the possibilities of creating distant satellites and using them for the purposes of interest to us here.

Observation of the displacement of the perigee of satellites is not the only way of using them for the purposes of verifying the general theory of relativity. With the aid of satellites, one can also investigate the effect of the gravitational displacement of frequency.

If radiation of frequency $v$ is sent from a satellite located very far from the earth (in practice, at a distance of more than several earth radii), then on earth the frequency will no longer be the same — by virtue of the effect of gravitational displacement it will increase by $\Delta v$, where

$$\frac{\Delta v}{v} = \frac{kM_{\delta}}{c^2 r_{\delta}} = 7 \times 10^{-10}, \tag{9}$$

where $M_{\delta}$ is the mass of the earth and $r_{\delta}$ is its radius. The frequency in this case increases (the wave length decreases); that is, the displacement of spectral lines appears violet.[12] This is clear, inasmuch as the photon is attracted to the earth and, consequently, its energy $hv$ and frequency $v$ increase.

For satellites closer to the earth the displacement of frequency is less than it should be from (9), since the potential difference $\phi_1 - \phi_2$ decreases (see (6) ). In this connection, for example, for a satellite which is at a height of 800 kilometers above the earth,

$$\frac{\Delta v}{v} = 7.6 \times 10^{-11}.$$

Even the maximum relative displacement of frequency (9) is 3000 times less than the gravitational displacement of frequency in the spectra of the sun, by virtue of which its observation by optical methods is not to be dreamed of. But in the case of radio waves the situation changes, and one will indeed be able to place a radio transmitter on a satellite (in contradistinction to the sun!). In radio waves, in view of the peculiarities of the radio apparatus on which we cannot dwell here, even the measurement of a relative displacement of frequency $\Delta v/v = 10^{-13}$ cannot be considered as the ultimate, and there already exists an instrument, the molecular generator, which guarantees a frequency stability $\Delta v/v = 10^{-10}$ to $10^{-11}$. Therefore measurement of the gravitational displacement of frequency by making use of satellites seems promising and alluring.

It must be said, however, that if accuracies of $\Delta v/v = 10^{-13}$ to $10^{-14}$ will be attainable in practice, then the effect of the general theory of relativity can be observed even without satellites, and simply on the earth! In fact, at a small height above the earth, the potential difference $\phi_1 - \phi_2$ in (6) is simply equal to $gH$, where $g = 981$ centimeters per second per second is the acceleration of the force of gravity on the earth and $H$ is the height of the transmitter above the receiver. Therefore $\Delta v/v = gh/c^2 = 1.09 \times 10^{-13}\,H$, where $H$ is measured in kilometers. When $H = 5$ kilometers (the transmitter is on a mountain), $\Delta v/v \simeq 5 \times 10^{-13}$; and when $H = 20$ kilometers (the transmitter is in an airplane or a pilot balloon), $\Delta v/v \simeq 2 \times 10^{-12}$. Thus the possibility of verifying the general theory of relativity directly on the earth is not excluded, but, of course, the utilization of satellites, where the displacement of frequency is hundreds and thousands of times greater, is considerably more real, at least today, when the value $\Delta v/v = 10^{-13}$ is still far from being attained. In this connection the more distant satellites have definite advantages, for which the effect under discussion is greater and the "disturbing" displacement of frequency caused by the presence in the satellite of a forward speed is less (we refer to the well-known Doppler effect).

We shall note, finally, that the utilization of artificial satellites will help solve one more very important problem connected with the general theory of relativity. We refer to the measurement of the brightness of the metagalaxy, that is, of the totality of star systems (galaxies) which lie beyond the limits of our galaxy. It is very difficult to measure this brightness from the surface of the earth, since the luminescence of the upper layers of the terrestrial atmosphere prevents this. The question of the brightness of the metagalaxy has great cosmological significance. But inasmuch as cosmology, which is concerned with the study of the structure of the Universe "as a whole," is closely connected with and in a theoretical way is based on the general theory of relativity, the determination of the brightness of the metagalaxy turns out to have a close bearing on the problems of this theory.

And so the utilization of artificial satellites of the earth opens up rather broad possibilities for the further experimental verification of the general theory of relativity. These experiments are difficult, and the satellites themselves have not yet been launched, but the progress

of science and technology gives every reason to hope that within the
next few years our ancient planet, together with its old satellite —
the moon — will also acquire a whole swarm of small satellite-labora-
tories.  And in these laboratories many important problems will be
solved, and new data will be obtained which are important for one of
the greatest scientific theories of all time — Einstein's general theory
of relativity.  (*Priroda*, September, 1956.  The author is identified
as "Corresponding Member of the USSR Academy of Sciences.")

---

[1] The questions touched on here are explained in more detail in the author's
paper "Experimental verification of the general theory of relativity," *Uspekhi
Fizicheskikh Nauk*, Vol. 59, No. 1, 1956, pp. 11–49.

[2] The words "tyagotenie" and "gravitatsiya" are synonyms.

[3] Here it is assumed that the velocity of propagation of gravitational effects
coincides with the velocity of light. Such an assumption seemed very probable
from the very beginning, and its correctness follows directly from the general
theory of relativity.

[4] Let us recall that all electromagnetic disturbances (waves) are propagated in
a vacuum with the identical velocity $c$, independent of the length of these waves,
which for X-rays amounts to hundred-millionths of a centimeter, and in case of
radiowaves amounts to many kilometers.

[5] The relative angular displacement is the ratio of the displacement after one
revolution $\delta\psi$ to the angle $2\pi$ which corresponds to one revolution of the planet.

[6] The perihelion of a planet also rotates under the influence of the perturbation
of other planets, in connection with which, the values indicated in the last column
of Table 1 determine not the entire deflection of the perihelion, but only the deflection not connected with the influence of the other planets.

[7] The law of motion is a gravity field $mu = F = kmM/r^2$, by virtue of the
equality of the heavy and inert masses of a body, appearing in both parts of the
equality and designated by one and the same letter $m$, acquires the form $u =
kM/r^2$, that is, does not depend on the mass $m$ of the body under consideration.
Hence it follows that all bodies under identical initial conditions move in a field
of gravity in the same way and, in particular, fall from a given height to the
earth in the same time (the latter occurs, of course, only in a vacuum where air
resistance can be disregarded).

[8] Formula (6) does not contain Planck's constant $h$ and therefore is, as a
matter of fact, classical (nonquantum). At the same time the use of the quantum
theory to obtain classical results is an entirely legitimate methodical device.

[9] By means of the very largest existing telescope (with a 5-meter mirror diameter) nebulae are successfully studied which are up to $2 \times 10^9$ light years $= 2 \times
10^{27}$ centimeters away from us. For comparison we point out that the distance
from the earth to the sun is equal to $1.5 \times 10^{13}$ centimeters, and the dimensions of
our galaxy do not exceed 100,000 light years $= 10^{23}$ centimeters.

[10] We note that for the moon the effect of the general theory of relativity can
be practically disregarded.

[11] For satellites the "effect of rotation" is larger than for Mercury for two
reasons: because the earth rotates 25 times faster than the sun and because the
satellite is much closer to the earth than Mercury is to the sun (Mercury is $5 \times
10^7$ kilometers away from the sun).

[13] This is precisely why expression (9) differs in sign from formula (7). From the general expression (6) we proceed at once to (9) by assuming $\phi_1 = 0$, and $\phi_2 = kM \, \delta / r \quad \delta$.

# 33. The Problem of Creating an Artificial Earth Satellite

*A. N. Nesmeyanov*

The past decade has been marked by unprecedented progress in science and technology.

The discovery of atomic energy and the possibility of its use, the advances of rocket technology, jet aviation, radar, and electronics — all this makes it possible to begin realizing a number of scientific and technical problems connected with interplanetary communications.

Theoretically the problem of sending a cosmic ship beyond the limits of the earth's atmosphere was solved as early as the beginning of the twentieth century by our outstanding compatriot K. E. Tsiolkovskii, who proved that the only means for such travel could be a rocket — a flying apparatus propelled by a jet engine, which creates thrust by emitting a stream of hot gases. K. E. Tsiolkovskii also pointed out that the creation of an artificial earth satellite would be the first necessary stage on the path to the realization of interplanetary flight.

From the very beginning, however, on the path to the realization of the first cosmic flight, great technical difficulties were encountered, to overcome which, large collectives of scientists and engineers have been working persistently for many years.

It was necessary to create a powerful engine capable of operating reliably for a sufficiently long time under extremely strained thermal conditions, but also having leightweight and strong rocket design capable of withstanding great loads during flight. At the same time, the design parameters of the rocket, the engine, and its fuel had to be in the aggregate such that the rocket would achieve a minimum velocity of 8 kilometers per second. Only by attaining such a velocity is there a possibility of creating an artificial earth satellite and thereby realizing the first step in the conquest of world space.

It was necessary to work out the optimum conditions of the rocket's

276

motion, ensuring the transfer of the satellite into an orbit with a height of several hundred kilometers.

To ensure the assigned regime of the rocket's motion and the transfer of the satellite to the assigned orbit, it was necessary to work out and create a very precise system of automatic rocket guidance which would operate reliably under the complicated conditions of flight.

Only by conducting extensive scientific work was it possible to overcome the technical difficulties which arose, sometimes very unexpectedly, in the process of solving this problem. Research in the field of the aerodynamics of supersonic velocities and in the field of radio-telecontrol, theoretical works on the dynamics of rocket motion and on the theory of automatic regulation, the search for new lightweight, strong, and heat-resisting materials, and for new high-caloric fuels, et cetera — all this was the foundation without which it would have been impossible to create a rocket suitable for solving the problem of an artificial earth satellite and the realization of interplanetary flight in the future.

The very creation of the artificial satellite as a carrier of scientific apparatus was a task the solution of which was possible only by the use of the latest achievements of science and technology in the most diverse fields. It was necessary to find miniature and lightweight sources of energy, miniature and lightweight apparatus for communication and telemetry, as well as automatic and telecontrol scientific apparatus capable of operating reliably for a long time under the conditions of interplanetary space.

As the result of many years of work by Soviet scientists and engineers to the present time, rockets and all the necessary equipment and apparatus have been created by means of which the problem of an artificial earth satellite for scientific research purposes can be solved.

The first Soviet artificial satellite will move at a comparatively short distance from the earth's surface (of the order of a few hundred kilometers). Thanks to this, scientific investigations of the phenomena taking place in the upper layers of the atmosphere will become possible.

It is well known what an important role the ionosphere, that mysterious laboratory within which are engendered many of the phenomena that take place in the upper atmosphere, plays in all the problems of the physics of the upper layers of the atmosphere. Scientists need a large amount of experimental data to understand the nature of the corpuscular radiation of the sun and of other phenomena. In this connection, up to the present time there remain under discussion many problems connected with the elucidation of the role which the ultraviolet and roentgen-like rays of the sun and cosmic radiation play in the formation of the ionosphere. We do not know the structure of the atmosphere at great heights, its temperature, pressure and density — parameters a knowledge of which is important not only to scientists, but also to engineers for calculating the motion of high-altitude aircraft, for example.

In the light of the latest, primarily rocket, investigations, it has become palpably clear how insufficient is our knowledge of the physics of the ionosphere. These investigations have shown that radically new methods are necessary in the study of the upper layers of the atmosphere, from the point of view of both theory and experiment.

With the aid of a new division of theoretical physics — magnetohydrodynamics — interesting conjectures and hypotheses have been suggested concerning the origin of cosmic rays, the aurorae polaris, and other phenomena in the upper layers of the atmosphere. Still absent, however, is a theory of the formation of the ionosphere, which corresponds to experimental data.

High-altitude launching of rockets opens up great possibilities here, making it possible to measure directly some of the parameters of the atmosphere.

In the USSR measurements of the electron concentration in the ionosphere, of the pressure and density of the atmosphere, etc., have been carried out by means of such launchings.

These measurements have yielded interesting factual material. The essential shortcoming of such measurements is their short duration. The necessity arises for working out methods of scientific investigation which make it possible to conduct an experiment for a long time in the upper layers of the atmosphere. This possibility is opened up by the creation of an artificial earth satellite.

In the forthcoming International Geophysical Year it is intended to launch several such satellites both in the USSR and in the U. S. by means of which a broad program of scientific research will be realized.

This research includes first of all the study of primary cosmic radiation. It is known that primary cosmic radiation consists in the main of hydrogen nuclei (protons) and of helium nuclei (alpha-particles) and to a considerably smaller extent of heavier nuclei (carbon, nitrogen, oxygen, and others). One of the disputed properties of primary cosmic radiation is the similarity between the curve of the average abundance of the elements in the universe and the curve of the charge distribution of the primary component of cosmic radiation. Such elements as lithium, beryllium, and boron are rare in nature, and the problem of the quantity of these nuclei in the composition of primary cosmic radiation has not yet been solved experimentally. In this connection the study of the properties of primary cosmic radiation can throw light on the problem of the wandering time of cosmic particles in world space and of the passage of cosmic rays.

This circle of problems should include a study of the variations of the intensity of cosmic rays at various heights and in various regions through which the artificial earth satellite will fly. The study of these phenomena is of essential significance for the problem of the origin of cosmic rays and for astrophysical problems, particularly for ascertaining the connection of variations in the outbursts on the sun with disturbances of the earth's magnetic field.

One of the tasks concerned with investigation of the ionosphere's laminar structure is the determination of the ion concentration. It has been established experimentally that this concentration changes with height. In this connection the receipt of information on the ionization of the atmosphere along the satellite's orbit is of exceptional interest.

Of the other ionospheric measurements one should note the mass-spectrometric measurements of the ionic composition of the ionosphere for the purpose of determining and defining more exactly its chemical structure.

Among the remarkable geophysical phenomena are the fluctuations (oscillations) of the earth's magnetic field. Measurements which have been carried out on the surface of the earth as well as by means of rockets have shown that the earth's magnetic field does not remain constant with time, that there exist so-called secular and short-periodic variations of the magnetic field. The nature of the secular variations in many respects still remains a mystery. As far as the short-periodic variations are concerned, the reasons for their formation are connected today with the existence in the upper layers of the atmosphere of systems of electric currents which are measured in hundreds of thousands of amperes. For example, it is supposed that the system of currents causing the solar secular variations of the magnetic field is located at a height of 100 to 120 kilometers.

In this connection the study of the change in the intensity of the magnetic field at great heights is of exceptional interest, since such a study will provide scientists with new data about the existence of a different type of short-periodic variations and the atmospheric currents associated therewith.

This interest is accentuated further by the fact that the magnetic variations are connected by well-known regularities with other physical phenomena—the aurorae polaris, the propagation of radio waves, the variations of cosmic rays, etc. Magnetic disturbances are especially closely connected with the aurorae polaris. It is supposed that both phenomena are caused by the corpuscular radiation of the sun. The nature and intensity of the corpuscular radiation, however, have not been sufficiently studied. At the same time, the theories of the aurorae polaris essentially rely on one assumption or another concerning the nature of the particles which are emitted by the sun. Therefore the question of the nature and intensity of the corpuscular radiation remains very important, and our ideas about the origin of the aurorae polaris and other phenomena in the upper layers of the atmosphere depend to a considerable degree on its solution.

An important task in the investigations by means of the artificial earth satellite is the study of micrometeors and meteors. These solid particles, which, for example, move with a velocity of 50 to 70 kilometers per second relative to the earth, are of interest not only to geophysicists and astronomers, but also to designers of rockets and satellites, since their action must be taken into consideration in the development and the design of the satellite. Calculations show that even small particles are capable of penetrating the external shell of the satellite. In this connection, it is necessary to know the intensity of the micrometeors as well as their energy. Obtaining the mass spectrum of micrometeors and meteors would make it possible to draw definite conclusions about the "meteor danger," an extremely important problem for future interplanetary communications.

We have touched on only a few of the experiments which will be carried out by Soviet scientists with the aid of artificial earth satellites. The results obtained by means of the satellites will considerably supplement the scientific data which will be accumulated during the International Geophysical Year.

Ensuring the necessary conditions for the normal operation of the scientific apparatus is the center of attention of our scientists and engineers, as well as a whole series of other problems on the successful solution of which depends the quality of the planned experiments. The creation and launching of artificial earth satellites is the first and most important stage in the matter of realizing interplanetary flights.

The creation and launching of a Soviet artificial earth satellite for scientific purposes during the International Geophysical Year will play an exceptional role in unifying the efforts of scientists of various countries in the struggle to conquer the forces of nature.  (*Pravda,* June 1, 1957. The author is identified as "Academician" and "President of the USSR Academy of Sciences.")

# 34. USSR Rocket and Earth Satellite Program for the IGY

*I. P. Bardin*

One of the most important studies during the International Geophysical Year (IGY) is the investigation of various geophysical phenomena in the upper layers of the atmosphere.

The program of the USSR for the IGY includes studies of the earth's atmosphere by launching rockets and man-made satellites.

These studies will give us reliable data on the structure of the atmosphere and its physics and also offer the data necessary for the solution of a number of practical problems: the improvement of the weather forecast service, radiowave propagation forecast, detailed determinations of the conditions for aircraft flights, etc.

As is known, vertical sounding of the atmosphere by means of rockets has been in progress in our country for a number of years.

During the IGY we intend to continue and develop this work.

Great opportunities for upper-atmosphere study open up in connection with the launching of the man-made satellite which will help scientists to conduct observations for a long time on the processes in the upper atmosphere.

In the Soviet Union, during the IGY the first launching of a man-made satellite for scientific purposes will be made.

At present there is a considerable number of proposals by Soviet scientists concerning the employment of rockets and man-made satellites for one measurement or another. The proposals cover practically all the main questions of the physics of the upper layers of the atmosphere and other problems.

The following is the preliminary program for this work.

### THE PHENOMENA IN THE UPPER ATMOSPHERE TO BE STUDIED WITH ROCKETS AND SATELLITES

1. Structural parameters of the atmosphere.
2. Optical properties.

3. Ultra-violet and X-ray solar radiation.
4. Corpuscular solar radiation and aurorae.
5. Cosmic rays.
6. Ionospheric phenomena.
7. Magnetic field of the earth.
8. Micrometeors and meteorites.
9. Physical and chemical processes in the upper layers of the atmosphere.

1. *Structural Parameters of the Atmosphere.*

Measurements will be taken of the pressure, temperature, and density of the air at various altitudes and also of the structure of the
atmosphere.

Together with the measurements of the density taken by manometers, certain data will be obtained by observation of the satellite's orbit.

During the movement of the satellite, owing to the atmosphere resistance, its orbit will gradually come closer to the earth. Studying
this evolution it will be possible to determine the law of density distribution with altitude.

2. *Optical Properties.*

Measurements will be made of the altitude and the brightness of
the fluorescence of individual layers of the atmosphere; the scatter-
ing of light in the atmosphere will also be studied, as well as optical
phenomena on the horizon.

3. *Ultra-violet and X-Ray Radiation.*

The air envelope is a filter for solar radiation. The atmosphere
passes light beams with a wavelength not less than 0.29.

The penetration of rockets and satellites into the upper layers of
the atmosphere will enable us to study the ultraviolet and X-ray portions of the solar spectrum, to determine the role of this solar radiation in the formation of the ionosphere, and to study the absorbtion
of the radiation in various layers of the upper atmosphere.

4. *Corpuscular Solar Radiation and Aurorae.*

Corpuscular emission of the sun calls forth sporadic violent variations in the earth's magnetic field and disturbances in the ionosphere.
Effected by the corpuscular streams from the sun, the ionospheric disturbances bring about long-period disturbances of short radiowave
propagation.

Solar corpuscles evince several other phenomena in the upper layers of the atmosphere — aurorae, for instance. However, the nature and the intensity of the corpuscular radiation remains to be studied.

It is intended to measure the intensity of the solar corpuscular radiation and to determine the nature of the corpuscles and the velocity of their penetration into the atmosphere, both during periods of calm and of great activity on the sun.

### 5. *Cosmic Rays.*

It is known that primary cosmic radiation, in the main, consists of hydrogen nuclei (protons), of helium nuclei (alpha particles) and, in much smaller number, of heavier nuclei (carbon, nitrogen, oxygen, etc.).

One of the properties of primary cosmic radiation is the similarity between the curve of the average distribution of the elements in the cosmic rays and the curve of the distribution of the charges of the primary component of cosmic radiation. Such elements as lithium, beryllium, and boron are rare in nature and the question regarding the number of these nuclei in primary cosmic radiation has not been studied experimentally. In this connection the study of the properties of primary cosmic radiation may shed light on the questions regarding the time of the cosmic particles' wandering in the space of the universe, and on the origin of cosmic rays.

Classed with the same range of questions should be the study of the variations of cosmic ray intensity at various altitudes and in different geographical regions.

### 6. *Ionospheric Physics.*

One of the problems regarding the structure of ionospheric layers is the determination of ion concentration. It has been established experimentally that the concentration varies with altitude.

In this connection, of great interest are the data on the ionization of the atmosphere along the orbit of a satellite, or along the trajectory of a rocket.

The study of radiowave passage through the ionospheric layers will in great measure improve our knowledge of the electron density and of the degree of radiowave attenuation.

As to other ionospheric measurements there will be mass-spectrometric measurements of the ion content of the ionosphere with a view to the determination and verification of its structure.

### 7. *Magnetic Fields.*

The short periodic variations of the earth's magnetic field are at present associated with the systems of electrical currents flowing in the upper layers of the atmosphere. Modern data indicate that rings of such currents are located in auroral polar zones (in northern and southern latitudes) and around the equator.

The important task of the scientific measurements to be made by means of the satellite is the proof of the existence of these currents, their nature, and the causes of their origin. The settlement of this problem will offer scientists new data to explain various short-period variations of the earth's magnetic field and their connection with solar and geophysical phenomena.

### 8. *Micrometeors and Meteorites.*

The problem of micrometeorites is of great scientific and practical importance. On the one hand, the presence of micrometeorites in the upper atmosphere predetermines a range of physical processes influencing the state of the atmosphere. On the other hand, micrometeorites and meteors present certain dangers for the satellite. Calculations show that even small particles with a velocity of 50 to 70 kilometers per second can break through the casing of the satellite. Therefore, it is important to know the concentration in space and the energy of micrometeorites. The study of the mass spectrum of micrometeorites and of meteors would help in drawing a definite conclusion regarding the "meteor danger" which is most important for future interplanetary travelling. To solve this problem instruments that record the impacts of meteorites (impact detectors) will be installed in the rockets and the satellites.

### 9. *Physical and Chemical Processes in the Upper Atmosphere.*

It is intended to launch various chemical reagents with the rockets into the upper atmosphere and to study the processes that occur during their interaction with the surrounding medium.

#### THE INSTRUMENTATION TO TRAVEL WITH ROCKETS AND SATELLITES

The entire geophysical equipment designed for the investigation of the upper atmosphere is housed in various containers. Some of the containers make up the vanguard part of the instrument rocket, which is detached from the rocket a certain time after termination of engine operation. These containers reach altitudes up to 200 kilometers.

The containers are equipped with radio telemetry or instruments with direct photographic recording. In the latter case the containers are saved.

### FIRING SITES

The vertical firings of the rockets for the purpose of studying the upper layers of the atmosphere will be conducted in three zones located approximately along the meridian 50 to 60 degrees East.

First zone — the Arctic, the Franz Joseph Land, 80 degrees North.

Second zone — the middle latitudes of the USSR, 50 to 60 degrees North.

Third zone — the Antarctic, mainly in the area of Mirny, 50 to 60 degrees South.

The launching of the satellites will be made from the USSR at a small angle to the meridian. The satellite will revolve around the earth and will be consequently observed in all the areas of the earth except the central areas of the Arctic and the Antarctic.

### ROCKET DISTRIBUTION BY ZONES AND YEARS

First zone — 1958, 25 firings.

Second zone — 1957, 30 firings; 1958, 40 firings.

Third zone — 1957-58, 30 firings.

### THE DISTRIBUTION OF THE STUDIED PARAMETERS BY CONTAINERS

At every firing of a rocket or the launching of a satellite, a definite area of the upper atmosphere investigations will be covered.

When the rockets take up containers of the first type, study will be made of the structural parameters of the atmosphere and of its optical properties, of the ultraviolet and X-ray parts of the solar spectrum, and of ionospheric phenomena and micrometeorites.

When containers of the other type are taken up with the rockets, the range of problems studied will include the corpuscular solar radiation, aurorae, and also the physical and chemical processes in the upper layers of the atmosphere.

When launching the man-made satellites, the program will include geophysical, physical and astrophysical experiments in various combinations, and also other investigations such as the observation of the relativity theory effect, the study of the shape of the earth, etc.

### SCHEDULE OF ROCKET AND SATELLITE FIRINGS

Firing of the rockets and satellites will take place at approximately even intervals throughout the International Geophysical Year, mainly

on World Days and on occasions of active solar processes, that is,
Special World Days.    (Submitted to the CSAGI at Brussels, June 10,
1957.   The author is identified as "Academician" and "President of
the USSR National IGY Committee and Vice President of the USSR
Academy of Sciences.")

# 35.  Observation of the Artificial Satellite

*A. A. Mikhailov*

As we know, during the Third International Geophysical Year artificial earth satellites will be launched.  Observation of the motion of these satellites will provide valuable information on the upper layers of the atmosphere and the shape and structure of the earth.

On astronomers of the Soviet Union there devolves the difficult and responsible task of organizing visual observations of artificial satellites.

The first satellites will have a visible stellar magnitude from 4 to 9 and a period of revolution of about 1½ hours.  They will be observable only during the dawn and dusk hours, and, as a result of their high angular velocity (up to 1 degree per second), the time they will be observable at any given point will not exceed 2 minutes for each passage.  Due to the earth's rotation and its non-spherical character the satellite's orbit will systematically shift relative to the earth's surface.

The probability is extremely small that two successive passages will be observable from the same place in one dawn or dusk period.

For visual observations of a satellite it is proposed to organize a network of special stations with 20-25 observers, not necessarily professional astronomers, each of which observes a small sector of the sky with the aid of a standard telescope with an input pupil of 50 millimeters and a field of vision of about 11 degrees.  Passage of the satellite through a definite point in the celestial sphere will be noted by some kind of recording deviced tied in with time signals.

It is possible that some satellites will be fitted with pulse gas discharge lamps, which will periodically give out light flashes.

This will permit visual observations to be conducted throughout the whole night.

The Astronomical Council of the Academy of Sciences USSR requests all astronomical organizations, all astronomers of the Soviet Union, and members of the All-Union Astronomical and Geodetic

Society to participate actively in preparations for the visual observations of artificial satellites.

Instructions and special apparatus for observations can be obtained through the Astronomical Council. (*Astronomicheskii Tsirkulyar*, No. 180, May 18, 1957; the same item appeared in *Astronomicheskii Zhurnal*, Vol. 34, No. 3, May-June, 1957, except that in the fifth paragraph the figures read "10-20 observers." The author is identified as Chairman of the Astronomical Council of the USSR Academy of Sciences and Corresponding Member of the USSR Academy of Sciences.)

# 36. Information for Radio Amateur Observers

*V. Vakhnin*

During the International Geophysical Year the USSR proposes to launch several artificial earth satellites equipped with radio transmitting apparatus. Radio observation of the signals of these satellites will make it possible to obtain new data on the structure of the ionosphere, to establish precisely the size, shape, and position of the satellite's orbit, and to obtain information on the processes taking place in the satellite during its flight. In addition to the professional radio services, radio amateurs must also participate in radio observations of the satellite. Since radio amateur observations will be of a popular character they can ensure extremely important data on the satellite's flight and on the state of the ionosphere.

The success of radio amateur observations and the value of the data obtained will depend largely on how well the amateurs take into consideration those peculiarities of reception which are associated with unusually high altitude, with unusually high speed, and with other peculiarities of the flight of a satellite, and on how well radio amateurs will be able to predict the time of repeated appearances of the satellite, etc.

The present article presents the information on artificial earth satellites necessary for radio amateurs and data on how the flight of the satellite influences the character of the signals received from it.

### ORBITS OF ARTIFICIAL EARTH SATELLITES

Artificial earth satellites will be launched by means of a rocket which will raise it to an altitude of several hundred kilometers and then accelerate it in a horizontal direction to a speed of about 8,000 meters per second (Figure 1), after which the rocket motors will stop and the satellite will separate from the rocket and move around the earth, making one revolution in approximately 1½ hours. The satellite's orbit will be approximately elliptical in shape; one focus of the ellipse will be at the center of the earth (Figure 2). Because of the orbit's ellipticity the altitude of the satellite will vary during each revolution; the point at which the altitude is greatest is called the apogee of the orbit, while the point of minimum altitude is the perigee. In order to determine completely the shape, size, and position of the orbit it is sufficient to indicate five quantities (Figure 3): the height of the perigee the height of the apogee; the inclination of the orbit, that is, the angle that the plane of the orbit forms with the plane of the equator; the longitude of the node, that is, the angle that the line of intersection of the orbital and equatorial planes forms with a direction, earlier assigned in the sky, lying in the plane of the equator (direction to the point of the vernal equinox); and, finally, the angular distance of the perigee from the node.

These quantities are called the elements of the orbit; their values at the launching of the satellite are determined by the launching point, the time of day at which the launching will take place, and the direction and speed at the moment of entry into the orbit.

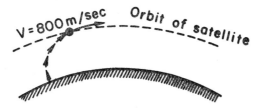

Figure 1. Diagram of satellite launching.

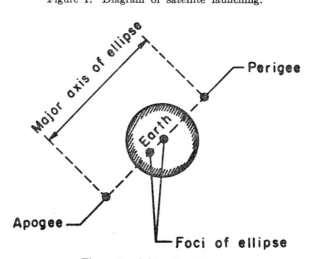

Figure 2. Orbit of satellite.

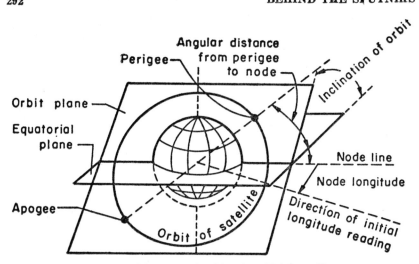

Figure 3.  Elements of orbit of artificial satellite.

After launching, the satellite will experience a slight braking due to friction in the upper layers of the atmosphere and, as a result, its flight speed will gradually decrease; at the same time the flight altitude will also decrease.[1]  After several days or weeks the flight altitude will be so reduced that the satellite will enter the denser layers of the atmosphere, will be greatly slowed down, will be heated by friction with the atmosphere, and will disintegrate.  The braking force and, consequently, the lifetime of the satellite will depend on the density of the upper layers of the atmosphere, which is known only approximately at the present time; therefore data on how rapidly the satellite is braked and disintegrates are of considerable scientific interest.

Radio amateur observations can help to more sharply define the values of the orbital elements and the amount of braking in the upper layers of the atmosphere.  At the end of the satellite's flight, amateur observations will be particularly valuable, since the satellite's entry into the dense layers of the atmosphere may take place in regions where there are no professional receiving sets.

REGION OF OBSERVATION OF THE ARTIFICIAL SATELLITE

A diagram of the relative movement of the satellite and its observers is shown in Figure 4.  The plane of the satellite's orbit does not participate in the rotation of the earth, whereas observers on the earth's surface move with the earth's rotation from west to east, as shown by the dotted lines of Figure 4.  During one revolution of the satellite (ap-

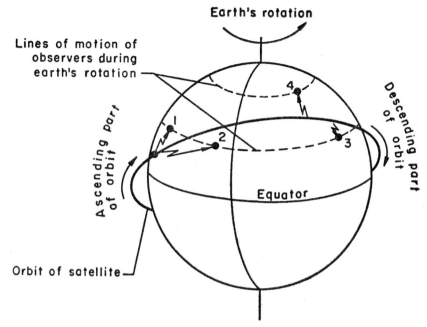

Figure 4. Motion of satellite and observers: (1) Position of observer during radio seance of ascending part of orbit. (2) Position of observer during second radio seance (on ascending part of next revolution of orbit). (3) Position of observer during radio seance of descending part of orbit. (4) Observer located close to northern limit of observation.

proximately 1.5 hours) an observer at the equator will have moved to the east 2,500 kilometers, an observer at 45° latitude will have moved 1,760 kilometers, and one at 60° will have moved 1,000 kilometers. The northern and southern limits of observation are determined by the inclination of the orbit: the more steeply the orbital plane is inclined, the farther north and south the satellite will pass in its movement.   In 24 hours the satellite will make about 16 revolutions, the trace of which will cover the earth's surface with an almost uniform "grid."   A satellite launched in the USSR will cover in its flight practically the entire populated area of the earth.

An observer located between the northern and southern limits of the region of observation will be able to observe the satellite, since, regardless of the longitude of his position, the earth's rotation will sooner or later cause him to approach the satellite's orbit and intersect its plane.   At any point on the earth south of the northern limit of the "orbital grid" and north of its southern limit the satellite will be observable twice a day: once on the "ascending" branch and once

on the "descending" branch of the orbit (Figure 4). In the northern-
most and southernmost regions both observations will be combined
into one.

The time during which the radio signal can be heard on one branch
will be determined by the speed of the satellite (8 kilometers per
second), the range of the radio facilities, and the distance between
the observation point and the trace of the given revolution of the
orbit (Figure 5). The average duration of one seance will be several
minutes.

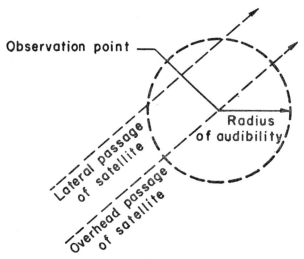

Figure 5.  Duration of audibility of satellite during overhead and lateral passages.

ROTATIONAL MOTION OF A SATELLITE AND ITS EFFECT
ON RADIO RECEPTION

The highest rate of rotation of the satellite will not exceed several
revolutions per minute. The effect of the rotational motion of the
satellite on radio reception will be determined first of all by the design
of the satellite's antennas: Sufficiently low fading will result if the
antennas on the satellite are so constructed that they radiate a cir-
cularly polarized wave while the antenna of the ground station is
designed for reception of a linearly polarized wave (Figure 6, a). In
this case reception of signals is ensured for almost any rotation of
the satellite. But when the satellite's antennas are located in a plane
which is directed toward the receiving point and perpendicular to the
direction of polarization of the receiving antenna (Figure 6, b), a
complete cessation of reception takes place, whereas for deviations
from this position, there is strong attenuation of the received signal.

The strong signal fading which occurs when the rotating satellite passes the position shown in Figure 6, b, is unlikely; it is more probable that there will be small fluctuations in signal strength when the rotating satellite passes a position intermediate between those shown in Figure 6, a and b.

### OTHER FORMS OF RADIO SIGNAL FADING

In addition to the above-described phenomena associated with rotation of the satellite, ordinary radio signal fading may occur either as a result of radio waves arriving at the receiving antenna by different paths (Figure 7), or as a result of reflection from the earth's surface.

The character of fading brought about by the first cause can be rather unusual. Since the satellite moves with enormus speed, the path traversed by the radio waves will change rapidly. Therefore,

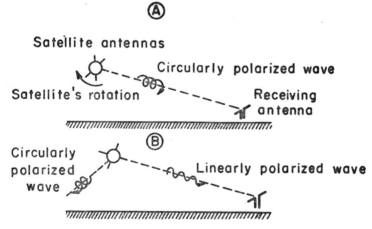

Figure 6. Reception of electromagnetic waves from satellite for different positions of satellite relative to receiving antenna.

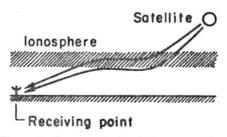

Figure 7. Passage of signals from satellite.

the moments when waves passing from different directions cancel each other and the moments when the waves reinforce each other can alternate very rapidly; thus fading will change from the slow oscillations in signal strength, to which radio amateurs are accustomed, into a rapid modulation of the signal with a frequency of tens or even hundreds of cycles per second.

The second type of fading—fading caused by the influence of the earth on the receiving antenna—can take place when the receiving antenna is suspended high above the earth (at a height of more than 10 to 15 kilometers). In this case, for a fixed angle of incidence of the wave, a wave arriving at the antenna directly and a wave reflected from the earth can cancel each other; thus a null is formed in the radiation pattern of the receiving antenna.

If the height at which the antenna is suspended exceeds the wave length by several times, several nulls will be formed in the radiation pattern. When signals are received from a rapidly moving satellite, the angle of approach of the wave will also change rather rapidly; therefore, the signal will periodically fade and swell (with a period of several seconds or several tens of seconds).

### THE DOPPLER EFFECT

The Doppler effect consists in the principle that as the radio receiver and the transmitter approach each other or move away from each other, the frequency of the signal arriving at the radio receiver varies in proportion to the rate of approach or separation.

During an approach the frequency of the signal increases; during separation, the frequency decreases.

Since the satellite's movement takes place with strict regularity and with a constant velocity, the variation in the frequency will also take place with strict regularity: when the satellite first appears, the rate of its approach will be a maximum, and, consequently, the frequency of the received signal will also be a maximum. During the satellite's approach the angle between the direction of its motion and the direction of its receiving points will increase, and the rate of its approach will begin to decrease gradually. Finally, as the angle between the direction of motion and the direction of reception becomes greater than 90°, the satellite will begin to recede from the receiver; the rate of recession will gradually increase and will become maximum before the signal stops. Correspondingly, the frequency of the Doppler effect will also vary. At first, the signal will be at its highest frequency, and then, as the satellite approaches the receiver, the frequency will begin to decrease rapidly. Finally, when the satellite passes the receiver and begins to recede, the frequency will tend toward a minimum. An approximate graph of the variation in radio signal frequency with time is shown in Figure 8.

The rate of variation in frequency during the satellite's flight past the receiving point will depend on the distance at which it passes; the closer the satellite comes to the receiver, the more rapidly will the frequency vary from maximum to minimum (see curves in Figure 8).

The entire period of frequency variation will last only two or three minutes; if the oscillator of the receiver is sufficiently stable and does not become detuned during reception, the Doppler effect can be

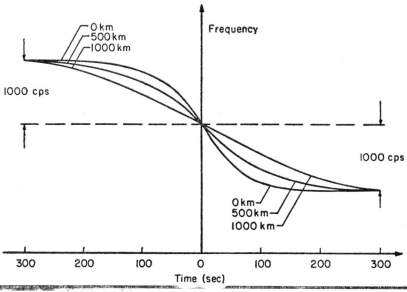

Figure 8. Graph of frequency variation (Doppler effect) depending on distance along earth's surface between observation point and plane of orbit.

easily detected and recorded, thereby providing important data on the position of the orbit relative to the receiving point. However, when the first radio signals are received from the satellite, the oscillator must be tuned, because the frequency of the tone at the middle of the seance will vary approximately 2,000 cycles per second for 40 megacycles and approximately 1,000 cycles per second for 20 megacycles; during the remainder of the seance the tuning of the oscillator should not be changed.[2]

PREDICTION OF REAPPEARANCES OF THE SATELLITE

As has already been indicated, the orbit of the satellite does not participate in the daily rotation of the earth; nor does the boundary between day and night participate in the earth's daily rotation. Therefore, the satellite will enter the earth's shadow and emerge from it always at the same latitude and will generally appear above a given latitude at the same local time, taken at the point of intersection of the orbit with the given parallel.[3] This law can easily be applied in predicting the reappearances of a satellite. The intersection would be especially simple if the period of the satellite's revolution were precisely 1 hour and 30 minutes. In this case, the satellite would pass above the same point of the earth at precisely the same time of day. As a matter of fact, the period of revolution may vary slightly; that is, the satellite, having passed above a certain point on a given day, may, on the following day, pass that point either more easterly or more westerly. Let us examine the case shown in Figure 9. Suppose that in the first days the satellite passes through point A at exactly 1200 hours local time, but that on subsequent days it intersects the same latitude more easterly (at point B); the local time of intersection at point B will be 1200 hours as before. However, the local time of point B is 15 minutes ahead of the local time of point A, for example: therefore, at point A the signal will be received 15 minutes earlier than on previous days. Conversely, it follows that if the satellite intersects a given latitude more westerly than on the previous day, its appearance at point A will be somewhat later than on previous days.

Since the period of revolution is not accurately known for the first days, then it will also not be known whether the satellite will pass more easterly or more westerly on subsequent days. It will be necessary, therefore, to begin observation again from the west, starting approximately 1 hour from the moment when the previous observation took place, and, if the satellite is not detected, to continue observation for about two hours. But if the satellite is observed and the seance takes place, the next observation should take place exactly 1.5 hours after the beginning of the first reception, in order to observe the subsequent revolution. After the end of the seance on the ascending branch, similar seances can be conducted on the descending branch.

USE OF RADIO AMATEUR OBSERVATIONS FOR
MORE PRECISE DEFINITION OF THE ORBIT

The task of the more precise definition of the orbit differs in prin-

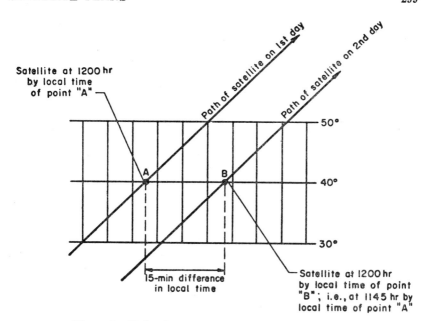

Figure 9. Path of reappearances of artificial satellite.

ciple, for example, from the task of determining the trajectory of an aircraft by radar, since we know in advance that the satellite cannot perform arbitrary motions in space, but for given initial data, can only traverse a completely definite trajectory. This circumstance perimts the use of more simple measurements than in the case of radar. Thus, for example, if the position of the satellite has been accurately found by bearings from five or six points, and the exact time of these bearings has been established, then the position of its orbit can be computed with an accuracy sufficient for practical purposes.

Doppler effect recordings can also be used to determine the orbit (Figure 8); from these recordings it is possible to determine the distance at which the satellite passed and the exact moment that it was at the minimum distance.

Therefore, in order to use radio amateur observations, it is extremely important to have recordings of signals on magnetic tape which can be used first to measure the Doppler effect, secondly to "synchronize" the recording obtained with the exact time. From the duration of the tones and pauses, information can also be obtained regarding certain processes occuring within the satellite itself.

Highly qualified radio amateurs and radio clubs can also build equipment which will make it possible to take direction bearings of the satellite. The times of the bearings must be synchronized with the exact time.

It should be noted that for control of the orbit, the signal having a frequency of 40 megacycles per second is of greastest value, since it is less distorted when the signal passes through the ionosphere.

Some variations in the equipment for receiving signals from the satellite will be described in subsequent articles; however, it is desirable that radio amateurs also suggest their own versions of receivers and direction finders as well as ways in which the recording can by synchronized with the exact time. (*Radio,* No. 6, June, 1957. Original title of this article was "Artificial Earth Satellites"; the subtitle appears here as the title.)

----

[1] As a result of the resistance of the atmosphere, and also the deviation of the gravitational field from the central, the above mentioned elements of the orbit will change slowly.

[2] It should be remembered that if the oscillator is tuned below the carrier frequency, the frequency of the audible tone will decrease; whereas if the oscillator is tuned above the carrier frequency, the frequency of the tone will rise.

[3] Local time is understood to mean not standard (zone) time but the time determined by the position of the sun at the point of observation. Here the displacement of the earth's shadow caused by the annual motion of the earth is not considered; for a completely accurate solution, it is necessary to consider not "local sun" but "local star" time. However, for practical purposes, radio amateurs need not take this inaccuracy into account.

# 37. Scientific Value of Radio Signals

*A. N. Kazantsev*

The program of the International Geophysical Year, in which the Soviet Union, as well as other countries, are taking part, includes the launching of artificial earth satellites. It is known that such artificial earth satellites will be launched in the Soviet Union and the United States.

The artificial earth satellite will be provided with two radio transmitters having frequencies of about 20 megacycles and 40 megacycles and radiated power of about 1 watt. These transmitters will operate continuously for a long time (determined by the capacity of their power supplies). At the same time radio receiving points and radio amateurs throughout the whole territory of the Soviet Union and abroad will be able to receive, repeatedly, the radio signals radiated by the satellite's transmitters.

Signals from the transmitters on the artificial satellite will be telegraph messages having a duration of 0.05 to 0.7 second. The message of one transmitter will correspond to a pause in the second transmitter.

For further work in designing radio apparatus for artificial satellites it is very important to know the conditions under which the apparatus will operate during flight. Therefore, signals from the first satellites will be used to obtain certain information about the conditions under which their apparatus operates. Changes in the physical conditions to which the apparatus on the satellite will be subjected will cause corresponding changes in the kind of radiated signals; these changes will be easily distinguished even when the signals of any of the transmitters are received by ear.

Some of the possible forms of signals are shown in Figure 1.

Every report from radio amateurs on the form of signals received from the satellites, with indication of the exact time of reception, will be of considerable value.

At the same time, observations of the variations in the received signal level, during the passage of the satellite in the zone of each re-

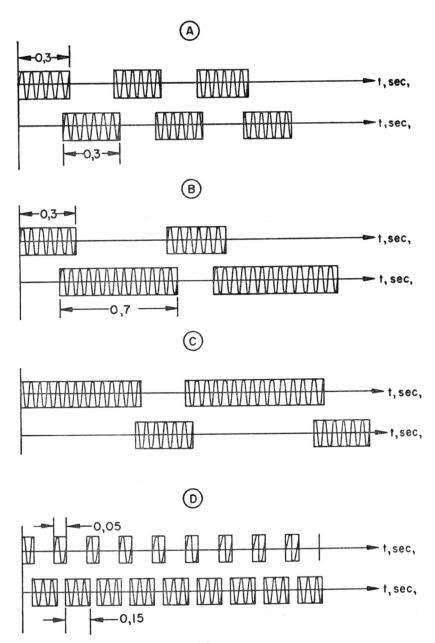

Figure 1.

302

ceiving point, will make it possible to obtain valuable information about the propagation of radio waves in the ionosphere which cannot be obtained by the usual method of study based on the reflection of signals radiated by a ground transmitter.

As we know, the ionosphere has a laminar structure; that is, it is observed to contain several ionization maxima (Figure 2). The main layers are the following: the E layer, located at an altitude of 100 to 140 kilometers; and the F layer, which, during daylight hours of the summer months, is divided into two layers—the $F_1$ layer, which lies at an altitude of about 200 kilometers, and the $F_2$ layer which has an ionization maximum lying at an altitude of the order of 250 to 400 kilometers (depending on the time of day and year).

The highest frequency at which radio waves are reflected from a given ionized layer, when their incidence on it is vertical, is known as the critical frequency. Knowing the critical frequency, it is easy to determine the value of electron concentration in the maximum of the layer. A knowledge of the critical frequencies and the altitudes of the ionized layers makes it possible to evaluate the conditions of propagation of short waves on radio communication lines. Long-distance radio communication on short waves is determined primarily by the reflection of radio waves from the $F_2$ layer, which has the highest electron concentration and, consequently, also the highest critical frequency.

The degree of electron concentration in the ionized layers, especially in the $F_2$ layer, is closely related to the 11-year cycle of solar activity. The International Geophysical Year coincides approximately with

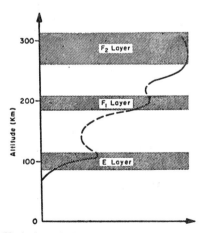

Figure 2. Variation of electron concentration with altitude.

the period of maximum solar activity. Therefore, all phenomena affected by the influence of the ionosphere on the propagation of radio waves will be most clearly expressed.

By means of the usual radiosonde methods employed at ionospheric stations, it is possible to form an idea of the structure of the ionosphere only up to the level of maximum ionization of the $F_2$ layer, since radio waves with frequencies higher than the critical frequencies of the $F_2$ layer pass through the ionosphere without returning to the earth.

Reception of radio radiation from the satellite will make it possible to obtain signals from the region of the ionosphere which radio waves, radiated from the earth's surface and which are reflected back to earth, can not penetrate.

During the International Geophysical Year the critical frequencies of the $F_2$ layer are expected to reach 10 megacycles per second in summer and 15 to 16 megacycles per second in winter. From this it is evident that the operating frequencies of transmitters in the artificial satellite are higher than the possible critical frequencies of the $F_2$ layer. Since the flight altitude of the satellite may exceed the altitude of maximum ionization of the $F_2$ layer, observations of signals sent from the satellite can provide certain information relative to the region lying above the maximum of the $F_2$ layer.

The highest frequency at which radio waves can be reflected from the ionosphere depends not only on the electron concentration of the ionized layer, but also on the angle of incidence of radio waves on the layer. The passage of the wave from vertical incidence to inclined incidence increases the magnitude of the frequency at which reflection is possible from a given ionized layer.

It is possible to assume approximately that the frequency of reflection for inclined incidence of radio waves on a layer is related to the frequency of reflection for vertical incidence by the so-called cosine laws, $f' = f/\cos \phi$, where $f'$ is the frequency of reflection for inclined incidence, f for vertical incidence, and $\phi$ is the angle of incidence (the angle between the direction of the beam and the vertical at the point of incidence of the beam on the reflecting layer).

In the flight of the satellite above the ionization maximum of the $F_2$ layer, radio waves will fall on this layer from the outside relative to the earth. Let us assume that a wave with frequency $f'$ falls on the region of maximum ionization of the $F_2$ layer, whose critical frequency is equal to $f_r$ at an angle of $\phi$ (Figure 3). It should be noted that in Figure 3 the reflection of rays and their passage through the ionized layer is represented schematically without taking into account

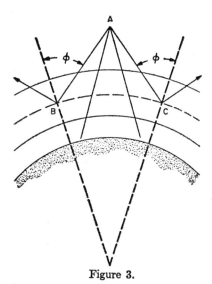

Figure 3.

the curvature of the trajectory of the radio waves in the ionized medium.

When the conditions for reflection of radio waves are observed, which can be approximately described in the following form: $f' \leq f_{F/2}/\cos \phi$, a radio wave reflected from the $F_2$ layer from the outside will go out into world space.

The earth's surface will receive only those falling from the satellite within a certain cone BAC (Figure 3). The angle at the apex of this cone will be less for a longer wave radiated from the satellite than for a shorter wave.

Because of this, at each point on the earth's surface the higher-frequency signals will be received first and then the lower-frequency signals; therefore, the moments of appearance and disappearance of the signals will not coincide with the moments of the optical rising and setting of the satellite.

The difference in times of appearance of radio signals of different frequencies will depend on the state of the ionosphere and on the flight altitude of the satellite in any given part of its trajectory. There-fore, it is of interest to record the moments of appearance and dis-appearance of signals from each of the transmitters in the satellite.

The signal levels at the point of reception are determined by two factors: the distance between the transmitter and receiver, and the absorption of radio waves in the ionosphere.

Here no attention is given to the influence of the directivity of the transmitting antennas, which can be taken into account during the statistical processing of the results of simultaneous observations at different receiving points.

During the movement of the satellite, from the time it rises until it sets, the distance $R$ between it and the point of reception will change rapidly. At the same time, the level of the signals must vary inversely as the distance, that is, $1/R$. The absorption of radio waves in the ionosphere will cause deviation from this law. It can be assumed that the coefficients of absorption for different frequencies in the radio wave band employed will be inversely proportional to the squares of the frequencies.

Thus, recordings of measurements of received signal levels (with indication of the exact ime of each measurement) will make it possible to obtain data on the absorption of radio signals along their entire path, including the region of the ionosphere which is inaccessible to investigation by means of the methods ordinarily employed.

The time dependence of the receiver input voltage during the receiving seance can be obtained by qualified radio amateurs possessing needle-type signal level indicators calibrated in advance by means of a standard signal generator. Each reading of the received signal level must be accompanied by the indication of the exact time (hours, minutes, seconds).

If the oscillator frequency of the receiver is so selected by calculation that the audible tone of the signal at an operating frequency of $f_1 = 20$ megacycles per second will be, say, 1500 cycles per second, then, from the moment of the appearance of the signal (the "rising" of the satellite) to its disappearance, the audible tone will vary continuously from a certain maximum audio frequency to a minimum (or vice versa). This variation in tone is caused by the Doppler effect and is analogous to the variation of the audible tone of a locomotive whistle for an observer standing on a platform as the train passes.

For a receiving point located in the orbital plane of the artificial satellite, the greatest frequency variation $\Delta f$ during operation on a frequency of $f_1 = 20$ megacycles per second will be approximately 500 cycles per second. Consequently, in our example the audible signal tone will vary from 2,000 cycles per second to 1,000 cycles per second. At the moment that the satellite crosses the zenith the tone will have a frequency of 1,500 cycles per second. Because of the Doppler effect, the greatest variation in the tone of the received signal, for an operating frequency of $f_2 = 40$ megacycles per second, will be about 1,000 cycles per second (to one side or the other of the mean value).

For receiving points located outside the orbital plane of the satellite (there will be, of course, a majority of such points), the frequency variation of the received signals, owing to the Doppler effect, will be less than in the above example, because of the decrease in the radial component of the satellite's velocity. The magnitude of frequency variations of the audible signal tone by means of an ordinary magnetic not only on the radial velocity of the satellite, but also on the state of the ionosphere through which the satellite will pass.

If the orbit of the satellite and the location of the receiving point are known precisely, then, from the magnitude of the variations in signal frequency, it is possible to draw conclusions about the state of the upper region of the ionosphere.

Each observer who receives the signals can record the frequency variations of the audible signal tone by means of an ordinary magnetic tape recorder (with fixed tuning of the oscillators; it is desirable to employ quartz frequency stabilization of the oscillators). Recordings should be made on both operating frequencies. Such recordings will be extremely valuable.

From the above it follows that radio amateurs who observe the radio signals from the artificial earth satellite can collect material the generalization of which will make it possible to obtain valuable information about the propagation of radio waves in the ionosphere and the properties of its upper area.

It is to be hoped that radio amateurs, both in the Soviet Union and abroad, will take an active part in the interesting work of observing radio signals from the satellite and thereby make a valuable contribution to the development of scientific research with the aid of the newest means — artificial earth satellites. (*Radio,* No. 6, June, 1957. Original title of the article was "Observation of Radio Signals From an Artificial Satellite and Their Scientific Value").

# Part Seven

# THE SPUTNIK

# 38.   Announcement of the First Satellite

*Tass*

For several years scientific research and experimental design work have been conducted in the Soviet Union on the creation of artificial satellites of the earth.

As already reported in the press, the first launching of the satellites in the USSR were planned for realization in accordance with the scientific research program of the International Geophysical Year.

As a result of very intensive work by scientific research institutes and design bureaus the first artificial satellite in the world has been created.   On October 4, 1957, this first satellite was successfully launched in the USSR.   According to preliminary data, the carrier rocket has imparted to the satellite the required orbital velocity of about 8000 meters per second.   At the present time the satellite is describing elliptical trajectories around the earth, and its flight can be observed in the rays of the rising and setting sun with the aid of very simple optical instruments (binoculars, telescopes, etc.).

According to calculations which now are being supplemented by direct observations, the satellite will travel at altitudes up to 900 kilometers above the surface of the earth; the time for a complete revolution of the satellite will be one hour and thirty-five minutes; the angle of inclination of its orbit to the equatorial plane is 65 degrees.   On October 5 the satellite will pass over the Moscow area twice — at 1:46 a.m. and at 6:42 a.m. Moscow time.   Reports about the subsequent movement of the first artificial satellite launched in the USSR on October 4 will be issued regularly by broadcasting stations.

The satellite has a spherical shape 58 centimeters in diameter and weighs 83.6 kilograms.   It is equipped with two radio transmitters continuously emitting signals at frequencies of 20.005 and 40.002 megacycles per second (wave lengths of about 15 and 7.5 meters, respectively).   The power of the transmitters ensures reliable reception of the signals by a broad range of radio amateurs.   The signals have the form of telegraph pulses of about 0.3 second's duration with a pause of the same duration.   The signal of one frequency is sent during the pause in the signal of the other frequency.

Scientific stations located at various points in the Soviet Union are tracking the satellite and determining the elements of its trajectory. Since the density of the rarefied upper layers of the atmosphere is not accurately known, there are no data at present for the precise determination of the satellite's lifetime and of the point of its entry into the dense layers of the atmosphere.   Calculations have shown that owing to the tremendous velocity of the satellite, at the end of its existence it will burn up on reaching the dense layers of the atmosphere at an altitude of several tens of kilometers.

As early as the end of the nineteenth century the possibility of realizing cosmic flights by means of rockets was first scientifically substantiated in Russia by the works of the outstanding Russian scientist K. E. Tsiolkovskii.

The successful launching of the first man-made earth satellite makes a most important contribution to the treasure-house of world science and culture.   The scientific experiment accomplished at such a great height is of tremendous importance for learning the properties of cosmic space and for studying the earth as a planet of our solar system.

During the International Geophysical Year the Soviet Union proposes launching several more artificial earth satellites.   These subsequent satellites will be larger and heavier and they will be used to carry out programs of scientific research.

Artificial earth satellites will pave the way to interplanetary travel and, apparently, our contemporaries will witness how the freed and conscientious labor of the people of the new socialist society makes the most daring dreams of mankind a reality.   (*Pravda*, October 5, 1957.)

# 39.  Report on the First Satellite

*Pravda*

On October 4, 1957, the entire world witnessed an outstanding event — the successful launching in the Soviet Union of the first artificial earth satellite.  The report of the launching of the satellite was received in all corners of the globe.  Its passage was recorded by many observers on all continents.  The creation of the satellite was the result of long, persevering research and design work in which large collectives of Soviet scientists, engineers, and industrial workers participated.

Theoretically, the question of the possibility of sending a cosmic ship beyond the limits of the earth's atmosphere was solved at the beginning of the twentieth century by the outstanding Russian scientist K. E. Tsiolkovskii who proved that the rocket must be the means for cosmic flight.  In his works K. E. Tsiolkovskii formulated a series of cardinal problems of interplanetary flight and pointed out that the creation of an artificial earth satellite would be the first necessary step.

Creation of an artificial earth satellite called for the solution of a number of very complex and fundamentally new scientific and technical problems.  The biggest difficulties were encountered in developing a carrier rocket to lift the satellite into its orbit.  To launch the satellite, a carrier rocket was created possessing a high degree of design perfection.  Powerful engines working under difficult thermal conditions were created.  The optimal regimes of the rocket's movement were worked out, ensuring its most effective utilization.  To ensure the assigned law of motion necessary to take the satellite to its orbit, a very precise and effective system of automatic rocket guidance was developed.

The solution of these as well as many other very complex tasks was made possible by the use of the newest achievements of science and technology in the most diverse fields, and, primarily, by the high technical level of rocket building in the USSR.  The creation of an artificial earth satellite in such a short time was ensured by the high level of scientific-technical potential in our country, the efficient and well-organized work of scientific research institutes, design bureaus, and industrial enterprises.

Great experimental work connected with the creation and development both of the separate aggregates and of the system as a whole preceded the launching of the satellite. The successful launching of the satellite has completely confirmed the correctness of the calculations and basic technical solutions made in creating the carrier rocket and the satellite.

The launching of the first satellite opens up an extensive scientific research program which will be continued during the International Geophysical Year in a series of subsequent artificial satellites, the creation of which will entail a further increase in their weight and dimensions. The creation of the satellite is the first step in the conquest of interplanetary space and the realization of cosmic flights.

The artificial satellite has the shape of a sphere. It was placed in the nose of the carrier rocket and covered by a protective cone. The rocket with the satellite was fired vertically. Soon after the firing, by means of a program device, the axis of the rocket began to deviate gradually from the vertical. At the end of the trajectory leading into the orbit, the rocket was at an altitude of several hundred kilometers and was moving parallel to the earth's surface with a velocity of about 8000 meters per second. After the rocket engine stopped, the protective cone was jettisoned, and the satellite separated from the rocket and began to move independently.

At present the satellite equipped with apparatus, the carrier rocket, and the protective cone are moving around the world. Since the speed of separation of the cone from the satellite and of the satellite from the rocket was not great, the carrier and the cone after a certain time found themselves at a comparatively small distance from the satellite, moving around the earth along orbits close to that of the satellite. Then, due to the difference in periods of revolution arising both from the relative speed at the moment of separation and from the different degrees of braking in the earth's atmosphere, all three bodies moved apart and in the process of subsequent motion they can now be found at the same moment over completely different points of the earth's surface.

### THE SATELLITE'S ORBIT

To a first approximation, the satellite's orbit is an ellipse, one focus of which is in the center of the earth. The flight altitude of the satellite above the earth's surface is not constant, but changes periodically, reaching a highest value of approximately 1000 kilometers. At present the orbit's perigee — its lowest point — is in the northern hemisphere.

The orientation of the orbit's plane relative to fixed stars remains almost constant. Since the earth rotates around its axis, then with each subsequent turn the satellite must appear over a different region, shifting with each turn approximately 24 degrees in longitude. The actual longitudinal displacement will be somewhat greater since the plane of the orbit will gradually turn around the earth's axis in the direction opposite to the earth's rotation because of the deviation of the gravitational field from the central. This movement of the plane of the orbit is not large and amounts to approximately one-fourth of a degree in longitude for each revolution. As a result of the relative movement of the earth and the plane of the orbit, each subsequent turn will be approximately 1500 kilometers to the west of the preceding one, at the latitude of Moscow. In the equatorial area the displacement will be greater and will amount to about 2500 kilometers.

The orbit's plane is inclined at an angle of 65 degrees to the equatorial plane. In this connection, the trace of the satellite passes over areas of the earth lying approximately between the north and south polar circles. Because of the earth's rotation around its axis, the angle of inclination of the trace to the equator differs from the angle of inclination of the orbit's plane. When crossing over to the northern hemisphere, the trace intersects the equator at an angle of 71.5 degrees in a northeast direction. Then the trace gradually turns completely to the east and, having touched the parallel corresponding to 65 degrees north latitude, turns to the south and crosses the equator in a southeast direction at an angle of 59 degrees. In the southern hemisphere the trace is tangent to the parallel corresponding to 65 degrees south latitude, after which it turns to the north and again crosses into the northern hemisphere.

With the passing of time, because of the braking of the satellite in the upper layers of the earth's atmosphere, the shape and size of the satellite's orbit will gradually change. Since the density of the atmosphere is extremely low at great altitudes where the satellite is moving the evolution of the orbit will take place very slowly at first. The height of the apogee will fall more rapidly than that of the perigee, and the orbit will gradually become more circular. When the satellite enters the denser layers of the atmosphere, the braking of

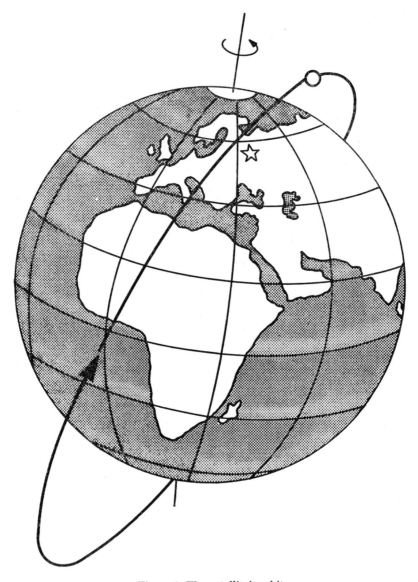

Figure 1. The satellite's orbit.

the satellite will bcome very strong. The satellite will grow hot and burn up like meteorites which arrive from interplanetary space and burn up in the earth's atmosphere.

At present the density of the upper atmosphere is not known with sufficient precision. Therefore, it is impossible as yet to forecast precisely the life time of the satellite in its orbit. The data on the density of the upper atmosphere available at present, as well as the results of the trajectory measurements that have been carried out, make it possible to say that the satellite will circle the earth for a long time.

At present the satellite's period of revolution is 96 minutes. As the orbit shrinks, the period will decrease. The rate at which the period changes will serve to indicate the rate at which the shape of the orbit changes. This is why the precise measurement of the satellite's period of revolution is an extremely important and responsible task.

The parameters of the Soviet artificial satellite's orbit make it possible to observe it on all the continents over a wide range of latitudes. This opens up great possibilities for the solution of various scientific problems. It can be pointed out that launching the satellite into such an orbit is a more difficult task than launching it into an orbit close to the equatorial plane. When launching along the equator it is possible to utilize to a large degree the speed of the earth's rotation around its axis for accelerating the rocket.

### OBSERVATION OF THE SATELLITE'S MOVEMENT

The most important component of the investigations conducted by means of the artificial earth satellite is the observation of its movement, the processing of the observations, and the forecasting, as a result of the processing, of the satellite's further movement. Observation of the satellite is conducted by radiotechnical means and also in observatories by means of optical instruments. In addition to specialists with their facilities, radio amateurs are widely attracted to make observations, as well as groups of amateur astronomers, conducting observations on astronomical posts by means of optical instruments specially manufactured for this purpose. At present, in the USSR 66 optical observation stations and 26 DOSAAF clubs with a large amount of radio tracking equipment are regularly conducting satellite observations. Moreover, thousands of radio amateurs are individually conducting observations of the satellite.

The scientific stations are conducting their observations by means of radiolocators and radio direction finders. Observation by optical

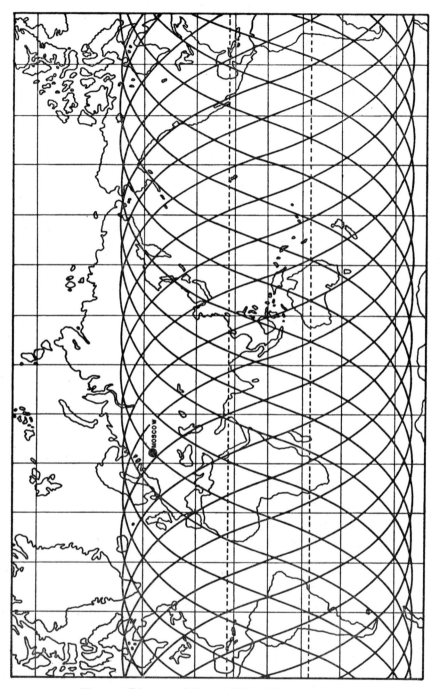

Figure 2. Diagram of the satellite's daily movement.

methods and photography of the satellite's movement are also being conducted.

Let us dwell on the methods of observation used by amateur astronomers and radio amateurs, since these methods are available to wide circles interested in the satellite's movement. Amateur astronomers have at their disposal a large number of specially manufactured telescopes with perfect optics and wide-angle vision. At the observation stations there are also sets of equipment making it possible to determine the satellite's position in the celestial sphere at a definite moment of time.

Since there is apparatus by means of which the optical station marks the satellite's position in the celestial sphere, measurements can be carried out with a precision of one degree, and the moment of time at which this position is marked, with an error of not more than one second. The optical station observes the artificial satellite in the morning or in the evening when the surface of the earth is plunged in darkness, and the satellite itself, which is at a great height, is illuminated by the sun.

It should be noted that observations of the satellite by means of astronomical instruments represent a well-known difficulty and differ from observations of ordinary astronomical bodies since the satellite moves across the sky very rapidly with a speed averaging about one degree per second.

To ensure reliability of observations, every optical station sets up one or two "optical barriers" of telescopes arranged along the meridian and in a vertical circle perpendicular to the satellite's visible orbit. Moreover, when looking for the satellite, a method based on the so-called principle of local time is employed. This method makes use of the fact that the satellite itself will pass through a given latitude at the local star time, which changes slowly as the orbit rotates in absolute space around the earth's axis because of the deviation of the gravitational field from the central one. Thanks to this, for a given station the satellite will, in the process of its movement, pass through a succession of points on the celestial sphere which may be called "expectation points." If the axis of the optical instrument is adjusted so that it is directed toward the next expectation point computed earlier on the celestial sphere, then sooner or later the satellite will inevitably be found.

Observations of the satellite are conducted by a large number of radio amateurs by means of radio receivers specially designed for this purpose. The wiring diagrams for these receivers and for their direction-finding attachments were published in the popular science radio-technical magazine *Radio*, long in advance of the satellite's launching.[1] Information on the satellite's movement, supplied by radio amateurs, can be used not only for studying the laws of the passage of radio waves through the atmosphere but also, especially when the radio amateur uses the direction-finding attachment, for a rough determination of the elements of the satellite's orbit.

Radio amateurs have already made a large number of satellite observations. In a number of places the passage of the satellite has been recorded by amateur astronomers. In a number of other places, unfortunately, cloudiness has made it impossible so far to conduct optical observations.

All the data of the scientific stations as well as the radio and optical observations of the amateurs are being collected and processed. As a result of the processing of these data, both the elements of the orbit and their secular variations are being determined. In the processing, the newest computing facilities, such as electronic computers, are being utilized. As a result of the processing, the parameters of the orbit are being defined more accurately and the satellite's movement is being forecast. Moreover, the data coming in from observation stations are being used for a number of geophysical investigations conducted by means of the satellite, such as the determination of the density of the atmosphere by the evolution of the parameters of the satellite's orbit, and so forth.

### DESCRIPTION OF THE SATELLITE

As reported earlier, the satellite has the shape of a sphere. Its diameter is 58 centimeters, its weight 83.6 kilograms. The hermetic casing of the satellite is made of aluminum alloys. Its surface is polished and specially treated. The casing contains all the satellite's apparatus, together with its sources of power. Before launching, the satellite is filled with gaseous nitrogen.

The antennas, in the form of four metal rods from 2.4 to 2.9 meters long, are attached to the outer surface of the casing. While the satellite is being raised into its orbit, the antenna rods are folded against the rocket's body. After the satellite's separation, the antennas turn on their hinges and occupy the position shown in the photograph. (See Figure 3.)

Moving along its orbit, the satellite periodically is subjected to sharp temperature variations — to heating by the sun's rays during its passage over the illuminated side of the earth, to cooling during its flight in the earth's shadow, to the thermal changes of the atmosphere, and so forth. Moreover, a certain amount of heat is also generated by the operation of the apparatus in the satellite. Thermally, the artificial satellite is an independent celestial body which is in radiant heat equilibrium with the surrounding space. Therefore, the problem of ensuring for a long time the normal temperature regime necessary in the satellite for the operation of its apparatus is, in principle, new and rather complex. Maintaining the necessary temperature regime in the first satellite is ensured by imparting to its surface suitable values of the solar radiation coefficients of emission and absorption and also by regulating the thermal resistance between the satellite's shell and the equipment inside by forced circulation of nitrogen within the satellite.

In the satellite there are two radio transmitters which continuously emit radio signals with frequencies of 20.005 and 40.002 megacycles (wave lengths of 15 and 7.5 meters, respectively). It should be noted that on the Soviet satellite, because of its relatively great weight it was possible to install radio transmitters of great power. This makes it possible to receive signals from the satellite over great distances, and enables a very large number of radio amateurs in all parts of the world to join in tracking the satellite. The first days of tracking the satellite's flight confirmed the possibility of the positive reception of its signals by ordinary amateur receivers at distances of several thousands of kilometers. Several cases of the reception of the satellite's signals at distances of up to 10,000 kilometers have been recorded.

### THE SATELLITE'S RADIO SIGNALS

The signals emitted by the radio transmitters on each of the frequencies have the form of telegraphic messages. The signal on one frequency occurs during a pause in the signal of the other frequency. The average duration of the signals on each of the frequencies is about 0.3 second. These signals are used for tracking the satellite's orbit and also for solving a number of scientific problems. To register the processes that are taking place in the satellite, it has been equipped with sensitive elements which change the frequencies of the telegraphic messages and the correlations between the duration of these messages and the pauses in accordance with changes in certain parameters in the satellite (temperature and others). While the signals from the satellite are being received they are recorded for subsequent decoding and analysis.

It should be considered that after a certain time the radio trans-

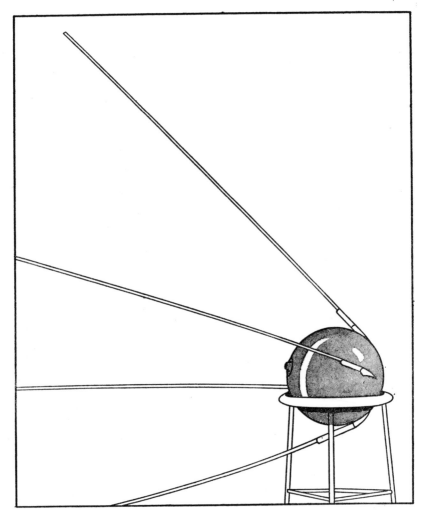

Figure 3. The Soviet artificial earth satellite.
(A drawing based upon a photograph of the satellite on a stand)

mitter will cease to function. This may occur, for example, if a meteoric particle pierces the satellite's casing or damages an antenna. Moreover, the satellite has a limited supply of electric energy. After the transmitter stops functioning, observation of the satellite will be conducted by optical methods and radiolocators.

Of great importance are observations of the propagation of the radio waves emitted by the satellite. So far, the basic information about the ionosphere has been obtained through study of radio waves sent from the earth and reflected from regions of the ionosphere lying below the level of maximum ionization of the ionospheric layers. It it not known at present, in fact, at what heights the upper boundary of the ionosphere lies. The launching of the satellite makes it possible to receive for a long time radio signals of two different frequencies from regions of the ionosphere that lie above the level of maximum ionization, and perhaps, above the ionosphere altogether — regions heretofore inaccessible for prolonged observations.

Measurements of the levels of the signals received and of the angles of refraction of radio waves of different frequencies makes it possible to obtain data on the attenuation of radio waves in the hitherto unexplored regions of the ionosphere and certain information on the structure of these regions.

The program of scientific measurements in artificial earth satellites is very extensive and embraces many divisions of the physics of the upper layers of the atmosphere and the study of cosmic space near the earth.

These questions include: the study of the state of the ionosphere, its chemical composition, pressure and density measurements, magnetic measurements, the study of the nature of the sun's corpuscular radiation, the primary composition and variations of cosmic rays, the ultraviolet and roentgen portions of the solar spectrum, as well as the electrostatic fields in the upper layers of the atmosphere and microparticles. Already the first satellite will yield information on a number of these questions.

Regarding the study of cosmic rays, the program provides for obtaining data on the relative content of the various nuclei in primary cosmic radiation. In particular, the relative content of lithium, beryllium, and boron nuclei will be determined, as well as highly charged nuclei. In this respect it will be possible to obtain data inaccessible to research methods previously employed.

The equipment installed in the satellite also makes it possible to study the variations of the total cosmic ray flux, the study of which is hampered by the great thickness of the atmosphere, which is above the apparatus when it is located on the earth. The data thus obtained will make it possible to reveal the daily, half-daily, and 27-day variations and to study their connection with the phenomena on the sun. The satellite makes it possible to conduct the above measurements over the entire globe.

The sun's shortwave radiation has not been studied so far because of its absorption by the atmosphere. The great heights at which the satellite is revolving make it possible to study the ultraviolet and roentgen portions of the solar spectrum and to reveal the variations in radiation intensity by means of instruments developed by our physicists. This is important, since according to modern ideas, the sun's short wave radiation causes the ionization of the upper layers of the atmosphere. Consequently, these results will shed new light on the processes of formation of the ionosphere. Since the sun's shortwave radiation is caused by the solar corona, data about it will make it possible to obtain new results about the structure of the solar corona.

The sun's corpuscular radiation, as well as its short wave radiation, plays a tremendous role in the processes that are taking place in the upper layers of the atmosphere. For this reason it is important to establish the nature of corpuscular radiation, its intensity, by the energetic spectrum of the particles ejected by the sun, and to explain the role of the sun's corpuscular radiation in the formation of the polar aurorae. These questions also will be settled by means of the equipment installed in the artificial earth satellites.

\* \* \*

The satellite's flight above the ionized layers of the atmosphere makes it possible to verify a number of conclusions made on the basis of one hypothesis or another concerning the circular currents existing in the upper layers of the atmosphere. Artificial satellites will also make it possible to study the rapid variations in the earth's magnetic field.

Of considerable interest is the study at great heights (of the order of 1000 kilometers) of electrostatic fields and the answer to the question whether the earth and its atmosphere is a charged or a neutral system. Besides the study of the ionosphere by the indirect methods of observing the passage of radio waves, the program of research in satellites provides for direct measurements of ion concentration at various heights and, in the future also, of the chemical composition of the ionosphere by mass spectrometric methods. If modern ideas that negative ions are absent at great heights are correct, these experiments will yield complete information on the composition of the ionosphere.

Without dwelling on all the scientific observations that are being, and will be, conducted in satellites during the International Geophysical Year, we shall mention the investigations of meteoric matter in the upper layers of the atmosphere. It is planned to obtain mass and velocity spectra of the microparticles that strike the atmosphere from cosmic space.

The artificial satellite is the first step in the conquest of cosmic space. For the transition to manned cosmic flights it is necessary to study the effects of the conditions of cosmic flight on living organisms. This study should be conducted in the first instance on animals. Just as it was done in high altitude rockets, the Soviet Union will launch a satellite having animals on board as passengers, and detailed observations of their behavior and the course of their physiological processes will be conducted.

It can be said with confidence that the realization of the planned program of scientific investigations by means of artificial earth satellites will play a revolutionary role in many problems of physics, geophysics, and astrophysics.

With the successful launching of the artificial earth satellite, science and technology are making a new, qualitative leap, taking the direct methods of scientific measurements into hitherto inaccessible cosmic space and paving wide roads for future interplanetary travels. (*Pravda*, October 9, 1957.)

---

[1] *Radio*, No. 7, July, 1957, pp 17-23; No. 8, August, 1957, pp 17-20.

# APPENDICES

*"One of the immediate tasks of the Commission is to organize work concerned with building an automatic laboratory for scientific research in space. Since outside the limits of the atmosphere, such a cosmic laboratory, which will revolve round the earth as its satellite for a long time, will permit observations that are not accessible for investigation under ordinary terrestrial conditions, scientists will be able to study conditions of life when the physicists will be able to observe the ultraviolet radiation of the sun, and to learn much concerning conditions...*

## APPENDIX A

## GOLD MEDAL ESTABLISHED FOR OUTSTANDING WORK IN THE FIELD OF INTERPLANETARY COMMUNICATIONS

The Presidium of the USSR Academy of Sciences at its September 24th meeting adopted a resolution establishing the K. E. Tsiolkovskii Gold Medal for outstanding work in the field of interplanetary communications.

K. E. Tsiolkovskii, the founder of astronautics, was the first to put the problem of flight in world space on a scientific basis. He devised a rocket aircraft for interplanetary communications and worked out the principles of the theory of the motion of this device. Tsiolkovskii showed, for the first time, that in order to overcome the force of the earth's attraction, it is necessary to make use of precisely the principle of jet propulsion and that only in this way can the necessary speed be provided. The scientist derived a fundamental formula in which he shows how the speed of this cosmic rocket can increase as its fuel gradually burns away.

The best papers by Soviet scientists working in the field of astronautics will be awarded the K. E. Tsiolkovskii Gold Medal. The Presidium of the USSR Academy of Sciences will award this medal once every three years for the most outstanding work in the field of interplanetary communications. (*Pravda*, September 25, 1954.)

## APPENDIX B

## COMMISSION ON INTERPLANETARY COMMUNICATIONS

A permanent interdepartmental Commission on Interplanetary Communications has been established under the Astronomy Council of the USSR Academy of Sciences. The Commission must coordinate and direct all work concerned with solving the problem of mastering cosmic space.

Comrade A. G. Karpenko, scientific secretary of the Commission, reported the following to a *Vechernyaya Moskva* correspondent:

"The problem of realizing interplanetary communications is undoubtedly one of the most important tasks among those which mankind will have to solve on the way to conquering nature. The successful solution of this task will become possible only as a result of the active participation of many scientific and technological collectives. It is precisely for the unification and guidance of those collective efforts of research workers that the permanent interdepartmental Commission on Interplanetary Communications has been established at the USSR Academy of Sciences. The Commission is headed by Academician L. I. Sedov and is composed of outstanding scientists—physicists, mechanical engineers, astrophysicists, and others—among them Academicians P. L. Kapitsa and V. A. Ambartsumyan, Corresponding Member of the USSR Academy of Sciences P. P. Parenago, Doctor of Physics and Mathematics B. V. Kukarkin, and others.

"One of the immediate tasks of the Commission is to organize work concerned with building an automatic laboratory for scientific research in space. Since it is outside the limits of the atmosphere, such a cosmic laboratory, which will revolve around the earth as its satellite for a long time, will permit observations of phenomena that are not accessible for investigation under ordinary terrestrial conditions. Thus, biologists will be able to study conditions of life when the force of gravity is absent; astrophysicists will be able to observe the ultraviolet and X-ray spectra of the radiation of the sun and the stars and to learn much about the processes which are taking place on these bodies. Such a laboratory will enable radiophysicists to study more completely the processes which take place in the ionosphere and to determine the most advantageous conditions for establishing radio communications with the space ships of the future. Geophysicists and geographers will be able to provide more accurate results in forecasting the weather and northern navigation by photographing at any moment the disposition of ice floes in the Arctic Ocean and of clouds in the atmosphere.

"The creation of a cosmic laboratory will be the first step in solving the problem of interplanetary communications and will enable our scientists to probe more deeply into the secrets of the universe." (*Vechernyaya Moskva*, April 16, 1955.)

APPENDIX C

INTERNATIONAL CONGRESS OF ASTRONAUTS

Soviet scientists Academician L. I. Sedov and Professor K. F. Ogorodnikov are in Copenhagen attending the International Congress of Astronauts as observers. At the press conference which took place yesterday in the building of the Soviet Legation, Academician L. I. Sedov told Danish and foreign reporters about the work of Soviet scientists in the field of astronautics.

"At the USSR Academy of Sciences," said Academician L. I. Sedov, "an interdepartmental commission has been formed for coordinating research work in the field of interplanetary communications. This commission consists of scientists of various specialities. Several very prominent experts are cooperating in it. Recently in the USSR much consideration has been given to research problems connected with the realization of interplanetary communications, particularly the problems of creating an artificial earth satellite. The practicability of technological artificial satellite projects is already well known to engineers, designers, and scientific workers engaged in or interested in rocket technology. In my opinion, it will be possible to launch an artificial earth satellite within the next two years, and there is a technological possibility of creating artificial satellites of various sizes and weights.

"From a technical point of view, it is possible to create a satellite of larger dimensions than that reported in the newspapers which we had the opportunity of scanning today. The realization of the Soviet project can be expected in the comparatively near future. I won't take it upon myself to name the date more precisely.

"We hope," continued Academician Sedov, "that specific problems of creating an artificial satellite will be discussed at this Congress. It seems to me that the time has come when it is possible to direct all forces and means toward mutual efforts for creating an artificial satellite and to switch the military potential in the technology of rockets to the peaceful and noble purposes of developing cosmic flights. I think that such work would be an important contribution to the cause of eliminating the cold war and would serve the cause of consolidating peace."

The Soviet scientist's announcement greatly interested the reporters. All newspapers today are publishing extensive accounts of the press conference. (A Tass dispatch from Copenhagen dated August 3, 1955. It appeared in *Pravda*, August 5, 1955.)

## "DISCOVERY OF A WORLD"—A BOOK REVIEW BY N. VARVAROV

The new book, *Discovery of a World*, by B. Lyapunov[1] is devoted to one of the most grandiose and important problems for the further progress of science and technology—the problem of mastering world space. In lively, fascinating, and laconic form the author tells not only about the achievements of jet technology, nuclear physics, electronic automatics, astronomy, and other fields of knowledge which have a direct bearing on the problem considered, but also about their brilliant prospects.

In the book, scientific fantasy is closely interwoven with the achievements of science and technology which open the way to the future.

In the first chapter the author considers in detail the fundamental obstacles standing in the way to world space; gravity and the resistance of the earth's atmosphere.

In the chapter "Explorers of Great Altitudes" the author talks about how our knowledge of the atmosphere has broadened.

The chapters "By Rocket into the Universe" and "Discovery of a World" are devoted to an account of the basic hypothical stages of mastering world space and the significance of the solution of this problem for the further progress of science and technology.

In fascinating form the author tells of journeys to the moon, Mars, Venus, and other planets of the solar system. At the same time the reader learns about the weather conditions prevailing on these planets and about the possibility of the existence of plant and animal life on them.

In the concluding chapter, "The Way to the Stars," the question of the possibility of flight beyond the limits of the solar system is considered.

This interesting and entertaining book by Engineer Lyapunov has, however, several very essential defects.

In many cases the author, while explaining a story, does not tell about the latest information on one question or another. Thus, for example, on page 70 he writes: ". . .Professor Oberth calculated that a rocket must travel 500 years before encountering a celestial wanderer (meteor—N.V.). Such an estimate is 30 years old. Contemporary data are far less optimistic; they greatly increase the probability of an encounter with a meteor." It is impossible to understand why one should cite a 30-year-old estimate when there is a more realistic estimate given by Doctor of Technical Sciences Professor K. P. Stanyukovich.

In explaining the flight-to-the-moon project advanced by English scientists, the author does not even mention the project of Soviet investigators, which, in our opinion, is more realistic.

Considering the questions of radio control of the cosmic rocket in flight, the author does not point out the work in this field by Candidate of Technical Sciences Yu. S. Khlebtsevich, who suggested a highly original project for the flight control of a rocket flying to the moon. Indicating that the sun, together with the neighboring stars, rotates around the center of the galaxy with a velocity of 240 kilometers per second, the author does not mention that this velocity was first determined by Soviet scientist Corresponding Member of the USSR Academy of Sciences P. P. Parenago.

All this bewilders the reader: 20 and 30 years ago many scientists were working in the field of astronautics, but who has done what in recent years is not known.

The author has not mentioned the work conducted in our country today on mastering cosmic space. But one should point out not only that the members of a public scientific organization—the astronautics section of the V. P. Chkalov Central Aeroclub—are engaged in this work, but that members of both the permanent interdepartmental Commission on Interplanetary Communications and the institutes of the USSR Academy of Sciences are doing important organizational and scientific work.

Despite the defects indicated, the book by B. V. Lyapunov will be read with interest by youth and will do it unquestionable good by broadening the concept of the universe. (*Tekhnika-Molodezhi*, September, 1955. The author is identified as "Chairman of the Astronautics Section of the V. P. Chkalov Central Aeroclub.")

¹ *Otkrytie Mira*, Izd. "Molodaya Gvardiya," Moscow, 1954, 160 pp.

## APPENDIX E
## COMPETITION FOR THE K. E. TSIOLKOVSKII GOLD MEDAL

The Presidium of the USSR Academy of Sciences announces the competition for the K. E. Tsiolkovskii Gold Medal.

The K. E. Tsiolkovskii Medal will be awarded to Soviet and foreign scientists for original work of major significance in the development of astronautics.

Work completed between 1950 and 1956 may be entered in the competition for the K. E. Tsiolkovskii Medal for 1957.

Work in competition for the K. E. Tsiolkovskii Medal may be submitted by scientific societies, scientific research institutes, higher educational institutions, public organizations and indivduals.

Work in competition for the K. E. Tsiolkovskii Medal should be submitted before April 1, 1957, to the Permanent Interdepartmental Commission for Coordination and Control of Scientific-Technical works in the Field of the Organization and Realization of Interplanetary Communications (Room 97, Bol'-shaya Gruzinskaya 10, Moscow D-56).

Works with the inscription "In competition for the K. E. Tsiolkovskii Medal" are to be presented in triplicate, typed or printed, together with references and a brief biography of the author and a list of his principal scientific works and inventions. (*Izvestiya*, September 28, 1956.)

APPENDIX F
# NOTICE TO RADIO AMATEURS

The Institute of Radio Engineering and Electronics of the USSR Academy of Sciences asks radio amateurs to report on the preparation for the reception of signals from satellites launched in the USSR, to send a description of the radio equipment, and after observation of the satellite, to report the radio signal data and to forward the magnetic tapes with the recorded signals to the address: Moscow, K-9, Makhovaya ul., 11, IRE AN SSSR.

In the report it is desirable to indicate:

1. The point of observation.
2. The date of observation.
3. The Moscow time (the beginning of reception, the end of reception, and the moment of greatest signal strength).
4. How the time was recorded (by an ordinary adjusted clock or if nationwide time signals were used).
5. The frequencies of the signals received.
6. The peculiarities of reception (signal fading, signal loss, and its origin by jump, etc.).
7. The speed of signal manipulation.
8. The moment of passage of the equisignal zone (when using the direction-finding unit) or the moment of the speediest passage (when using the Doppler effect).
9. The meteorological conditions at the moment of reception (cloudiness, precipitation, etc.).
10. Type of receiver or receiving apparatus.
11. Type of antenna and its installation point (surrounding objects).
12. Type of recorder and magnetic tape speed (in millimeters per second).
13. The observer's surname, name, and patronymic, and his exact address and radio amateur experience.

Immediately at the end of reception of the signals please report briefly by telegram the place of reception, the date, the time (Moscow), and the signal frequency to the address: Moskva—Sputnik. (*Radio,* No. 7, July, 1957. The article did not appear under any title.)

APPENDIX G
# REGULATIONS OF THE INTERDEPARTMENTAL COMMISSION ON INTERPLANETARY COMMUNICATIONS

Regulations concerning the Interdepartmental Commission for the Coordination and Control of Scientific-Theoretical Work in the Field of Organization and Accomplishment of Interplanetary Communications of the Astronomical Council of the USSR Academy of Sciences.

1. The fundamental task of the Interdepartmental Commission for the Coordination and Control of Scientific-Theoretical Work in the Field of Organization and Accomplishment of Interplanetary Communications is to assist in every way the development of scientific-theoretical and practical work in the Soviet Union concerning questions of studying cosmic space and the achievement of interplanetary communications.

2. The Commission is charged with:

(a) Taking actions which secure the active participation of academic and branch scientific research establishments in work for the investigation of cosmic space.

(b) Organization of work on drawing up problems, plans, and programs of scientific investigations on the fundamental trends of astronautics.

(c) Broad attraction of scientific-research establishments, of universities and individual investigators to the solution of problems to secure the realization of flight into cosmic space.

(d) Coordination of scientific activities of individual research institutions on problems of astronautics.

(e) Popularization of the tasks and achievements in the field of astronautics.

3. The Interdepartmental Commission on Interplanetary Communications inquires into plans and reports concerning the activities of scientific research institutes which work on the program controlled by the Commission.

4. The Commission at its discretion summons coordinating meetings and scientific-theoretical conferences concerning the problems of astronautics.

5. The Commission organizes competitions and carries out the examination of scientific research works submitted in the competition for the K. E. Tsiolkovskii Gold Medal.

6. The Commission through the Foreign action of the USSR Academy of Sciences maintains connections with scientific organizations in foreign countries, which are working in the field of investigation of cosmic space and the achievement of interplanetary communications.

7. The Interdepartmental Commission on Interplanetary Communications comes under the Astronomical Council of the USSR Academy of Sciences. (Submitted by Academician L. I. Sedov to the International Astronautics Federation in October, 1957.)

APPENDIX H

## MEMBERS OF THE INTERDEPARTMENTAL COMMISSION ON INTERPLANETARY COMMUNICATIONS

List of Members of the Interdepartmental Commission on Interplanetary Communications of the Astronomical Council of the USSR Academy of Sciences.

1. Sedov, L. I. — Academician, Chairman
2. Petrov, G. I. — Corresponding Member of the USSR Academy of Sciences, Vice Chairman
3. Levin, B. Yu. — Doctor of Physico-Mathematical Sciences
4. Lavrent'ev, M. A. — Academician, Mathematical Institute of the USSR Academy of Sciences
5. Kapitsa, P. L. — Academician, Physical Laboratory of the USSR Academy of Sciences
6. Bogolyubov, N. N. — Academician, Mathematical Institute of the USSR Academy of Sciences
7. Blagonravov, A. A. — Academician, Mechanical Engineering Institute of the USSR Academy of Sciences

| | | |
|---|---|---|
| 8. | Ambartsumyan, V. A. | Academician, President, Armenian SSR Academy of Sciences |
| 9. | Lebedev, S. A. | Academician, Institute of Precision Mechanics and Computer Engineering of the USSR Academy of Sciences |
| 10. | Parenago, P. P. | Corresponding Member of the USSR Academy of Sciences, State Astronomical Institute |
| 11. | Ginzburg, V. L. | Corresponding Member of the USSR Academy of Sciences, Physical Institute of the USSR Academy of Sciences |
| 12. | Trapeznikov, V. A. | Corresponding Member of the USSR Academy of Sciences, Institute of Automatics and Telemechanics of the USSR Academy of Sciences |
| 13. | Petrov, B. N. | Corresponding Member of the USSR Academy of Sciences, Institute of Automatics and Telemechanics of the USSR Academy of Sciences |
| 14. | Frank-Kamenetskii, D. N. | Doctor of Chemical Sciences |
| 15. | Khaikin, S. E. | Doctor of Physico-Mathematical Sciences, Chief of the Astronomical Observatory |
| 16. | Pokrovskii, G. I. | Doctor of Technical Sciences, Military Air Academy |
| 17. | Vanichev, A. P. | Doctor of Technical Sciences |
| 18. | Pobedonostsev, Yu. A. | Doctor of Technical Sciences |
| 19. | Duboshkin, G. N. | Doctor of Physico-Mathematical Sciences |
| 20. | Stanyukovich, K. P. | Doctor of Technical Sciences, Moscow Higher Technical College im. Bauman |
| 21. | Bolkhovitinov, V. F. | Doctor of Technical Sciences, Military Air Academy |
| 22. | Florov, Yu. A. | Chief Designer, Central Scientific Institute of Aircraft Engine Construction im. Baranov |
| 23. | Barabashev, N. P. | Academician, Ukrainian SSR Academy of Sciences |
| 24. | Masevich, A. G. | Candidate of Physico-Mathematical Sciences |
| 25. | Markov, A. V. | Doctor of Physico-Mathematical Sciences |
| 26. | Okhotsimskii, D. E. | Candidate of Physico-Mathematical Sciences |
| 27. | Karpenko, A. G. | Scientific Secretary of the Commission |

(Submitted by Academician L. I. Sedov to the International Astronautical Federation in October, 1957.)

# BIBLIOGRAPHY

# I. BOOKS AND MONOGRAPHS

Abiants, V. Kh., *Reaktivnye dvigateli* (Jet engines), Izd. *Znanie*, Moscow, 1955, 32 pp.
Stenogram of a public lecture read in Moscow before the All-Union Society for the Propagation of Political and Scientific Information, Series 4, No. 24.

Abramovich, G. N., *Gazovaya dinamika vozdushno-reaktivnykh dvigatelei* (Gas dynamics of air reactive engines), Izd. BNT, Moscow, 1947.

————, *Prikladnaya gazovaya dinamika* (Applied gas dynamics), Gostekhizdat, Moscow, 1951, 511 pp; 2d ed., 1953, 736 pp.
A textbook for higher technical schools and aviation institutes.

Agrenich, A., *Ot kamnya do sovremennogo snaryada* (From stone to modern missile), Voenizdat, Moscow, 1954, 163 pp.
A historical sketch.

Aizerman, M. A., *Lektsii po teorii avtomaticheskogo regulirovaniya* (Lectures on the theory of automatic control), Gostekhizdat, Moscow, 1956, 427 pp.
Bibliography contains 369 references.

Ambartsumyan, V. A., E. R. Mustel', A. B. Severnyi, and V. V. Sobolev, *Teoreticheskaya astrofizika* (Theoretical astrophysics), V. A. Ambartsumyan (ed.), Gostekhizdat, Moscow, 1952, 636 pp.

Aralazorov, M. S., *Konstantin Eduardovich Tsiolkovskii, ego zhizn' i deyatelnost'* (Konstantin Eduardovich Tsiolkovskii, his life and work), Gostekhizdat, Moscow, 1952, 128 pp.

Armstrong, G., *Aviatsionnaya meditsina* (Aviation medicine), Izd. Inostrannoi Literatury, Moscow, 1954, 518 pp.
This is a translation of the book by H. G. Armstrong, *Principles and practice of aviation medicine*, The Williams and Wilkins Company, Baltimore, 3d ed., 1952.

*Atmosfera Zemli* (The earth's atmosphere), Goskul'tprosvetizdat, Moscow, 1953, 424 pp.
A collection.

*Atmosfery Zemli i planet* (The atmospheres of the earth and planets), G. P. Kuiper (ed.), Izd. Inostrannoi Literatury, Moscow, 1951.
This is a translation of the book *The atmospheres of the earth and planets*, G. P. Kuiper (ed.), The University of Chicago Press, Chicago, 1949, vii + 366 pp., 16 plates. Chapter IV, "The Upper Atmosphere Studied from Rockets" ("Izuchennie verkhnikh sloev zemnoi atmosfery s pomoshch'yu raket") is frequently referred to in the Russian literature.

Baev, L. K., and I. A. Merkulov, *Samolet-raketa: Reaktivnaya aviatsiya* (The rocket airplane: Jet aviation), 2d ed., Gostekhizdat, Moscow, 1953, 64 pp. See the review by G. V. E. Thompson, *Journal British Interplanetary Society*, Vol. 13, No. 1, January, 1954, p. 59.

Barabashev, N. P., *Issledovanie fizicheskikh uslovii na Lune i planetakh* (Investigation of the physical conditions of the moon and the planets), Izd. Khar'kovskogo Gosudarstvennogo Universiteta, Khar'kov, 1952, 272 pp.

Bobrov, N. N., *Bol'shaya zhizn': Konstantin Eduardovich Tsiolkovskii* (A great life: Konstantin Eduardovich Tsiolkovskii), Aviaavtoizdat, Moscow and Leningrad, 1937, 168 pp.

Bolgarskii, A. V., and V. K. Shchukin, *Rabochie protsessy v zhidkostno-reaktivnykh dvigatelyakh* (Working processes in liquid rocket engines), Oborongiz, Moscow, 1953, 424 pp.
A textbook for aviation institutes. Appendix IV lists basic data for sixteen rocket engines—thirteen German, two American, and one British. The bibliography lists 32 references.

*Bol'shaya Sovetskaya Entsiklopediya* (Large Soviet Encyclopedia), 2d ed.:
"Bespilotnaya aviatsiya" (Pilotless aviation), Vol. 5, September 19, 1950, pp. 76–77.
"Zhidkostno-reaktivnyi dvigatel' " (Liquid-jet engine), Vol. 16, October 18, 1952, p. 132.
"Mezhplanetnye soobshcheniya" (Interplanetary communications), by M. K. Tikhonravov, Vol. 27, June 18, 1954, pp. 51–53.
"Porokhovoi raketnyi dvigatel' " (Powder rocket engine), Vol. 34, June 20, 1955, p. 178.
"Puskovye raketnye prisposobleniya" (Rocket launching devices), Vol. 35, June 23, 1955, pp. 312–313.
"Raketa" (Rocket), by M. K. Tikhonravov and B. V. Lyapunov, Vol. 35, July 23, 1955, pp. 665–668.
"Reaktivnoe vooruzhenie" (Rocket armament), by V. F. Zamkovets, Vol. 36, September 14, 1955, pp. 139–140.
"Reaktivnyi dvigatel' " (Reactive engine), by N. V. Inozemtsev, Vol. 36, September 14, 1955, pp. 142–150.

Britske, E. V., *et al.*, *Termokhimicheskii konstanty neorganicheskikh veshchestv* (Thermochemical constants of inorganic substances), Izd. Akademii Nauk SSSR, Moscow, 1949.

Chechik, P. O., *Radioteknika i electronika v astronomii* (Radiotechnology and electronics in astronomy), Gosenergizdat, Moscow and Leningrad, 1953, 104 pp.

Chernyshev, N. G., *Khimiya raketnykh topliv* (Chemistry of rocket fuels), Gosenergoizdat, Moscow and Leningrad, 1948, 352 pp.
This book contains an analysis of the properties and a critical evaluation of a large number of rocket fuels actual and potential.

————, *Rol' russkoi nauchno-tekhnicheskoi mysli v razrabotke osnov reaktivnogo letaniya* (The role of Russian scientific-technical thought in developing the principles of jet flight), Izd. MVTU im. Baumana, Moscow, 1949.

————, *Problema mezhplanetnykh soobshchenii v rabotakh K. E. Tsiolkovskogo i drugikh otchestvennykh uchenykh* (The problem of interplanetary communications in the works of K. E. Tsiolkovskii and other native scientists), Izd. *Znanie*, Moscow, 1953, 32 pp.

Dobronravov, V. V., *Kosmicheskaya navigatsiya* (Cosmic navigation), Izd. *Znanie*, Moscow, 1956, 32 pp.
A public lecture read before the All-Union Society for the Propagation of Political and Scientific Information, Series 4, No. 7.

Esnault-Pelterie, R., *Kosmicheskie polety* (Cosmic flights), Prof. A. A. Kosmodem'yanskii (ed.), Oborongiz, Moscow, 1950, 148 pp.
Translation from the French *l'Astronautique*, 1935.

Fedulov, I. F., and V. A. Kireev, *Uchebnik fizicheskoi khimii* (Textbook of physical chemistry), 4th ed., Goskhimizdat, Moscow, 1954, 487 pp.

Feodos'ev, V. I., and G. B. Sinyarev, *Vvedenie v raketnuyu tekhniku* (Introduction to rocket technology), Oborongiz, Moscow, 1956, 376 pp.
A textbook for higher technical institutions. Well illustrated (289 figures). The bibliography lists 27 references.

Fesenkov, V. G., *Kosmicheskoe prostranstvo* (Cosmic space), Izd. Akademii Nauk Kazakhskoi SSR, Alma Ata, 1948, 17 pp.

*Fizika i khimiya reaktivnogo dvizheniya* (Physics and chemistry of jet propulsion), A. S. Sokolnik (ed.), Gosinoizdat, Moscow: Sbornik 1, 1948, 235 pp.; Sbornik 2, 1949, 200 pp.; Sbornik 3, 1949, 188 pp.
These are collections of papers translated from the English, French, and German. There is a review of Sbornik 1 by A. D. Petrov in *Uspekhi Khimii*, Vol. 18, No. 3, 1949, p. 372. Sbornik 2 was used as a reference by M. K. Tikhonravov in his *Bol'shaya Sovetskaya Entsiklopediya* article on "Mezhplanetnye soobshcheniya."

Gil'zin, K. A., *Raketnye dvigateli* (Rocket engines), Oborongiz, Moscow, 1950, 84 pp.

————, *Ot rakety do kosmicheskogo korablya* (From rocket to cosmic ship), Oborongiz, Moscow, 1954, 112 pp.
This book is a second, revised edition of the author's *Raketnye dvigateli* published in 1950. Chapter 6 "Budushchee raketnykh dvigateli" (Future of rocket engines)

discusses long-range high-speed flights, earth satellites, interplanetary flights, and atomic-rocket technology. This popular book has had two printings (August 25, 1954, and February 18, 1955) of 25,000 copies each.

————, *Puteshestvie k dalekim miram* (Voyage to distant worlds), Detgiz, Moscow, 1956, 280 pp.
This is the most comprehensive of the recent Soviet books on astronautics.

Glushko, V. P., *Zhidkoe toplivo dlya reaktivnykh dvigatelei* (Liquid fuel for jet engines), Part 1, Izd. VVIA, Moscow, 1936, 224 pp.
Course of lectures given at the Military Air Academy.

Godnev, L. N., *Vychislenie termodinamicheskikh funktsii po molekulyarnym dannym* (Computing thermodynamic functions from molecular data), Gostekhizdat, Moscow, 1956, 419 pp.

Gukhman, A. A., and N. V. Ilyukhin, *Osnovy ucheniya o teploobmene pri techenii gaza s bol'shoi skorost'ya* (Fundamentals of heat exchange in high speed gas flow), Mashgiz, Moscow, 1951, 226 pp.

Il'yashenko, S. M., *Bystree zvuka: O reaktivnykh dvigatelykh* (Faster than sound: About jet engines), Voenizdat, Moscow, 1948, 56 pp.

————, *Reaktivnaya tekhnika* (Jet technology), Izd. DOSARM, Moscow, 1951, 78 pp.

Inozemtsev, N. V., *Osnovy termodinamiki i kinetiki khimicheskikh reaktsii* (Principles of thermodynamics and kinetics of chemical reactions), Mashgiz, Moscow, 1950, 209 pp.

————, *Osnovy teorii reaktivnykh dvigatelei* (Principles of the theory of jet engines), Izd. DOSAAF, Moscow, 1952, 200 pp.

————, and V. S. Zuev, *Aviatsionnye gazoturbinnye dvigateli* (Aviation gas turbine engines), Oborongiz, Moscow, 1949, 468 pp.

Kalinovskii, A. B., and N. Z. Pinus, *Aerologiya: Metody aerologicheskikh nablyudenii* (Aerology: Methods of aerological observation), Gidrometeoizdat, Leningrad, 1951, 452 pp.
This is a textbook for hydrometeorological institutes. Chapter XII, "Primenenie raket dlya issledovaniy atmosfery" (Use of rockets for investigation of the atmosphere), pp. 400–409, has sketches of three rockets: the first Soviet meteorological rocket designed in 1933 by M. K. Tikhonravov, the V-2 rocket, and the Wac-Corporal rocket. It also has a table of basic characteristics for the V-2 and Wac-Corporal rockets. The chapter lists fourteen references, three of which are papers by M. V. Machinskii and A. N. Shtern, N. A. Rynin, and M. K. Tikhonravov which were presented at the All-Union Conference on the Study of the Stratosphere held in Leningrad, March 31–April 6, 1934.

Karagodin, V. M., *Nekotorye voprosy mekhaniki tela peremennoi massy*

(Some problems in the mechanics of a body of variable mass), Moskovskii aviatsionnyi tekhnologicheskii institut, No. 63, Oborongiz, Moscow, 1956, 30 pp.

Karpenko, A. G., *Problemy kosmicheskikh poletov* (The problems of cosmic flights), Izd. *Znanie*, Moscow, 1955, 24 pp.
> A popular lecture given at the Polytechnical Museum in the cycle "Contemporary problems of astronautics." All-Union Society for the Propagation of Political and Scientific Information, Series 4, No. 25.

Khitrin, L. I., *Fizika goreniya i vzryva* (The physics of combustion and explosion), Izd. Moskovskogo Universiteta, Moscow, 1957, 442 pp.

Khlebtsevich, Yu. S., *Radioteleupravlenie kosmicheskimi raketami* (Radio-telecontrol of cosmic rockets), Izd. *Znanie*, Moscow, 1955, 32 pp.
> From a Sunday lecture given at the Polytechnical Museum in the cycle "Contemporary problems of astronautics." All-Union Society for the Propagation of Political and Scientific Information, Series 4, No. 39.

Klement'ev, S. D., *Avtomatika i telemekhanika* (Automatics and telemechanics), F. E. Temnikov (ed.), Gostekhizdat, Moscow, 1955, 292 pp.
> This book is a popular exposition of a rapidly developing subject. It contains a two-part bibliography that lists 15 popular-science books and 24 technical books. Of particular interest is Chapter XII, "Radiotelemekhanika" (Radiotelemechanics), pp. 258–282, which discusses, among other things, radio guidance of aircraft and of the V-2 missile. Pages 277–282 are devoted to a discussion of the method of telemetering used in connection with the high-altitude research with V-2 rockets at White Sands, New Mexico, in 1946. The information, including a sketch of a V-2 rocket equipped for study of the ionosphere, and block diagrams of the airborne telemetering unit and of the ground-station telemetering system, was ostensibly, though not admittedly, taken from the two-part article entitled "Telemetering from V-2 rockets" by V. L. Heeren, C. H. Hoeppner, J. R. Kauke, S. W. Lichtman, and P. R. Shifflett in *Electronics*, Vol. 20, No. 3, March, 1947, pp. 104–105; Vol. 20, No. 4, April, 1947, pp. 124–127.

Knorre, G. F., *Topochnye protsessy* (Combustion processes), Gosenergoizdat, Moscow, 1951.

———, *Chto takoe gorenie?* (What is combustion?), Gosenergoizdat, Moscow, 1955, 224 pp.
> A popular scientific exposition of the physical principles of the process of combustion.

Kolesnikov, A. A., *Osnovy teorii reaktivnykh dvigatelei* (Principles of the theory of jet engines), Voenizdat, Moscow, 1947, 124 pp.

Kondratyuk, Yu. V., *Zavoevanie mezhplanetnykh prostranstv* (Conquest of interplanetary spaces), Novosibirsk, 1929; P. I. Ivanov (ed.), 2d ed., Oborongiz, Moscow, 1947, 84 pp.

Kooy, J., and J. Uytenbogaart, *Dinamika raket* (Dynamics of rockets), Prof. A. A. Kosmodem'yanskii (ed.), Oborongiz, Moscow, 1950, 328 pp.
A translation of the book *Ballistics of the future, with special reference to the dynamical and physical theory of the rocket weapons.*

Korolev, S. P., *Raketnyi polet v stratosfere* (Rocket flight in the stratosphere), Voenizdat, Moscow, 1934, 108 pp.
A pioneer work in the study of the upper atmosphere.

Kosmodem'yanskii, A. A., *Obshchie teoremy mekhaniki tela peremennoi massy* (General theorems of the mechanics of a body of variable mass), Izd. VVIV (Voenno-vozdushnoi inzhenernoi akademii imeni Zhukovskogo), Moscow, 1946, 16 pp.

————, *Mekhanika tel peremennoi massy; teoriya reaktivnogo dvizheniya* (Mechanics of bodies of variable mass; theory of jet propulsion), Izd. VVIA (Voenno-vozdushnoi inzhenernoi akademii imeni Zhukovskogo), Moscow, 1947, 110 pp.

————, *Znamenityi deyatel' nauki Konstantin Eduardovich Tsiolkovskii* (Famous man of science Konstantin Eduardovich Tsiolkovskii), 2d ed., Voenizdat, Moscow, 1954, 1936 pp.

Kozhevnikova, T. B., *Kryl'ya nashei rodiny* (Wings of our motherland), Goskul'tprosvetizdat, Moscow, 1953, 104 pp.

Kozlov, A. S., *Teoriya aviatsionnykh giroskopicheskikh priborov* (Theory of aeronautical gyroscopic instruments), Oborongiz, Moscow, 1956, 256 pp.
A textbook for aeronautical institutes.

Kukarkin, B. V., *Stroenie i razvitie zvezdnogo mira* (Structure and development of the celestial world), P. P. Parenago (ed.), Izd. *Pravda*, Moscow, 1951, 21 pp.
Stenogram of a public lecture read in Moscow.

*Kurs teorii goreniya, detonatsii i vzryva* (A course in the theory of combustion, detonation, and explosion): Kniga I., "Teplovoi vzryv i rasprostranenie plameni v gazakh" (Thermal explosion and propagation of flames in gases), by Ya. B. Zel'dovich and V. V. Voevodskii; Kniga II., "Turbulentnoe i geterogennoe gorenie" (Turbulent and heterogeneous combusion), by Ya. B. Zel'dovich and D. A. Frank-Kamenetskii; Izd. Moskov. Mekhan. Inst., Moscow, 1947, 300 pp.
Reviewed in *Uspekhi Khim*, Vol. 17, 1948, pp. 277–278.

Langemak, G. E., and V. P. Glushko, *Rakety, ikh ustroistvo i primenenie*

(Rockets, their construction and utilization), ONTI, Moscow, 1935, 118 pp.

Leshkovtsev, V. A., *Atomnaya energiya* (Atomic energy), Gostekhizdat, Moscow and Leningrad, 1954, 72 pp.; 2d ed. 1955, 64 pp.

Levinson, Ya. I., *Aerodinamika bol'shikh skorostei* (Aerodynamics of high speeds), 2d ed., B. Ya. Shumyatskii (ed.), Oborongiz, Moscow, 1950, 352 pp.

Lomakin, A. Ya., *Tsentrobezhnye i propellernye nasosy* (Centrifugal and propeller pumps), GONTI, Moscow, 1950.

Lyapunov, A. M., *Obshchaya zadacha ob ustoichivosti dvizheniya* (General problem of steady motion), Gostekhizdat, Moscow, 1950, 471 pp.

Lyapunov, B. V., *Problema mezhplanetnykh puteshestvii v trudakh otechestvennykh uchenykh* (The problem of interplanetary travels in the works of native scientists), Izd. *Pravda*, Moscow, 1951, 24 pp.

————, *Rasskazy ob atmosfere* (Stories about the atmosphere), Detgiz, Moscow and Leningrad, 1951, 96 pp.
The chapter "Raketa—oruzhie nauki" (Rocket—weapon of science), pp. 82–94, is devoted to high-altitude rockets for investigating the atmosphere.

————, *Bor'ba za skorost'* (The struggle for speed), Izd. *Molodaya Gvardiya*, Moscow, 1952, 236 pp.
The chapters "Shturm zvukovogo bar'era" (Storming the sonic barrier), pp. 114–139, and "Kosmicheskii reis" (Cosmic trip), pp. 140–163, are devoted to rocket technology and the prospects of its development.

————, *Raketa: Raketnaya tekhnika i reaktivnaya aviatsiya* (Rocket: Rocket technology and jet aviation), Voenizdat, Moscow, 1954, 128 pp

————, *Otkrytie mira* (Discovery of a world), Izd. *Molodaya Gvardiya*, Moscow, 1954, 160 pp.
For a review of this book, see Appendix D.

————, *Rasskazy o raketakh* (Stories about rockets), 2d ed., Gosenergizdat, Moscow and Leningrad, 1955, 174 pp.
There are five "stories" or chapters in this book. Chapter 5, "Ot fantazii k nauke" (From phantasy to science), pp. 136–165, contains the following sections: 1. Interplanetary travels; 2. The founder of celestial navigation; 3. Artificial earth satellite; 4. Extra-terrestrial station; 5. On the way to the cosmic ship; 6. The road into the universe. The bibliography lists 39 references.

————, *Upravlyaemye snaryady* (Guided missiles), Voenizdat, Moscow, 1956, 139 pp.
A popular account based on non-Russian sources. In the series "Nauchno-populyarnaya biblioteka soldata i matrosa."

————, *Bor'ba za skorost'* (The struggle for speed), 2d ed., Gostekhizdat, Moscow, 1956, 208 pp.

There is a review by Academician A. Blagonravov of this book in *Nauka i Zhizn'*, Vol. 24, No. 5, May, 1957, p. 60.

Malkov, M. P., and K. F. Pavlov, *Spravochnik po glubokomu okhlazhdeniyu v tekhnike* (Handbook on deep refrigeration in technology), Gostekhizdat, Moscow, 1947, 411 pp.

*Mekhanika: Sbornik statei* (Mechanics: Collection of papers), V. V. Dobronravov (ed.), No. 50, Oborongiz, Moscow, 1956, 382 pp.

This collection of 19 papers was published in connection with the 125th anniversary in 1955 of the Moscow Higher Technical College *imeni* Bauman (Bauman Institute). The papers are devoted to the various fields of theoretical mechanics: general analytical dynamics, theory of vibrations, mechanics of a variable mass, gyroscopes, ballistics, friction and wear of machines, gas dynamics, and mathematical analysis. The authors include V. V. Dobronravov, I. N. Veselovskii, N. Ya. Golovin, A. N. Obmorshev, K. P. Stanyukovich, P. V. Orekhov, M. B. Sizov, L. G. Tikhonova, S. M. Ibin, M. F. Khromeenkov, V. P. Kutler, V. F. Krotov, R. Ya. Shostak, and N. V. Sakharov. Of special interest is the paper by Student V. F. Krotov, "Raschet optimal'noi traektorii dlya perekhoda rakety na zadannuyu krugovuyu traektoriyu vokrug Zemli" (Calculation of the optimum trajectory for the transition of a rocket to a given circular trajectory around the earth), pp. 313–334.

Merkin, D. R., *Giroskopicheskie sistemy* (Gyroscopic systems), Gostekhizdat, Moscow, 1956, 300 pp.

The bibliography lists 57 references.

Merkulov, I. A., *Reaktivnaya aviatsiya* (Jet aviation), Izd. *Znanie*, Moscow, 1954, 30 pp.

All-Union Society for the Propagation of Political and Scientific Information, Series 4, No. 26.

————, *Kosmicheskie rakety* (Cosmic rockets), Izd. *Znanie*, Moscow, 1955, 32 pp.

From a Sunday lecture given at the Polytechnical Museum in the cycle "Contemporary problems in astronautics." All-Union Society for the Propagation of Political and Scientific Information, Series 4, No. 36.

Meshcherskii, I. V., *Raboty po mekhanike tel peremennoi massy* (Works on the mechanics of bodies of variable mass with preface and introductory paper by Prof. A. A. Kosmodem'yanskii), Moscow and Leningrad, 1949, 276 pp.

This volume includes the following classic papers: "Dinamika tochki peremennoi massy" (Dynamics of a point of variable mass), 1897, and "Uravneniya dvizheniya tochki peremennoi massy v obshchem sluchae" (Equations of motion of a point with variable mass in the general case), 1904.

Mikheev, M. A., *Osnovy teploperedachi* (Principles of heat transfer), 3d ed., Gosenergoizdat, Moscow, 1953, 393 pp.

Mikoni, K. S., *Sverkhvysotnye polety—budushchee reaktivnykh dvigatelei* (Super high altitude flights—the future of jet engines), Izd. *Molodaya Gvardiya*, Moscow, 1932, 112 pp.

Moskovskii, V. P., and P. T. Astashenkov (eds.), *Problemy ispol'zovaniya atomnoi energii—sbornik statei* (Problems of utilizing atomic energy—a collection of papers), 2d ed., Voenizdat, Moscow, 1956, 624 pp.
Pages 164–179 are devoted to an article entitled "Rakety dlya mezhplanetnykh pereletov" (Rockets for interplanetary flights), by K. P. Stanyukovich. It is an extension of the material presented by the author in Chapter 7.

Naumenko, M., "Raketnaya artilleriya russkoi armii" (Rocket artillery of the Russian army), in the collection: *Iz istorii razvitiya russkoi voenno-tekh-nicheskoi mysli* (From the history of the development of Russian military-technical thought), Voenizdat, Moscow, 1952, pp. 64–87.
An outline of Russian rocket artillery of the 19th century.

Noordung, Hermann, *Problema puteshestviya v mirovom prostranstve* (The problem of travel in world space), ONTI, Glavnaya aviatsionnaya redakt-siya, Moscow and Leningrad, 1935, 96 pp.
An abridged translation by B. M. Ginzburg from the German.

Oberth, H., *Puti osushchestvleniya kosmicheskikh poletov* (*Wege zur Raum-schiffahrt*), B. V. Raushenbakh (ed.), Oborongiz, Moscow, 1948, 232 pp.
Abridged translation of the third German edition.

Ogorodnikov, K. F., *Na chem Zemlya derzhitsya* (What supports the earth), 4th ed., Gostekhizdat, Moscow, 1953, 32 pp.

Oparin, A. I., and V. G. Fesenkov, *Zhizn' vo vselennoi* (Life in the universe), Izd. Akademii Nauk SSSR, Moscow, 1956, 224 pp.
Discussion is limited almost entirely to the habitability of the planets of the solar system.

OSOAVIAKHIM (Society for the Promotion of Defense and Aero-Chemical Development), Stratospheric Committee, Reactive Section, *Reaktivnoe dvizhenie* (Reactive motion), Leningrad and Moscow, 1925, two volumes.

Perel'man, Ya. I., *Mezhplanetnye puteshestviya* (Interplanetary travels), 1915; 10th ed., ONTI, Glavnaya redaktsiya nauchno-populyarnoi i yunosheskoi literatury, Leningrad and Moscow, 1935, 272 pp.
This book was a best seller. More than 150,000 copies were printed—50,000 in the 10th edition.

———, *Polet na Lunu* (Flight to the moon), 1924.

———, *Raketoi na Lunu* (By rocket to the moon), 1930; 3d ed., 1933; 4th ed., Detgiz, Moscow, 1935, 80 pp.

———, *Tsiolkovskii, ego zhizn', izobreteniya i nauchnye trudy* (Tsiolkovskii, his life, inventions, and scientific works), 1932.

———, *K zvezdam na rakete* (By rocket to the stars), 2d ed., Izd. *Ukrainskii Rabotnik*, Khar'kov, 1934, 80 pp.

———, *Tsiolkovskii: Zhizn' i tekhnicheskie idei* (Tsiolkovskii: His life and technical ideas), ONTI, Glavnaya redaktsiya nauchno-populyarnoi i yunosheskoi literatury, Moscow and Leningrad, 1937, 168 pp.

Petrov, V. P., *Upravlyaemye rakety i snaryady* (Guided rockets and missiles), Izd. DOSAAF, Moscow, 1957.
Popular treatment of the principles of construction and operation of rockets and guided missiles.

Pokrovskii, G. I., *Napravlennoe deistvie vzryva* (The directed effect of explosion), Voenizdat, Moscow, 1942.

Primenko, A. E., *Reaktivnye dvigateli, ikh razvitie i primenenie* (Jet engines, their development and application), V. A. Popov (ed.), Oborongiz, Moscow, 1947, 191 pp.

———, *Gazovye turbiny i primenenie ikh v aviatsii* (Gas turbines and their application in aviation), G. S. Zhiritsko (ed.), Oborongiz, Moscow, 1950, 155 pp.

*Raketnaya tekhnika* (Rocket technology), No. 1, I. T. Kleimenov, G. E. Langemak, M. K., Tikhonravov, *et al.* (eds.), ONTI Glavnaya redaktsiya aviatsionnoi literatury, Moscow and Leningrad, 1936, ii + 145 pp.
Collection of papers. Contents: G. E. Langemak, "O edinoi terminologii i sisteme oboznachenii v raketnoi tekhnike" (On a single terminology and system of designations in rocket technology); M. K. Tikhonravov, "Primenenie raket dlya issledovaniya stratosfery" (Use of rockets for investigation of the stratosphere); V. I. Dudakov, "Teoriya poleta krylatoi rakety" (Theory of flight of winged rockets); K. E. Tsiolkovskii, "Energiya khimicheskogo soedineniya veshchestv i vybor sostavnykh chastei vzryva dlya raketnogo dvigatelya" (Energy of chemical combination of substances and choice of explosion components for rocket engines); Yu. A. Pobedonostsev, "O ratsional'nykh razmerakh i vesa rakety" (On rational dimensions and weight of rockets); M. P. Dryazgov, "Voprosy dinamiki porokhovykh krylatykh raket" (Problems of dynamics of winged powder rockets); F. A. Tsander, "Teplovoi raschet raketnogo dvigatelya na zhidkom toplive" (Heat analysis of liquid fuel rocket engines); F. A. Tsander, "Primenenie metallicheskogo topliva v raketnykh dvigatelyakh" (Use of metallic fuels in rocket engines); F. Yakaitis, "Formuly dlya istecheniya gazov iz sopla s uchetom peremennykh teploemkostei" (Formulas for gas flow from nozzles taking into account variable heat capacities)

Rankin, R. A., *Matematicheskaya teoriya dvizheniya neupravlyaemykh raket* (Mathematical theory of the motion of unguided rockets), Gosinoizdat, Moscow, 1951, 160 pp.

Translation of the paper "Mathematical theory of the motion of rotated and unrotated rockets," *Philosophical Transactions of the Royal Society of London*, Series A, Vol. 241, No. 837, March 23, 1949, pp. 457–585.

*Reaktivnoe dvizhenie* (Jet propulsion), A. A. Butlerov, A. A. Verner, P. S. Dubenskii, I. A. Merkulov, M. K. Tikhonravov, A. G. Kostikov (eds.), ONTI, Glavnaya redaktsiya obshchetekhnicheskoi literatury, Leningrad and Moscow, 1935, 154 pp.

Collection of papers by members of the Reactive Group of the Military-Scientific Committee of the Central Council of OSOAVIAKHIM SSSR. Contents: V. A. Davidov, "Puti razvitiya aviatsii i reaktivnoe dvizhenie" (Ways of development of aviation and jet propulsion); L. S. Dushkin, "Osnovnye polozheniya obshchoi teorii reaktivnogo dvizheniya" (Basic assumptions of the general theory of jet propulsion); V. P. Vetchinkin, "Vertikal'noe dvizhenie raket" (The vertical motion of rockets); V. P. Vetchinkin, "Neskol'ko zadach po dinamike reaktivnogo samoleta" (Some problems on the dynamics of the jet airplane); M. K. Tikhonravov, "Ustroichivost' rakety v polete" (Stability of a rocket in flight); I. A. Merkulov, "Postroenie traektorii reaktivnykh apparatov, obladayushchikh nachalnoi skorost'yu" (Construction of trajectories of reactive devices possessing an initial velocity); F. Frankl', "Vikhrevoe dvizhenie i obtekanie tel v plosko parallel'nom techenii sverkhzvukovoi skorosti" (Vortical motion and flow around bodies in a plane parallel current with supersonic velocity); E. S. Shchetinkov, "Primenenie kislorodnykh reaktivnykh dvigatelei na samolete" (The use of oxygen jet engines on aircraft); V. I. Dudakov, "Raschet razbega samoleta so startovymi raketami" (Calculation of rocket assisted aircraft takeoff run); V. I. Dudakov, "Raschet tormozheniya posleposadochnogo probega samoleta s pomoshch'yu raket" (Calculation of the braking effect of rockets on the landing run of aircraft).

*Reaktivnoe dvizhenie* (Jet propulsion), No. 2., P. S. Dubenskii, I. M. Merkulov, M. K. Tikhonravov, *et al.* (eds.), ONTI, Glavnaya redaktsiya aviatsionnoi literatury, Moscow and Leningrad, 1936, 140 pp.

Collection of papers by members of the Reactive Section of the Stratospheric Committee of the Central Council of OSOAVIAKHIM. Contents: K. E. Tsiolkovskii, "Trudy o kosmicheskoi rakete" (Works on cosmic rockets); K. E. Tsiolkovskii, "Toplivo dlya rakety" (Fuel for rockets); M. K. Tikhonravov, "Formula Tsiolkovskogo" (Tsiolkovskii's formula); M. K. Tikhonravov, "Puti ispol'zovaniya luchistoi energii dlya kosmicheskogo poleta" (Ways of using radiant energy for cosmic flight); V. S. Zuev, "O vertikal'nom polete rakety" (On the vertical flight of rockets); F. Lyakaitis, "Raschet raketnykh dvigatelei po entropiinym diagrammam" (Analysis of rocket engines by means of entropy diagrams); V. N. Prokof'ev, "O k.p.d. vozdushno-reaktivnogo dvigatelya i rakety" (On the efficiency of air jet engines and rockets); V. N. Prokof'ev, "Vliyanie koefitsienta Koriolisa na tyagi i k.p.d. raketnogo dvigatelya" (Effect of Coriolis' coeffecent on the thrust and efficiency of rocket engines); G. V. Averbukh, "Voprosy izmerenii v raketnoi tekhnike" (Problems of measurement in rocket technology).

Rodnykh, A. A., *Rakety i kosmicheskie korabli* (Rockets and cosmic ships), 2d ed., Gosmashmetizdat, Leningrad and Moscow, 1934, 63 pp.

Rosser, J., R. Newton, and G. Gross, *Matematicheskaya teoriya poleta neupravlyaemykh raket* (Mathematical theory of the flight of unguided rockets), Prof. A. A. Kosmodem'yanskii (ed.), Gosinoizdat, Moscow, 1950, 304 pp.

Translation of the book *Mathematical theory of rocket flight*, McGraw-Hill Book Co., Inc., New York, 1947.

Rynin, N. A., *Mezhplanetnye soobshcheniya* (Interplanetary communications), published in nine volumes over the period 1928–1932:

    I.    *Mechty, legendy i pervye fantazii* (Dreams, legends, and first fantasies), Leningrad, 1928, ix + 109 pp.

    II.    *Kosmicheskie korabli: Mezplanetnye soobshcheniya v fantaziyakh romanistov* (Cosmic ships: Interplanetary communications in the fantasies of novelists), P. P. Soikin Publishing House, Leningrad, 1928, 160 pp.

    III.    *Luchistaya energiya v fantaziyakh romanistov i v proektakh uchenykh* (Radiant energy in the fantasies of the novelists and in projects of scientists), Leningrad, 1930, 152 pp.

    IV.    *Rakety i dvigateli pryamoi reaktsii: Istoriya, teoriya i tekhnika* (Rockets and direct reaction motors: History, theory, and technology), Leningrad, 1929, 213 pp.

    V.    *Teoriya reaktivnogo dvizheniya* (Theory of jet propulsion); reprint from *Sbornik Leningradskogo Instituta Inzhenerov Putei Soobshcheniya*, No. 101, 1929, 64 pp.

    VI.    *Superaviatsiya i superartilleriya* (Superaviation and superartillery), Leningrad, 1929, 218 pp.

    VII.    *Russkii izobretatel' i uchenyi Konstantin Eduardovich Tsiolkovskii: Ego biografiya, raboty i rakety* (Russian inventor and scientist Konstantin Eduardovich Tsiolkovskii: His biography, works, and rockets), Leningrad, 1931, 112 pp.

    VIII.    *Teoriya kosmicheskogo poleta* (Theory of cosmic flight), Izd. Akademii Nauk SSSR, Leningrad, 1932, 358 pp.

    IX.    *Astronavigatsiya: Letopis' i bibliografiya* (Astronavigation: Chronicle and bibliography), Izd. Akademii Nauk SSSR, Leningrad, 1932, 218 pp + x pp.

For a comprehensive review of this treatise by Prof. Rynin, see G. V. E. Thompson, "A famous Russian encyclopedia of astronautics," *Journal of the British Interplanetary Society*, Vol. 13, July, 1954, pp. 192–202; Vol. 13, November, 1954, pp. 301–313; Vol. 15, March–April, 1956, pp. 82–91.

————, *Metody osvoeniya stratosfery* (Methods of mastering the stratosphere), 1931.

Sänger, E., *Tekhnika raketnogo poleta* (Technology of rocket flight), 2d ed., V. A. Shtokolov (ed.), Oborongiz, Moscow, 1947, 300 pp.
Translation from the German *Raketenflugtechnik*, 1933.

Sedov, L. I., *Metody podobiya i razmernosti v mekhanike* (Methods of similarity and dimensionality in mechanics), 2d ed., Gostekhizdat, Moscow, 1951, 193 pp.

Sharonov, V. V., *Mars* (Mars), Izd. Akademii Nauk SSSR, Moscow and Leningrad, 1947, 180 pp.

————, *Est' li zhizn' na drugikh planetakh?* (Is there life on the other planets?), Voenizdat, Moscow, 1952, 46 pp.

Shternfel'd, A. A., *Vvedenie v kosmonavtiku* (Introduction to cosmonautics), ONTI, Glavnaya redaktsiya aviatsionnoi literatury, Leningrad and Moscow, 1937, 320 pp.
Translation from the author's original French manuscript.

————, *Polet v mirovoe prostranstvo* (Flight into world space), Gostekhizdat, Moscow and Leningrad, 1949, 140 pp.; 2d ed., 1957, 256 pp.
There is a review by F. I. Ordway of the French edition of this book (*Le vol dans l'espace cosmique*, P. Kolodkine (trans.), Les Éditeurs Français Réunis, 1954, 195 pp.) in *Journal of Astronautics*, Vol. 2, No. 3, Fall, 1955, p. 132.

————, *Mezhplanetnye polety* (Interplanetary flights), Gostekhizdat, Moscow, 1955, 56 pp.; 2d ed., 1956, 48 pp.
Nauchno-populyarnaya biblioteka No. 82.

————, *Iskusstvennye sputniki Zemli* (Artificial earth satellites), Gostekhizdat, Moscow, 1956, 180 pp.
Chapter X, "Pravovye i drugie voprosy" (Legal and other problems), poses the question: To whom does upper atmospheric space belong?

Sinyarev, G. B., and M. V. Dobrovol'skii, *Zhidkostnye raketnye dvigateli; teoriya i proektirovanie* (Liquid rocket engines; theory and design), Oborongiz, Moscow, 1955, 488 pp.
A textbook for technical schools. Contains many numerical examples which illustrate the design principles and computational methods. The bibliography lists 43 references.

Smurov, G. S., *Polet bystree zvuka* (Flight faster than sound), Izd. *Pravda*, Moscow, 1950, 28 pp.

Solodovnikov, V. V., *Vvedenie v statisticheskuyu dinamiku sistem avtomaticheskogo upravleniya* (Introduction to the statistical dynamics of automatic control systems), Gostekhizdat, Moscow and Leningrad, 1952, 368 pp.

Sonkin, M., *Russkaya raketnaya artilleriya: Istoricheskie ocherki* (Russian rocket artillery: Historical sketches), Voenizdat, Moscow, 1949, 116 pp.; 2d ed., 1952, 196 pp.

*Spravochnik .khimika* (Chemist's handbook), B. P. Nikol'skii (ed.), Goskhimizdat, Moscow, 1951–1952, 3 vols.

*Spravochnik mashinostroitelya* (Mechanical engineer's handbook), Vol. 1, N. S. Acherkan (ed.), Mashgiz, Moscow, 1950; 2d ed., 1954.

Stanyukovich, K. P., *Neustanovivshiesya dvizheniya sploshnoi sredy* (Unsteady motions of a continuous medium), Gostekhizdat, Moscow, 1955, 804 pp.
The bibliography lists 49 references.

———, *O kosmichesikh poletakh* (Concerning cosmic flights), Izd. *Molodaya Gvardiya*, Moscow, 1956, 31 pp.

Storonkin, A., *Ob usloviyakh termodinamicheskogo ravnovesiya mnogokomponentnykh sistem* (On thermodynamic equilibrium conditions in multicomponent systems), Izd. Leningradskogo Gosudarstvennogo Ordena Lenina Universiteta, Leningrad, 1948, 122 pp.
The bibliography lists 26 references.

Sushkov, V. V., *Tekhnicheskaya termodinamika* (Technical thermodynamics), 5th ed., V. A. Kirillin (ed.), Gosenergoizdat, Moscow, 1953, 336 pp.

Sutton, G., *Raketnye dvigateli* (Rocket engines), Gosinoizdat, Moscow, 1952, 328 pp.
Translation of the book *Rocket propulsion elements: An introduction to the engineering of rockets*, John Wiley & Sons, New York, 1947.

Sytinskaya, N. N., *Est' li zhizn' na drugikh planetakh?* (Is there life on the other planets?), Gozkul'tprosvetizdat, Moscow, 1952, 60 pp.

*Teplofizicheskie svoistva veshchestv. Spravochnik* (Thermal physical properties of substances. Handbook), N. B. Vargaftik (ed.), Gosenergoizdat, Moscow and Leningrad, 1956, 367 pp.

*Terminologiya zhidkostnykh raketnykh dvigatelei* (Terminology of liquid rocket engines), Izd. Akademii Nauk SSSR, Moscow, 1953, 27 pp.
This is No. 16 of the series *Sborniki Rekomenduemykh Terminov* (Collections of recommended terms) prepared by the USSR Academy of Sciences' Committee on Technical Terminology. The members of the section on liquid rocket engines were L. S. Dushkin (leader), V. F. Berglezov, M. Yu. Gollender, R. M. Fedorov, and A. I. Polyanii. The members of the scientific subcommission on aviation terminology of the KTT AN SSSR were Professor Doctor of Technical Sciences N. V.

Inozemtsev (leader), Professors Doctors of Technical Sciences V. I. Dmitrievskii, A. A. Dobrynin, G. S. Skubachevskii, Candidate of Technical Sciences N. G. Dubravskii, Colonel K. I. Folomkin, Candidates of Technical Sciences L. G. Sheremet'ev, V. N. Kostrov. It was approved by representative of the Scientific Commission on Aviation Terminology Corresponding Member of the USSR Academy of Sciences (now Academician) B. S. Stechkin.

Tikhonravov, M. K., *Raketnaya tekhnika* (Rocket technology), ONTI, Glavnaya aviatsionnaya redaktsiya, Moscow, 1935, 79 pp.

Tikhov, G. A., *Astrobiologiya* (Astrobiology), Izd. *Molodaya Gvardiya*, Moscow, 1953, 68 pp.

*Trudy Vesesoyuznoi konferentsii po izucheniyu stratsfery 31 marta–6 aprelya 1934 g.* (Proceedings of the All-Union conference on the study of the stratosphere 31 March–6 April 1934), Izd. Akademii Nauk SSSR, Leningrad and Moscow, 1935, xxiv + 927 pp. with figures and 19 tables. Among the 87 papers presented at this conference were the following: N. A. Rynin, "Metody osvoeniya stratosfery" (Methods of mastering the stratosphere); M. V. Machinskii and A. N. Shtern, "Nauchnye problemy reaktivnogo dvizheniya" (Scientific problems of jet propulsion) and "Problemy dvigatelei pryamoi reaktsii" (Problems of direct reaction engines); M. K. Tikhonravov, "Primenenie raketnykh letatel'nykh apparatov" (The use of rocket flying devices); S. P. Korolev, "Polet reaktivnykh apparatov v stratosfere" (Flight of reactive devices in the stratosphere); M.-V. Machinskii, "O gorizontal'nom polete stratoplana" (On the horizontal flight of a stratoplane); F. Frankl', "Aerodinamika bol'shikh skorostei" (Aerodynamics of high speeds).

Tsander, F. A., *Problema poleta pri pomoshchi raketnykh apparatov* (Problem of flight by means of rocket devices), M. K. Tikhonravov (ed.), Oborongiz, Moscow, 1947, 240 pp. Originally published in Moscow, 1932.

Tsiolkovskii, K. E., *Trudy po raketnoi tekhnike* (Works on rocket technology), M. K. Tikhonravov (ed.) Oborongiz, Moscow, 1947, 368 pp.

————, *Sobranie sochinenie* (Collected works), Izd. Akademii Nauk SSSR, Moscow: Tom pervyi. *Aerodinamika* (Vol. 1. Aerodynamics), 1951, 266 pp. Tom vtoroi. *Reaktivnye letatel'nye apparaty* (Vol. 2. Reactive flying devices), 1954, 456 pp.

These volumes contain the following often-referred-to papers:
"Issledovanie mirovykh prostranstv reaktivnymi priborami" (Investigation of world spaces by reactive instruments), 1903.
"Raketa v kosmicheskoe prostranstvo" (Rocket into cosmic space), 1903 and 1924.
"Issledovanie mirovykh prostranstv" (Investigation of world spaces), 1926.
"Kosmicheskaya raketa" (Cosmic rocket), 1927.
"Kosmicheskie reaktivnye poezda" (Cosmic reactive trains), 1929.
"Tseli zvezdoplavaniya" (Goals of astronavigation), 1929.
"Zvezdoplavatelyam" (To astronavigators), 1930.
"Reaktivnyi aeroplan" (Reactive airplane), 1930.
"Stratoplan polureaktivnyi" (Semireactive stratoplane), 1930.

Valier, Max, *Polet v mirovoe prostranstvo kak tekhnicheskaya vozmozhnost'*
(Flight into world space as a technical possibility), S. A. Shorygin
(trans.), V. P. Vetchinkin (ed.), ONTI, Glavnaya redaktsiya nauchno-
populyarnoi i yunosheskoi literatury, Moscow and Leningrad, 1935,
335 pp.

Vanichev, A. P., *Termodinamicheskii raschet goreniya i istecheniya v oblasti
vysokokh temperatur* (Thermodynamic calculation of combustion and flow
in the region of high temperatures), Izd. BNT, Moscow, 1947.

————, and G. F. Knorre, *Obobshchennye raschetnye formuly gazovogo
analiza* (Generalized computing formulas of gas analysis), Izd. BNT,
Moscow, 1946.

Varvarov, N. A., *Iskusstvennyi sputnik Zemli* (Artificial earth satellite), Izd.
*Sovetskaya Rossiya*, Moscow, 1957, 32 pp.

Vasil'ev, M. V., *Puteshestviya v Kosmos* (Voyages into the cosmos), Goskul't-
prosvetizdat, Moscow, 1955, 176 pp.; 2d ed., Izd. *Sovetskaya Rossiya*,
1957, 256 pp.

Vasil'eva, O. M., *Nemetsko-Russkii slovar po raketnoi tekhnike* (German-
Russian dictionary on rocket technology), Yu. A. Pobedonostsev (ed.),
Gostekhizdat, Moscow and Leningrad, 1950, 212 pp.
  This dictionary contains about 7000 German terms with their translations pertaining
  for the most part to liquid-fuel jet engines and rockets. The source material for the
  terms in the dictionary consists of technical literature (books and periodicals)
  published in Germany from 1940 to 1945 and various technical material from
  German commercial firms, organizations, and institutions engaged in the production
  and use of rockets.

Vereshchagin, I. F., *Nekotorye zadachi teorii dvizheniya raket* (Some problems in the theory of rocket motion), Kirgiskii gosudarstvennyi pedagogi-
cheskii institut, Frunze, 1947, 79 pp.
  This is a dissertation for the degree of Candidate of Physico-Mathematical Sciences,
  prepared under the scientific supervision of Professor A. A. Kosmodem'yanskii,
  defended June 24, 1948, and approved February 14, 1949.

*Voprosy meditsiny pri mezhplanetnykh poletakh* (Problems of medicine in
interplanetary flights), V. I. Yazdovskii (ed.), Izd. Inostrannoi Literatury,
Moscow, 1955, 164 pp.
  This is a collection of 22 abridged translations of papers from Western periodicals
  —16 from the *Journal of Aviation Medicine*, 4 from the *Journal of the British
  Interplanetary Society*, one from the *Scientific American*, and one from *Revue de
  pathologie générale et comparée*. The bibliography lists 130 references.

Vorontsov-Vel'yaminov, B. A., *Ocherki o vselennoi* (Essays about the universe), Gostekhizdat, Moscow, 1951, 524 pp.

Vukalovich, M. P., and I. I. Novikov, *Uravnenie sostoyaniya real'nykh gazov* (Equation of state of real gases), Gosenergoizdat, Moscow, 1948, 339 pp.

Vukalovich, M. P., *et al.*, *Termodinamicheskie svoistva gazov* (Thermodynamic properties of gases), Mashgiz, Moscow, 1953, 373 pp.

Wimpress, R. N., *Vnutrennyaya ballistika porokhovykh raket* (Internal ballistics of powder rockets), Gosinoizdat, Moscow, 1952, 192 pp.
Translation of the book *Internal ballistics of solid-fuel rockets: Military rockets using dry-processed double-base propellant as fuel*, McGraw-Hill Book Co., Inc., New York, 1950.

Zel'dovich, Ya. B., and A. I. Polyarnyi, *Raschety teplovykh protsessov pri vyskoi temperature* (Calculations of thermal processes at high temperatures), Izd. Byuro Novoi Tekh. bez Goroda, Moscow, 1947, 68 pp.
The bibliography lists 16 references. Reviewed in *Uspekhi Fizicheskikh Nauk*, Vol. 34, 1948, pp. 462–463.

Zel'dovich, Ya. B., and A. S. Kompaneets, *Teoriya detonatsii* (Theory of detonation), Gostekhizdat, Moscow, 1955, 268 pp.

Zigel', F., *Zagadka Marsa* (The riddle of Mars), Detgiz, Moscow and Leningrad, 1952, 96 pp.

## II. PERIODICALS

Alekseev, P. P., *et al.*, "Raketnye issledovaniya atmosfery" (Rocket investigations of the atmosphere), *Meteorologiya i Gidrologiya*, No. 8, August, 1957, pp. 3–13.
The authors of this paper—P. P. Alekseev, E. A. Besyadovskii, G. I. Golyshev, M. N. Isakov, A. M. Kasatkin, G. A. Kokin, N. S. Livshchits, N. D. Masanova, E. G. Shvidkovskii—are members of the Tsentral'naya Aerologicheskaya Observatoriya (Central Aerological Observatory). The paper describes the equipment mounted in the nose of the meteorological rocket and the results obtained, i.e., temperature, pressure, and density at 2-km intervals from 0 to 80 km. The results are compared with similar U.S. data.

Al'pert, Ya. L., "Ionosfera" (The ionosphere), *Priroda*, Vol. 45, No. 1, January, 1956, pp. 13–23.
The rocket data used in this paper were taken from an unspecified American source. Figure 1 is a photograph of an atmospheric research V-2 rocket on a launching pad.

Balakhovskii, I. S., and V. B. Malkin, "Biologicheskie problemy mezhplanet-

nykh poletov" (Biological problems of interplanetary flights), *Priroda,* Vol. 45, No. 8, August, 1956, pp. 15–21.
For translation, see Chapter 12.

Baldov, A., "Samolety-snaryady" (Missile aircraft), *Krasnaya Zvezda,* No. 161, July 14, 1956, p. 4.

———, and I. Kucherov, "Upravlyaemye snaryady: Avtonomye sistemy upravleniya" (Guided missiles: Autonomous guidance systems), *Krasnaya Zvezda,* No. 51, March 2, 1956, p. 2.

Blagonravov, A. A., "Issledovanie verkhnikh sloev atmosfery pri pomoshchi vysotnykh raket" (Investigation of the upper layers of the atmosphere by means of high-altitude rockets), *Vestnik Akademii Nauk SSSR,* Vol. 27, No. 6, June, 1957, pp. 25–32.
This paper is a survey of the high-altitude rocket research work conducted in the Soviet Union since 1947.

———, " 'Mikeniks illyustreited' zayavlyaet pravo na Lunu" (*Mechanics Illustrated* claims a right to the Moon), *Ogonek;* No. 29, July, 1957, p. 22.
Academician Blagonravov criticizes the article by Pierre J. Hass entitled "Let's claim the moon now!" (*Mechanics Illustrated,* February, 1957, pp. 70–72, 160). He condemns the idea of any one nation's claiming the moon and proposes that all countries pool their scientists and resources to solve the great problems of today. "We would be pleased to establish permanent and firm contact with the scientists of the United States working in astronautics as well as with American interplanetary rocket societies."

Borisov, V., "Doroga k zvezdam" (The road to the stars), *Znanie-Sila,* Vol. 25, No. 4, April, 1950 pp. 7–8.
For translation, see Chapter 1.

Bulgakov, B. V., and Ya. N. Roitenberg, "K teorii silovykh giroskopicheskikh gorizontov" (On the theory of power gyroscopic horizons), *Izvestiya Akademii Nauk SSSR, Otdelenie Tekhnicheskikh Nauk,* No. 3, 1948, pp. 289–292.
The sections have the following captions: "Principle of power gyroscopic stabilization," "Equations of motion of a power gyroscopic horizon," and "Possibility of obtaining an 84-minute period and of compensating for ballistic deviations."

Burche, E., "Stranitsy proshlogo: Rozhdenie reaktivnoi aviatsii" (Pages of the past: The birth of jet propulsion), *Tekhnika-Molodezhi,* Vol. 20, No. 4, April, 1952, p. 36.

Butkov, K. V., and R. B. Rozenbaum, "Chastota kolebanii atomov v molekule ftora, termodinamicheskie funktsii ftora i konstanta ravnovesiya $F_2 \leftrightarrows 2F$ v intervale temperatur ot 298.1 do 5000°K" (The vibration frequency of atoms in the fluorine molecule; thermodynamic functions of fluorine and the equilibrium constant $F_2 \leftrightarrows 2F$ in the temperature interval from 298.1 to 5000°K), *Zhurnal Fizicheskoi Khimii*, Vol. 24, No. 6, June, 1950, pp. 706–713.

The thermodynamic functions in this paper are an extension of those of G. M. Murphy and J. E. Vance, "Thermodynamic properties of hydrogen fluoride and fluorine from spectroscopic data," *Journal of Chemical Physics*, Vol. 7, September, 1939, pp. 806–810. The high temperatures suggest Soviet interest in fluorine as an oxidant in rocket propulsion.

Chebotarev, G. A., "Kosmicheskii bumerang" (Cosmic boomerang), *Znanie-Sila*, Vol. 23, No. 2, February, 1957, pp. 28–29.

For translation, see Chapter 20.

————, "Simmetrichnaya traektoriya rakety dlya poleta vokrug Luny" (A symmetrical rocket trajectory for flight around the moon), *Byulleten' Instituta Teoreticheskoi Astronomii*, Vol. 6, No. 7 (80), 1957, pp. 487–492.

This is the technical paper on which the preceding popular article in *Znanie-Sila* was based.

Chugaev, Yu., and E. Tsarev, "Televidenie v upravlenii snaryadami" (Television in the guidance of missiles), *Krasnaya Zvezda*, No. 59, March 10, 1956, p. 3.

Danilin, B. S., V. V. Mikhnevich, A. I. Repnev, and E. G. Shvidkovskii, "Zadacha izmereniya davleniya i plotnosti vysokikh sloev atmosfery s pomoshch'yu iskusstvennogo sputnika Zemli" (Problem of the measurement of pressure and density of the upper layers of the atmosphere with the aid of an artificial Earth satellite), *Uspekhi Fizicheskikh Nauk*, Vol. 63, No. 1, September, 1957, pp. 205–225.

This paper is devoted to an analysis of the physical contents of the problem of measuring pressure and density of the upper layers of the atmosphere when using an artificial earth satellite for this purpose.

Dobronravov, V. V., "*Iskusstvennyi sputnik Zemli*" (Artificial satellite of the earth), *Kryl'ya Rodiny*, Vol. 7, No. 8, August, 1956, pp. 19–22.

————, "Kosmicheskaya navigatsiya" (Cosmic navigation), *Nauka i Zhizn'*, Vol. 23, No. 10, October, 1956, pp. 19–22.

————, "Na puti v kosmos" (On the way into the cosmos), *Kryl'ya Rodiny*, No. 6, June, 1957, pp. 20–22.

The author discusses Von Braun's space station project, the Soviet high-altitude rocket experiments with dogs, and proposed manned high-altitude rocket flights.

————, et al., "Na puti k zvezdam" (On the way to the stars), *Tekhnika-Molodezhi*, Vol. 22, No. 7, July, 1954, pp. 1–7.

For translation, see Chapter 3.

Drobinin, I. N., and S. E. Dunaev, "Pumps for low-boiling liquids," *Khimicheskoe Mashinostroenie*, Vol. 8, No. 5, 1939, pp. 11–12.
Abstracted in *Chemical Abstracts*, Vol. 33, 1939, 8058².

———, "Perevozka zhidkogo kisloroda na dal'nie rasstoyaniya" (Long-distance transportation of liquid oxygen), *Kislorod*, No. 1, 1946, pp. 33–39.

———, "Dvukhstupenchatyi nasos vysokogo davleniya dlya zhidkogo kisloroda" (Two-stage high-pressure pump for liquid oxygen), *Kislorod*, No. 4, 1947, pp. 39–45.

———, "Plunger pump for liquid oxygen," USSR Patent No. 68,921, July 21, 1947.
See *Chemical Abstracts*, Vol. 43, 1949, 6010i.

Egorov, V. A., "Nekotorye voprosy dinamiki poleta k Lune," (Some questions on the dynamics of flight to the moon), *Doklady Akademii Nauk SSSR*, Vol. 113, No. 1, March 1, 1957, pp. 46–49.
For translation, see Chapter 21.

———, "O nekotorykh zadachakh dinamiki poleta k Lune" (On some problems of the dynamics of flight to the moon), *Uspekhi Fizicheskikh Nauk*, Vol. 63, No. 1, September, 1957, pp. 73–117.
A summary of this paper is found in the preceding article

Evgen'ev, F., "Astrobiologiya" (Astrobiology), *Nauka i Zhizn'*, Vol. 21, No. 1, January, 1954, pp. 46–47.
This is a review of the book *Astrobiologiya* by G. A. Tikhov.

Fal'kovich, S. V., "K teorii sopla Lavalya" (On the theory of the Laval nozzle), *Prikladnaya Matematika i Mekhanika*, Vol. 10, No. 4, 1946, pp. 503–512.
For translation, see National Advisory Committee for Aeronautics Technical Memorandum 1212, April, 1949.

———, "Ploskoe dvizhenie gaza pri bol'shikh sverkhzvukovykh skorostyakh" (Plane motion of a gas at hypersonic velocities), *Prikladnaya Matematika i Mekhanika*, Vol. 11, No. 4, 1947, pp. 459–464.
For translation, see National Advisory Committee for Aeronautics Technical Memorandum 1239, October, 1949.

Fedorov, E. K., "V preddverii kosmicheskogo prostranstva" (On the threshold of cosmic space), *Literaturnaya Gazeta*, No. 69 (3725), June 8, 1957, pp. 1–2.
The author is a Corresponding Member of the USSR Academy of Sciences and chairman of the Soviet IGY Committee for rocket and satellite research. This paper describes the equipment (but not the rockets) used and the results obtained by Soviet scientists in sampling the upper atmosphere and in observing the behavior of dogs launched by rocket to altitudes of about 100 km. It discusses briefly the USSR rocket and satellite program for the IGY. It is illustrated with four photo-

graphs: a research rocket during takeoff, a rocket nose section containing optical instruments, a research rocket nose section making a parachute landing, and a close-up of an instrument container after landing.

———, "Issledovaniya verkhnikh sloev atmosfery pri pomoshchi raket i iskusstvennykh sputnikov Zemli" (Investigation of the upper layers of the atmosphere by means of rockets and artificial earth satellites), *Priroda*, Vol. 46, No. 9, September, 1957, pp. 3–12.
This paper is a more formal presentation of the material discussed in the previous article.

Fesenkov, V. G., "Zvezdnye miry" (Star worlds), *Tekhnika-Molodezhi*, Vol. 22, No. 3, March, 1954, pp. 5–10.

———, "Problemy astronavtiki" (Problems of astronautics), *Vestnik Akademii Nauk Kazakh SSR*, Vol. 11, No. 1, January, 1955, pp. 3–11; also published in *Priroda*, Vol. 44, No 6, June, 1955, pp. 11–18.
For translation, see Chapter 7.

Gantmakher, F. R., and L. M. Levin, "Ob uravneniyakh dvizheniya rakety" (On the equations of motion of a rocket), *Prikladnaya Matematika i Mekhanika*, Vol. 11, No. 3, 1947, pp. 301–312.
For translation, see National Advisory Committee for Aeronautics Technical Memorandum 1255, April, 1950.

Gil'zin, K. A., "Pered startom v kosmos" (Before the start into the cosmos), *Znanie-Sila,* Vol. 30, No. 9, September, 1955, pp. 29–32.

———, "Via intercontinental passenger rocket liner from Leningrad to New York and return," USSR *Illustrated Monthly,* No. 5, 1956, pp. 6–7, 48.
An imaginary trip from the land of make-believe.

Ginzburg, V. L., "Eksperimental'naya proverka obshchei teorii otnositel'nosti i iskusstvennye sputniki Zemli" (Experimental verification of the general theory of relativity and artificial earth satellites), *Priroda*, Vol. 45, No. 9, September, 1956, pp. 30–39.
For translation, see Chapter 32.

———, "Ispol'zovanie iskusstvennykh sputnikov Zemli dlya proverki obshchei teorii otnositel'nosti" (Utilization of artificial earth satellites for the verification of the general theory of relativity), *Uspekhi Fizicheskikh Nauk*, Vol. 63, No. 1, September, 1957, pp. 119–122.
This is a short résumé of a paper by the author in *Uspekhi Fizicheskikh Nauk*, Vol. 59, No. 1, 1956, pp. 11–49.

Glushko, V. P., "Stantsiya vne Zemli" (Station beyond the earth), *Nauka i Tekhnika*, Leningrad, Vol. 4, No. 40, October 8, 1926, pp. 3–4.
A popular article by an early Russian rocket pioneer.

————, "Konstantin Eduardovich Tsiolkovskii—K 100-letiyu so dnya rozhdeniya" (Konstantin Eduardovich Tsiolkovskii—On the centennial of his birthday), *Vestnik Akademii Nauk SSSR*, Vol. 27, No. 9, September, 1957, pp. 53–60.

A biographical sketch by one of Tsiolkovskii's early disciples who is now a Corresponding Member of the USSR Academy of Sciences.

Gol'denberg, S. A., "Turbulent transfer in heat exchange, diffusion, and chemical processes," *Izvestiya Akademii Nauk SSSR, Otdelenie Tekhnicheskikh Nauk*, No. 5, May, 1950, pp. 689–694.

Abstracted in *Chemical Abstracts*, Vol. 45, 1951, 9929b.

————, "Turbulent heterogeneous combustion," *Izvestiya Akademii Nauk SSSR, Otdelenie Tekhnicheskikh Nauk*, No. 8, August, 1950, pp. 1154–1164.

Abstracted in *Chemical Abstracts*, Vol. 46, 1952, 1336h.

————, "The process of turbulent combustion in a high-temperature region, *Izvestiya Akademii Nauk SSSR, Otdelenie Tekhnicheskikh Nauk*, No. 7, July, 1951, pp. 1025–1030.

Abstracted in *Chemical Abstracts*, Vol. 46, 1952, 10832h.

Gorelov, A., "O poletakh v mirovoe prostranstvo" (On flights into world space), *Nauka i Zhizn'*, Vol. 23, No. 6, June, 1956, pp. 59–60.

This article is a review of two books: *Puteshestviya v kosmos* by M. Vasil'ev and *Puteshestvie k dalekim miram* by K. A. Gil'zin.

Gringauz, K. I., and M. Kh. Zelikman, "Izmerenie kontsentratsii polozhitel'-nykh ionov vdol' orbity iskusstvennogo sputnika Zemli" (Measurement of the concentration of positive ions along the orbit of an artificial earth satellite), *Uspekhi Fizicheskikh Nauk*, Vol. 63, No. 1, September, 1957, pp. 239–252.

According to the authors, the most suitable parameter to be measured by the direct investigation of the properties of the ionosphere by means of artificial satellites is the concentration of positive ions. In the literature there is an almost unanimous opinion that at the altitudes through which the orbits of artificial satellites will pass (the area of the F-layer and above) negative ions are practically absent; if this is so, then the determination of the positive ion concentration is equivalent to the determination of the free electron concentration—a basic physical characteristic of the ionosphere.

Grishin, A., "Upravlyaemye snaryady: Samonavedenie" (Guided missiles: Homing guidance), *Krasnaya Zvezda*, No. 74, March 29, 1955, p. 2.

Gurvich, A. M., and A. V. Frost, "Stroenie, chastoty normalnykh kolebanii i termodinamicheskie funktsii svobodnykh radikalov metila, metilena, metina i dikarbona" (Structure, normal vibration frequencies, and thermodynamic functions of the methyl, methylene, methyne, and dicarbon free radicals), *Uchenye Zapiski Moskovskogo Universiteta*, No. 64, 1953, pp. 129–143.

This paper presents tables of free energy function, entropy, and enthalpy from 298.16° to 5000°K for $CH_3$, $CH_2$, CH, and $C_2$.

Imyanitov, I. M., "Izmerenie elektrostaticheskikh polei v verkhnikh sloyakh zemnoi atmosfery" (Measurement of electrostatic fields in the upper layers of the earth's atmosphere), *Uspekhi Fizicheskikh Nauk*, Vol. 63, No. 1, September, 1957, pp. 267–282.

The author considers the peculiarities of measurements of electrostatic fields in the upper layers of the atmosphere and methods for building equipment suitable for these measurements.

Isakov, P. K., "Problemy nevesomosti" (The problems of weightlessness), *Nauka i Zhizn'*, Vol. 22, No. 12, December, 1955, pp. 17–20.

For translation, see Chapter 11.

Ishlinskii, A. Ya., "Dve zametky o teorii dvizheniya rakety" (Two notes on the theory of rocket motion), *Doklady Akademii Nauk SSSR*, Vol. 53, No 7, September 1, 1946.

The English version of this paper appeared in *Comptes Rendus (Doklady) de l'Académie des Sciences de l'URSS*, Vol. 53, No. 7, September 10, 1946, pp. 595–596.

Karpenko, A. G., "Kosmicheskaya Laboratoriya" (Cosmic laboratory), *Moskovskaya Pravda*, No. 193, August 14, 1955, p. 1.

For translation, see Chapter 29.

————, and G. A. Skuridin, "Sovremennye problemy kosmicheskikh poletov" (Contemporary problems of cosmic flights), *Vestnik Akademii Nauk SSSR*, Vol. 25, No. 9, September, 1955, pp. 19–30.

For translation, see Chapter 8.

————, "Problemy mezhplanetnykh poletov" (Problems of interplanetary flights), *Oktyabr'*, Vol. 32, No. 9, September, 1955, pp. 140–147.

Karpenko, A. G., and M. L. Lidov, "O temperaturnom rezhime iskusstvennogo sputnika Zemli" (On the temperature regime of an artificial earth satellite), *Izvestiya Akademii Nauk SSSR, Seriya Geofizicheskaya*, No. 4, 1957, pp. 527–533.

This is one of the first papers released by the Interdepartmental Commission on Interplanetary Communications. It was received by the editor on October 18, 1956.

Kedrov, F., "Fotonnaya raketa" (The photon rocket), *Oktyabr'*, No. 7, July, 1957, pp. 169–171.

This article is based largely on material developed by Sänger and by Strenghill in 1956, plus a comment by Soviet physicist L. E. Gurevich on the problem of cosmic travels at speeds approaching that of light.

Kharitonov, A., "Upravlyaemye snaryady: Teleupravlenie" (Guided missiles: Remote control), *Krasnaya Zvezda,* No. 66, March 19, 1955, p. 3.

Khlebtsevich, Yu. S., "Radioteleupravlyaemye kosmicheskie rakety" (Radio-telecontrolled cosmic rockets), *Radio,* Vol. 5, May, 1955, p. 17.

———, "En fusée radioguidée vers la Lune" (By radiogúided rocket to the moon), *Études Soviétiques* (Paris), Vol. 8, No. 89, August, 1955, pp. 65–68.

———, "Doroga v kosmos" (The road into the cosmos), *Nauka i Zhizn',* Vol. 22, No. 11, November, 1955, pp. 33–37.
For translation, see Chapter 18.

———, " 'Tank' laboratories on the moon," *Soviety Weekly* (London), No. 738, March 22, 1956, p. 7.

———, "Put' na Lunu otkryt" (The path to the moon is open), *Tekhnika-Molodezhi,* Vol. 24, No. 5, May, 1956, pp. 33–35.

———, "Kogda poyavitsya iskusstvennyi sputnik Zemli?" (When will an artificial earth satellite appear?), *Literaturnaya Gazeta,* No. 81, July 10, 1956, p. 1.

———, "Real'na li ideya poleta na Mars?" (Is the idea of flight to Mars real?), *Literaturnaya Gazeta,* No. 86, July 21, 1956, p. 2.

———, "Polet na Veneru" (Flight to Venus), *Nauka i Zhizn',* Vol. 24, No. 8, August, 1957, pp. 53–56.
The author projects his original unmanned lunar tankette-laboratory project to Mars and to Venus.

———, "Luna-Venera-Mars proekt kosmicheskogo poleta" (Moon-Venus-Mars cosmic flight project), *Literaturnaya Gazeta,* No. 111, September 14, 1957, pp. 1–2.
This is a popular account of a Soviet project that calls for the dispatching of instrumented, but unmanned, rockets weighing not more than 50 tons to the moon (between 1960 and 1965) and to Venus and Mars (between 1962 and 1967).

———, *et al.,* "Na puti k zvezdam" (On the way to the stars), *Tekhnika-Molodezhi,* Vol. 22, No. 7, July, 1954, pp. 1–7.
For translation, see Chapter 3.

Khvastunov, M., "K solntsu" (To the sun), *Tekhnika-Molodezhi,* Vol. 22, No. 3, March, 1954, p. 10.

Khvostikov, I. A., "Stroenie i sostav stratosfery i ionosfery" (Structure and composition of the stratosphere and the ionosphere), *Vestnik Akademii Nauk SSSR*, Vol. 18, No. 1, January, 1948, pp. 17–31.

A paragraph on p. 29 of this report speaks disparagingly of the experimental results obtained from American V-2 rocket flights in the stratosphere.

————, "Ozon v stratosfere" (Ozone in the stratosphere), *Uspekhi Fizicheskikh Nauk*, Vol. 59, No. 2, June, 1956, pp. 229–323.

Pages 254–258 of this comprehensive study (which lists 134 references) are devoted to a presentation and a discussion of the data obtained from the American rocket flights of October 10, 1946, April 2, 1948, June 14, 1949, and January 25, 1950, above New Mexico, and originally reported by the U.S. Naval Research Laboratory and the Johns Hopkins Applied Physics Laboratory. This is in marked contrast to Khvostikov's comment in his 1948 report.

Kölle, Heinz H., "Wird in der Sowjet-Union eine Mondrakete gebaut?" (Is a moon rocket being built in the Soviet Union?), *Weltraumfahrt*, No. 1, January, 1952, pp. 9–10.

For translation, see Chapter 16.

Korobko-Stefanov, A., "Puteshestvie k dalekim miram" (Travel to distant worlds), *Tekhnika-Molodezhi*, Vol. 24, No. 12, December, 1956, pp. 28–29.

This is a review of the book *Puteshestvie k dalekim miram* by K. A. Gil'zin.

Kosmodem'yanskii, A., "Ekstremal'nye zadachi dlya peremennoi massy" (Extremal problems for a point of variable mass), *Doklady Akademii Nauk SSSR*, Vol. 53, No. 1, July 1, 1946, pp. 17–19.

The English version of this paper appeared in *Comptes Rendus (Doklady) de l'Académie des Sciences de l'URSS*, Vol. 53, No. 1, July 10, 1946, pp. 17–19.

————, "K. E. Tsiolkovskii, osnovopolozhnik sovremennoi raketodinamiki" (K. E. Tsiolkovskii, founder of modern rocket dynamics), *Trudy po istorii tekhniki Akademii Nauk*, No. 1, January, 1952, pp. 20–34.

Kozlovskaya, S. V., "Ekologicheskie tipy planetnykh atmosfer" (Ecological types of planetary atmospheres), *Priroda*, Vol. 45, No. 2, February, 1956, pp. 82–84.

The author considers the chemistry of the atmospheres of the planets of the solar system from the biological point of view. The article contains 6 references.

Kruchinin, V., "Zenitnye upravlyaemye snaryady" (Antiaircraft guided missiles), *Krasnaya Zvezda*, No. 57, March 8, 1956, p. 2.

Kucherov, I., "Radioupravlyaemye rakety" (Radio-guided rockets), *Radio*, No. 8, August, 1955, pp. 50–53.

For translation, see Chapter 22.

Kudryashev, L. I., "An approximate solution of the problem of heat exchange under the conditions of free motion of a liquid at the laminar boundary layer of the wall," *Izvestiya Akademii Nauk SSSR, Otdelenie Tekhnicheskikh Nauk,*No. 2, February, 1951, pp. 253–256.

Kukarkin, B., "Nauka o proiskhozhdenii mirov" (Science of the origin of the planets), *Tekhnika-Molodezhi*, Vol. 21, No. 5, May, 1953, pp. 11–13.

———, "Observatoriya zavtrashnego dnya" (Observatory of tomorrow), *Tekhnika-Molodezhi*, Vol. 21, No. 5, May, 1953, p. 14.

Kushnerevskii, Yu. V., "V verkhnikh sloyakh atmosfery" (In the upper layers of the atmosphere), *Nauka i Zhizn'*, Vol. 24, No. 3, March, 1957, pp. 11–13.

The last few paragraphs of this paper deal briefly with the proposed use of rockets and satellites during the forthcoming International Geophysical Year.

Levin, B., "Proiskhozhdenie Zemli i planet" (Origin of the earth and the planets), *Nauk i Zhizn'*, Vol. 19, No. 10, October, 1952, pp. 25–28.

Lisovskaya, M. S., "O traektoriyakh poleta rakety vokrug Luny" (On rocket flight trajectories around the moon), *Byulleten' Instituta Teoreticheskoi Astronomii*, Vol. 6, No. 8 (81), 1957, pp. 550–565.

This paper points out the existence conditions of rocket orbits that encompass the earth and the moon and pass at an arbitrarily small distance from the moon. A method of graphical integration is developed by means of which five symmetrical orbits of the indicated type are constructed.

Lyapunov, B., "Skorost'" (Speed), *Tekhnika-Molodezhi*, Vol. 20, No. 6, June, 1952, pp. 19–21.

———, "Mezhplanetnye puteshestviya" (Interplanetary voyages), *Nauka i Zhizn'*, Vol. 20, No. 6, June, 1953, pp. 33–35.

———, "Laboratoriya v kosmose" (Laboratory in space), *Tekhnika-Molodezhi*, Vol. 21, No. 8, August, 1953, pp. 33–37.

———, "Stantsiya vne Zemli" (Station outside the earth), *Znanie-Sila*, No. 9, September, 1954, pp. 11–15.

———, "Samolet-raketa-snaryad" (Rocket-missile-airplane), *Ogonek*, Vol. 33, No. 18 (1455), May, 1955, pp. 19–20.

———, "U poverkhnosti vozdushnogo okeana" (Near the surface of the air ocean), *Tekhnika-Molodezhi*, Vol. 23, No. 12, December, 1955, pp. 9–13.

———, "Upravlyaemye snaryady" (Guided missiles), *Kryl'ya Rodiny*, Vol. 7, No. 7, July, 1956, pp. 17–19.

Mandel'shtam, S. L., and A. I. Efremov, "Issledovaniya korotkovolnovogo ultrafioletovogo izlucheniya solntsa" (Investigation of shortwave ultraviolet solar radiation), *Uspekhi Fizicheskikh Nauk*, Vol. 63, No. 1, September, 1957, pp. 163–180.

This paper presents new results on the experimental and theoretical work on the study of short wave solar (i.e., photosphere, chromosphere, corona) radiation. It also discusses the variation in the intensity of the radiation and suggests experiments to be conducted by means of artificial satellites in order to resolve this problem.

Merkulov, I. A., "Kosmicheskie rakety" (Cosmic rockets), *Kryl'ya Rodiny*, Vol. 7, No. 4, April, 1956, pp. 8–11.

———, et al., "Na puti k zvezdam" (On the way to the stars), *Tekhnika-Molodezhi*, Vol. 22, No. 7, July, 1954, pp. 1–7.

For translation, see Chapter 3.

Metreveli, G., "Sputnik Zemli" (Earth satellite), *Voennye Znaniya*, No. 3, March, 1957, pp. 20–22.

This article is based, for the most part, on Project Vanguard information.

Mikhnevich, V. V., "Izmerenie davleniya v verkhnei atmosfere" (Measurement of pressure in the upper atmosphere), *Uspekhi Fizicheskikh Nauk*, Vol. 63, No. 1, September, 1957, pp. 197–204.

The author describes the apparatus and the results of pressure measurements in the upper layers of the atmosphere (50 to 100 km) with the aid of nonstabilized containers. The results are compared with previously published American data.

Mirtov, B. A., "Raketnye issledovaniya sostava atmosfery na bol'shikh vysotakh" (Rocket investigations of the composition of the atmosphere at high altitudes), *Uspekhi Fizicheskikh Nauk*, Vol. 63, No. 1, September, 1957, pp. 181–196.

A part of this report was presented at the International Congress on Rockets and Guided Missiles, Paris, December 3–8, 1956, for a translation of which, see Chapter 10.

———, and V. G. Istomin, "Issledovanie ionnogo sostava ionizirovannykh sloev atmosfery" (Investigation of the ion composition of the ionized layers of the atmosphere), *Uspekhi Fizicheskikh Nauk*, Vol. 63, No. 1, September, 1957, pp. 227–238.

This paper presents a discussion of the problems involved in the study of the ion spectrum of the ionosphere by means of an artificial earth satellite equipped with a Bennett-type radio-frequency mass spectrometer.

(Morizov, V. M.), "Davlenie, plotnost' i temperatura zemnoi atmosfery na vysotakh do 160 km" (Pressure, density, and temperature of the earth's atmosphere at heights up to 160 km), *Uspekhi Fizicheskikh Nauk*, Vol. 48, No. 4, December, 1952, pp. 609–613.

This article, signed "V. M.," presents data obtained from rocket tests performed at White Sands, New Mexico, from 1946 to 1950 and reported by R. J. Havens, R. T. Koll, and H. E. LaGow, "The pressure, density, and temperature of the earth's atmosphere to 160 kilometers," *Journal of Geophysical Research,* Vol. 57, No. 1, 1952, pp. 59–72.

Nesmeyanov, A. N., "Problema sozdaniya iskusstvennogo sputnika Zemli" (The problem of creating an artificial earth satellite), *Pravda,* No. 152, June 1, 1957, p. 2.
For translation, see Chapter 33.

———, "Nado mechtat'!" (One must dream!), *Komsomol'skaya Pravda,* No. 160, June 9, 1957, p. 1.
This hortative article contains the following paragraph: "Soon, literally in the next months, our planet earth will acquire another satellite, a satellite created by the hands of man. But in contradistinction to the moon this satellite from the very first minutes of its flight will begin to be of visible, tangible benefit to people. This diminutive and short-lived laboratory will signal to us by radio waves what is taking place at an altitude of several hundred kilometers; in particular, it will throw light on the secrets of the ionosphere and cosmic rays. The thought, will, and labor of people will create and send this artificial cosmic body along its celestial orbit. The technical difficulties that stood in the way of the solution of this most grandiose task have been overcome by our scientists. The apparatus by means of which this extremely bold experiment can be realized has already been created."

Nesterenko, G., "Atomnyi samolet budushchego" (Atomic airplane of the future), *Kryl'ya Rodiny,* Vol. 7, No. 1, January, 1956, pp. 12–14.
For translation, see Chapter 23.

Novinskii, G., and M. Shofman, "Fantaziya prevratitsya v real'nost'" (Fantasy will turn into reality), *Nauka i Zhizn',* Vol. 24, No. 1, January, 1957, p. 60.
This is a review by two physicians of the book *Voprosy meditsiny pri mezhplanetnykh poletakh.*

Novoselov, V. S., "Nekotorye voprosy mekhaniki peremennykh mass s uchetom vnutrennego dvizheniya chastits. I" (Some questions of the mechanics of variable masses including the internal motion of the particles. I), *Vestnik Leningradskogo Universiteta, Seriya Matematiki, Mekhaniki i Astronomii,* No. 19, 1956, pp. 100–113. "Nekotorye voprosy mekhaniki peremennykh mass s uchetom vnutrennego dvizheniya chastits. II" (Some questions of the mechanics of variable masses including the internal motion of the particles. II), *Vestnik Leningradskogo Universiteta, Seriya Matematiki, Mekhaniki i Astronomii,* No. 1, 1957, pp. 130–140.
This series of papers is based on the author's Candidate's dissertation, which he defended in Leningrad State University in 1952. Part I is a generalization of Meshcherskii's equation for the case of the relative motion of particles. Part II considers the laws of variation of kinetic energy for systems and bodies of variable mass.

Ogorodnikov, K. F., "VI Mezhdunarodnyi kongress po astronavtike" (The sixth international congress on astronautics), *Vestnik Leningradskogo Universiteta, Seriya Matematiki, Mekhaniki i Astronomii*, Vol. 11, No. 1, January, 1956, pp. 184–187.

Okhotsimskii, D. E., "K teorii dvizheniya raket" (On the theory of rocket propulsion), *Prikladnaya Matematika i Mekhanika*, Vol. 10, No. 2, 1946, pp. 251–272.

————, and T. M. Eneev, "Nekotorye variatsionnye zadachi, svyazannye s zapuskom iskusstvennogo sputnika Zemli" (Some variational problems connected with the launching of an artificial earth satellite), *Uspekhi Fizicheskikh Nauk*, Vol. 63, No. 1, September, 1957, pp. 5–32.
This article studies the problem of launching an artificial earth satellite into its orbit. It is assumed that the launching will take place by means of a rocket booster consisting of one or more stages. The subject of investigation is the law of the change in time of the direction of thrust of the jet engines in order to ensure the introduction of the satellite in a given orbit with minimum fuel consumption. The most advantageous rate of fuel consumption is also investigated.

————, and G. P. Taratynova, "Opredelenie vremeni sushchestvovaniya iskusstvennogo sputnika Zemli i issledovanie vekovykh vozmyshchenii ego orbity" (Determination of the lifetime of an artificial earth satellite and the investigation of the specular perturbations of its orbit), *Uspekhi Fizicheskikh Nauk*, Vol. 63, No. 1, September, 1957, pp. 33–50.
The results of this investigation are presented in tabular and in graphical form. Values of the velocity at perigee and of lifetime (expressed as a parameter $v$ in units of $m^3/kg\text{-sec}^2$) have been computed for various values of the height of perigee and of apogee.

Perel'man, R. G., "Atomnye dvigateli" (Atomic engines), *Nauka i Zhizn'*, Vol. 23, No. 1, January, 1956, pp. 26–32.
For translation of section on atomic rocket engines, see Chapter 24.

Petrov, B., "Na puti v kosmos" (On the way into the cosmos), *Krasnaya Zvezda*, No. 117, May 19, 1957, p. 4.
This item by a Corresponding Member of the USSR Academy of Sciences consists of notes on papers presented by American (James, Small), British (Dorling), and Soviet (Poloskov, Pokrovskii) delegates at the First International Congress on Rockets and Guided Missiles in Paris, December 3–8, 1956.

Petrov, V., "Televidenie budushchego: Ispol'zovannie iskusstvennogo sputnika Zemli dlya vsemirnogo televizionnogo veshchaniya" (Television of the future: Utilization of artificial earth satellite for worldwide television broadcasting), *Radio*, No. 6, June, 1956, pp. 28–31.
For translation, see Chapter 31.

————, "Iskusstvennye sputniki Zemli i vsemirnyi teletsentr" (Artificial earth satellites and the world telecenter), *Zvezda*, No. 4, April, 1957, pp. 160–164.

This paper is essentially the same as the preceding one.

————, and A. Sochivko, "Mezhkontinental'nye ballisticheskie snaryady" (Intercontinental ballistic missiles), *Voennye. Znaniya*, No. 7, July, 1957, pp. 13–16.

The authors discuss in turn the following missiles: Sänger's "antipodal bomber," the German V-1, the Snark, and the Atlas. Their reference sources for the American missiles are *Missiles and Rockets* (February, 1956) and *Air Force* (June, 1956). Further discussion is devoted to ballistic missile trajectories in general, to the terminal portions of ballistic missile trajectories of variable range, and to the zone of possible interception of ballistic rockets by means of antirockets.

Pobedonostsev, Yu., "Ob iskusstvennom sputnike Zemli" (On the artificial earth satellite), *Vestnik Vozdushnogo Flota*, Vol. 38, No. 9, 1955, pp. 87–96.

This article is admittedly based on information gleaned from the Western Press. Its illustrations include photographs of the Corporal and Viking rockets and of the 230 ton thrust rocket engine test stand at the White Sands Proving Grounds and a map of the guided missile flight test range at Cape Canaveral, Cocoa, Florida.

Pokrovskii, A. V., "Comment se comportent les animaux à 100 km d'altitude" (How animals behave at an altitude of 100 km), *Etudes Soviétiques*, No. 106, January, 1957, pp. 65–70.

This is the complete text in French of the report presented by A. V. Pokrovskii at the International Congress on Rockets and Guided Missiles in Paris, December 3–8, 1956. For translation, see Chapter 14.

Pokrovskii, G. I., "Iskusstvennyi sputnik Zemli" (Artificial earth satellite), *Izvestiya*, August 19, 1955, p. 3.

For translation, see Chapter 30.

Poloskov, S. M., and T. N. Nazarova, "Issledovanie tverdoi sostavlyayushchei mezhplanetnogo veshchestva s pomoshch'yu raket i iskusstvennykh sputnikov Zemli" (Investigation of the solid component of interplanetary matter by means of rockets and artificial earth satellites), *Uspekhi Fizicheskikh Nauk*, Vol. 63, No. 1, September, 1957, pp. 253–265.

Two of the most pressing problems to be solved in connection with the motion of rockets and artificial earth satellites in the upper layers of the atmosphere are the determination of the flux of meteoric particles and their kinetic energy. The authors discuss various methods by which data on the solid components of interplanetary matter can be obtained.

Pugachev, V. S., "Obobshchenie zadachi o krivoi pogoni" (Generalization of the problem of the pursuit curve), *Prikladnaya Matematika i Mekhanika*, Vol. 10, No. 4, 1946, pp. 525–528.

————, and V. Marisov, "Upravlyaemye snaryady: Ustroistvo i sposoby primeneniya" (Guided missiles: Construction and methods of use), *Krasnaya Zvezda*, No. 38, February 15, 1955, p. 3.

Radzievskii, V. V., and B. E. Gel'fgat, "Ob ogranichennoi zadache dvukh tel peremennoi massy" (On the restricted problem of two bodies of variable mass), *Astronomicheskii Zhurnal*, Vol. 34, No. 4, July–August, 1957. pp. 581–587.
The restricted problem of two bodies, for the case when the mass *m* of the central body varies with time *t* as $dm/dt = -\alpha m^n$, is investigated. It is proved that for any value of *n*, the problem is reduced to the problem of two bodies with constant mass, moving under the influence of their mutual gravitational attraction, which is disturbed by a quasi-elastic force and the force of friction. The values of these two disturbing forces remain very small even if the mass of the central body decreases by two.,

Raspevin, K., "Pervye puteshestvenniki v kosmos" (The first travellers into the cosmos), *Trud*, No. 40, February 16, 1957, p. 4.
This article is illustrated with photographs of some of the dogs used by Soviet scientists to study canine behavior during rocket flights up to altitudes of 110 km. For details, see Chapter 14.

Roitenberg, Ya. N., "Mnogogiroskopnaya vertikal" (The multigyroscopic vertical), *Prikladnaya Matematika i Mekhanika*, Vol. 10, No. 1, 1946, pp. 101–124.
This paper discusses, among other things, the ballistic deviation of multigyro verticals with a small free oscillation period.

(Rozenberg, G. V.), "Opredelenie struktury ozonnogo sloya do vysoty 70 km" (Determination of the structure of the ozone layer to a height of 70 km), *Uspekhi Fizicheskikh Nauk*, Vol. 49, No. 2, February, 1953, pp. 320–324.
This article, signed "G. R.," makes brief mention of rocket test data.

————, "Svodka raketnykh dannykh o stroenii vysokikh sloev atmosfery na yanvar' 1952 g." (Summary of rocket data on the structure of the upper layers of the atmosphere to January, 1952), *Uspekhi Fizicheskikh Nauk*, Vol. 50, No. 1, May, 1953, pp. 145–152.
This article, signed "G. R.," is based entirely on the paper by the Upper Atmosphere Rocket Research Panel, "Pressures, densities, and temperatures in the upper atmosphere," *Physical Review*, Vol. 88, No. 5, December 1, 1952, pp. 1027–1032.

Rozenblat, V. V., "Pered poletom v kosmos" (Before flight into the cosmos), *Nauka i Zhizn'*, Vol. 23, No. 11, November, 1956, pp. 25–28.
For translation, see Chapter 13.

Ruze, Mishel', "Iskusstvennie sputniki Zemli" (Artificial earth satellites), *V zashchitu mira*, Vol. 4, No. 52, September, 1955, pp. 29–35.

Ryabchikov, E., "Shturm kosmosa" (Storming the cosmos), *Ogonek*, No. 23, June 2, 1957, pp. 6–7.
This is a popular account of the results of Soviet rocket soundings of the upper atmosphere and of the behavior of three dogs—Al'bina, Malyshka, and Kozyavka—during rocket flights up to altitudes of 110 km.

————, "Sputnik Zemli" (Earth satellite), *Ogonek*, No. 24, June 9, 1957, pp. 25–26.
In this popular article the author describes how launching an artificial earth satellite will take place and discusses the significance of the information to be obtained therefrom. The article is illustrated with four photographs: a research rocket during takeoff, a rocket nose section making a parachute landing, a dog in its container following a parachute landing after a rocket flight into the upper atmosphere, and a research-rocket nose section containing optical instruments.

Sedov, L. I., "Ob obshchem videm uravnenii kinetiki khimicheskikh reaktsii v gazakh" (General form of equations of kinetics of gaseous reactions), *Doklady Akademii Nauk SSSR*, Vol. 60, No. 1, April 1, 1948, pp. 73–76.
Sedov gives a theoretical treatment of chemical kinetics, taking into account the effects of viscosity, diffusion, mixing of gases, and variations in temperature and pressure.

————, "Teoreticheskaya gazovaya dinamika v Moskovskom universitete" (Theoretical gas dynamics at Moscow University), *Vestnik Moskovskogo Universiteta*, Vol. 10, No. 4–5, April–May, 1955, pp. 85–99.
This is primarily a review of 210 published works by members of the mechanico-mathematical and higher physico-technical faculties of the Moscow University. The bibliography lists 13 monographs and textbooks and 197 journal articles and separate works.

————, "O poletakh v mirovoe prostranstvo" (On flights into world space), *Pravda*, September 26, 1955, p. 4.
For translation, see Chapter 9.

————, "Combustion, Applied Mechanics and Space Travel," *New Times* (Moscow), No. 47, November 15, 1956, pp. 29–30 (in English).
See Chapter 25.

————, "O dvizhenii gaza pri zvezdnykh vspyshkakh" (On the movement of gas in stellar outbursts), *Doklady Akademii Nauk SSSR*, Vol. 111, No. 4, December 1, 1956, pp. 780–782.
This is the paper that Sedov presented at the Sixth Symposium on Combustion at New Haven on August 20, 1956.

————, "Problemy kosmicheskikh poletov" (Problems of cosmic flights), *Pravda*, No. 163, June 12, 1957, p. 6.
This is a somewhat more comprehensive, but no more informative, survey than Sedov's previous effort in *Pravda*, No. 269, September 26, 1955.

————, and K. A. Nikitin, "Mezhdunarodnaya konferentsiya po raketnym dvigatelyam" (International conference on rocket engines), *Vestnik Akademii Nauk SSSR*, Vol. 26, No. 6, June, 1956, pp. 104–106.

This is a brief account of some of the papers presented at the First International Meeting of the Forschungsinstitut für Physik der Strahlantriebe, February 6–8, 1956, in Freudenstadt, Schwarzwald, near Stuttgart, Germany. It is illustrated with a photograph of K. A. Nikitin, L. I. Sedov, E. Sänger, and R. W. Porter.

Seifert, Howard S., Mark M. Mills, and Martin Summerfield, "Fizika rakety" (Physics of a rocket), *Uspekhi Fizicheskikh Nauk*, Vol. 34, No. 1, 1948, pp. 34–71; Vol. 34, No. 3, 1948, pp. 334–370; Vol. 34, No. 4, 1948, pp. 560–591.

This is a translation by M. L. Antol'skii of the three-part article "The Physics of Rockets," *American Journal of Physics*, Vol. 15, No. 1, January–February, 1947, pp. 1–21; Vol. 15, No. 2, March–April, 1947, pp. 121–140; Vol. 15, No. 3, May–June, 1947, pp. 255–272.

Seryapin, A. D., *et al.*, "Na puti k zvezdam" (On the way to the stars), *Tekhnika-Molodezhi*, Vol. 22, No. 7, July, 1954, pp. 1–7.

For translation, see Chapter 3.

Sharonov, V. V., "Soveshchanie po voprosam fiziki Luny i planet" (Conference on the problems of the physics of the moon and the planets), *Vestnik Leningradskogo Universiteta, Seriya Matematiki, Mekhaniki i Astronomii*, No. 13, 1956, pp. 151–152.

This conference, convoked by the Commission on the Physics of the Planets (under the Astronomical Council of the USSR Academy of Sciences), was held in the astronomical observatory of the Leningrad State University, February 10–11, 1956. More than 50 scientists participated. The two principal topics for discussion were (1) the questions of planetology connected with the problems of astronautics, and primarily, the question of the state of the moon's surface, and (2) the exchange of opinions and plans for observations of the coming great opposition of Mars in September, 1956. Professor N. P. Barabashev, conference chairman and director of the Khar'kov University observatory, pointed out that the importance of planetology is growing substantially in connection with the demands of cosmonautics and that at the same time the responsibility of planetary, and especially of lunar, investigators is increasing. M. K. Tikhonravov, Vice Chairman of the Commission on Interplanetary Communications, enumerated the basic questions the answers to which astronauts expect from the science of planetology.

Shaurov, N., and N. Shlyapnikov, "Proekt raketnogo dvigatelya I. I. Treteskogo" (I. I. Treteskii's rocket engine project), *Vestnik Vozdushnogo Flota*, Vol. 38, No. 5, 1955, pp. 78–84.

This is an interesting historical article based on an unpublished manuscript dated March 13 (old style), 1849, by a 28-year-old field engineer junior captain entitled "O sposobakh upravlyat' aerostatami" (On methods of controlling aerostats), 105 pages, 34 diagrams. In one method black powder was fed from a hopper in measured amounts by means of slots in a flywheel into a combustion chamber where it was ignited and the resulting product gases were allowed to flow through an orifice into a tank with horizontal and vertical pipes which exhausted into the atmosphere.

Shorin, S. N., "The role of radiative energy in combustion processes," *Izvestiya Akademii Nauk SSSR, Otdelenie Tekhnicheskikh Nauk*, No. 7, July, 1950, pp. 995–1015.
Abstracted in *Chemical Abstracts*, Vol. 45, 1951, 8361c.

Shorygin, S. A., "Bibliografiya. Chto chitat' o vozmozhnosti mezhplanetnykh puteshestvii" (Bibliography. What to read concerning the possibility of interplanetary travels), *Nauka i Zhizn'*, Vol. 3, No. 1, January, 1936, pp. 61–63.
Twenty-six books are listed and annotated. The authors include Ya. I. Perel'man, K. S. Mikoni, A. A. Rodnykh, N. A. Rynin, S. P. Korolev, Herman Noordung, Max Valier, K. E. Tsiolkovskii, N. N. Bobrov, Yu. V. Kondratyuk, F. A. Tsander, and M. K. Tikhonravov. Two of the books are collections of papers by various authors: *Reaktivnoe dvizhenie* (Jet propulsion), 1935, 154 pp.; and *Trudy vsesoyuznoi conferentsii po izucheniyu stratosfery 31 marta–6 aprelya 1934 g.* (Works of the All-Union conference for investigating the stratosphere, March 31 to April 6, 1934), 1935, xxiv + 927 pp.

Shternfel'd, A. A., "On fuel consumption by a rocket crossing the atmosphere with constant acceleration," *Comptes Rendus (Doklady) de l'Académie des Scientes de l'URSS*, Vol. 49, No. 9, December 30, 1945, pp. 629–632 (in English).
Communicated by L. S. Leibenson, Member of the Academy, August 25, 1945.

———, "Marshruty mezhplanetnykh korablei" (Routes of interplanetary ships), *Tekhnika-Molodezhi*, Vol. 20, No. 5, May, 1952, pp. 18–23.

———, Nakanune kosmicheskogo poleta" (On the eve of cosmic flight), *Tekhnika-Molodezhi*, Vol. 21, No. 2, February, 1953, pp. 31–34.

———, "Mezhplanetnye puteshestviya" (Interplanetary voyages), *Kryl'ya Rodiny*, Vol. 4, No. 8, August, 1953, pp. 18–20.

———, "Paradoksy kosmonavtiki" (Paradoxes of cosmonautics), *Tekhnika-Molodezhi*, Vol. 22, No. 1, January, 1954, pp. 26–29.

———, "Mezhplanetnye polety" (Interplanetary flights), *Molodzh' mira*, Vol. 12, December, 1954, pp. 30–32.

———, "Problemy kosmicheskogo poleta" (Problems of cosmic flight), *Priroda*, Vol. 43, No. 12, December, 1954, pp. 13–22.
For translation, see Chapter 5.

———, "Orbital'nye korabli" (Orbital ships), *Tekhnika-Molodezhi*, Vol. 23, No. 5, May, 1955, pp. 28–31.

————, "Polet na Lunu" (Flight to the moon), *Kryl'ya Rodiny*, Vol. 6, No. 9, September, 1955, pp. 19–20.

————, "Polet v kosmos" (Flight into the cosmos), *Znanie-Sila*, Vol. 31 No. 12, December, 1956, p. 18.

This is a short but enthusiastic review of the book *Puteshestviya v kosmos* (Travels into the cosmos) by M. Vasil'ev. Shternfel'd discusses several of the book's blunders, but concludes that these do not at all belittle the value of the book.

————, *et al.*, "Na puti k zvezdam" (On the way to the stars), *Tekhnika-Molodezhi*, Vol. 22, No. 7, July, 1954, pp. 1–7.

For translation, see Chapter 3.

Stanyukovich, K. P., "Priroda tyagoteniya" (The nature of gravity), *Nauka i Zhizn'*, Vol. 21, No. 1, January, 1954, pp. 21–23; also *Tekhnika-Molodezhi*, Vol. 22, No. 12, December, 1954, pp. 3–7.

————, "Trip to the moon: Fantasy and reality," *News: A Soviet Review of World Events*, No. 11, June 1, 1954, pp. 28–29 (in English).

See Chapter 17.

————, "Problemy mezhplanetnykh polet" (Problems of interplanetary flights), *Krasnaya Zvezda*, August 10, 1954, p. 3.

For translation, see Chapter 4.

————, "Silovye polya" (Fields of force), *Tekhnika-Molodezhi*, Vol. 22, No. 12, December, 1954, p. 8.

————, "Raketa i ee budushchee" (The rocket and its future), *Krasnaya Zvezda*, December 19, 1954, p. 3.

A review of the book *Raketa* by B. V. Lyapunov.

————, "Iskusstvennyi sputnik Zemli" (Artificial satellite of the earth), *Krasnaya Zvezda*, August 7, 1955, p. 3.

For translation, see Chapter 28.

————, "Rendezvous with Mars," *News: A Soviet Review of World Events*, No. 20, October 16, 1956, pp. 25–26 (in English).

See Chapter 19.

————, *et al.*, "Na puti k zvezdam" (On the way to the stars), *Tekhnika-Molodezhi*, Vol. 22, No. 7, July, 1954, pp. 1–7.

For translation, see Chapter 3.

Svetlova, L. P., "Mezhplanetniye perelety" (Interplanetary flights), *Rabotnitsa i Selyanka* (The woman worker and the peasant woman), Vol. 31, No. 4, April, 1955, pp. 22–23.

Taratynova, G. P., "O dvizhenii iskusstvennogo sputnika v netsentral'nom pole tyagoteniya Zemli pri nalichii soprotivleniya atmosfery" (On the motion of an artificial earth satellite in the earth's noncentral gravitational field in the presence of atmospheric drag), *Uspekhi Fizicheskikh Nauk*, Vol. 63, No. 1, September, 1957, pp. 51–58.

Tikhonravov, M. K., "Polet na Lunu" (Flight to the moon), *Pionerskaya Pravda*, No. 79, October 2, 1951, p. 2.
For translation, see Chapter 15.

Tikhov, G. A., "Novaya nauka—astrobiologiya" (New science—astrobiology), *Nauka i Zhizn'*, Vol. 18, No. 11, November, 1951, pp. 15–18.

———, "Astrobiologiya" (Astrobiology), *Tekhnika-Molodezhi*, Vol. 20, No. 11, November, 1952, pp. 23–27.

Tkachev, L. I., "O 84-minutnom periode dlya sistem so svyazannymi i svobodnymi giroskopami" (Concerning the 84-minute period for systems with coupled and free gyroscopes), *Prikladnaya Matematika i Mekhanika*, Vol. 13, No. 2, April 16, 1949, pp. 217–218.
In this note the author shows that the Schuler (84-minute) period is not an exclusive property of pendulum-like instruments, but also occurs in systems with "coupled" and "free" gyroscopes.

Tsitsin, F. A., "Zhizn' vo Vselennoi" (Life in the universe), *Nauka i Zhizn'*, Vol. 24, No. 1, January, 1957, pp. 45–49.
The author, a scientist at the State Astronomical Institute *imeni* Shternberg, discusses the conditions necessary for life, whether these conditions exist on the planets, and the possibility of life beyond the limits of the solar system.

Varvarov, N. A., "Problemy poleta v kosmicheskoe prostranstvo" (Problems of flight into cosmic space), *Sovetskii Flot*, May 29, 1955, p. 2.
For translation, see Chapter 6.

———, "O novykh knigakh; Otkrytie mira" (About new books; Discovery of a world), *Tekhnika-Molodezhi*, Vol. 23, No. 9, September, 1955, p. 29.
A review of the book *Otkrytie mira* by B. Lyapunov. For translation, see Appendix D.

———, "Iskusstvennye sputniki Zemli" (Artificial satellites of the earth), *Nauka i Zhizn'*, Vol. 24, No. 2, February, 1957, pp. 17–21.
This article is based, for the most part, on Project Vanguard information.

———, "Televidenie so sputnika Zemli" (Television from an earth satellite), *Sovetskaya Aviatsiya*, No. 171, July 21, 1957, p. 2.
The subject of this article is treated at greater length by V. Petrov in Chapter 31: "Television of the Future." It is interesting to note that Varvarov is identified as "Chairman of Astronavigation Section of DOSAAF SSSR."

———, *et al.*, "Na puti k zvezdam" (On the way to the stars), *Tekhnika-Molodezhi*, Vol. 22, No. 7, July, 1954, pp. 1–7.
For translation, see Chapter 3.

Vasilevskii, L., and M. Tarnopol'skii, "Gorod v mezhplanetnom prostranstve" (City in interplanetary space), *Yunost'*, No. 8, August, 1956, pp. 102, 106.
Pages 102 through 104 of this article are a Russian paraphrase of the article "Now They're Planning a City in Space" by H. O. Johansen, with drawings by Ray Pioch, which was published in *Popular Science Monthly*, Vol. 168, No. 5, May, 1956, pp. 92–98, and based on an engineering study, by Darrel C. Romick of the Goodyear Aircraft Company, of a giant earth satellite which would accommodate 20,000 people. Pages 105 and 106 of the article are captioned "Realen li etot proekt?" (Is this project feasible?) and present a discussion of Romick's project by three leading Russian space flight experts: Prof. Kirill Stanyukovich (Member of the USSR Academy of Sciences Interdepartmental Commission on Interplanetary Communications), A. A. Shternfel'd (Laureate of the International Encouragement Prize in Astronautics), and Prof. S. D. Balakhovskii (Laboratory director of the USSR Academy of Sciences Institute of Biochemistry).

Vassiliev, M., "L'exploration des espaces cosmiques" (Exploration of cosmic spaces), *Études Soviétiques* (Paris), Vol. 7, No. 75, June, 1954, pp. 70–72.

Vavilov, V. S., V. M. Malovetskaya, G. N. Galkin, and A. P. Landsman, "Kremnievye solnechnye batarei kak istochniki elektricheskogo pitaniya iskusstvennykh Zemli" (Silicon solar batteries as electric power sources for artificial earth satellites), *Uspekhi Fizicheskikh Nauk*, Vol. 63, No. 1, September, 1957, pp. 123–129.
This paper considers the operating principle of a semiconductor converter with P-N-transformation, methods of increasing the efficiency of transformation, the volt-ampere load characteristics of an experimental silicon photoelement, and the effect of temperature on the electromotive force of silicon photoelements.

Vernov, S. N., V. L. Ginzburg, L. V. Kurnosova, L. A. Razorenov, and M. I. Fradkin, "Issledovanie sostava pervichnogo kosmicheskogo izlucheniya" (Investigation of the composition of primary cosmic rays), *Uspekhi Fizicheskikh Nauk*, Vol. 63, No. 1, September, 1957, pp. 131–148.
This survey article lists 48 references. It discusses existing cosmic-ray data and indicates what advances can be made by making cosmic-ray flux measurements with the aid of artificial satellites.

Vernov, S. N., Yu. I. Logachev, A. Ye. Chudakov, and Yu. G. Shafer, "Issledovanie variatsii kosmicheskogo izlucheniya" (Research on the variations of cosmic radiation), *Uspekhi Fizicheskikh Nauk*, Vol. 63, No. 1, September, 1957, pp. 149–162.
This paper discusses the various phenomena which may be studied by means of equipment installed on a satellite: (*a*) time variations of intensity of primary cosmic radiations; (*b*) terrestrial and interplanetary magnetic fields; (*c*) the earth's albedo for cosmic radiation; (*d*) the structure of fluxes emitted by the sun.

Vladimirskii, V., "Novye istochniki energii dlya raket" (New sources of energy for rockets), *Krasnaya Zvezda*, No. 71, March 24, 1957, p. 3.
The new sources of energy referred to in the article are the atomic hydrogen, oxygen,

and nitrogen found in the upper atmosphere. Without mentioning any reference, the author describes the experiment carried out on March 14, 1956, at Holloman Air Force Base, New Mexico, when 18½ lb of nitric oxide gas was released into the free atmosphere at a height of approximately 106 km by means of an Aerobee X1-A Rocket. In the presence of the NO as a catalyst, the atomic oxygen recombined to form molecular oxygen, and the energy of recombination of atomic oxygen was converted to a large extent into light energy. For further details see J. Pressman, *et al.*, "Synthetic Atmospheric Chemiluminescence Caused by the Release of NO at 106 km," *Journal of Chemical Physics*, Vol. 25, No. 1, July, 1956, p. 187.

*Voprosy raketnoi tekhniki. Sborniki sokrashchennykh perevodov i referatov inostrannoi periodicheskoi literatury* (Problems of rocket technology. Collections of abridged translations and abstracts of foreign periodical literature), *Gosinoizdat,* Moscow, Vols. 1–7, 1951–1957.

Yatsunskii, I. M., "O vliyanii geofizicheskikh faktorov na dvizhenie sputnika" (On the effect of geophysical factors on a satellite's motion), *Uspekhi Fizicheskikh Nauk,* Vol. 63, No. 1, September, 1957, pp. 59–71.

Yur'ev, I. M., "K raschetu sopel" (On the calculation of nozzles), *Prikladnaya Matematika i Mekhanika,* Vol. 19, No. 1, pp. 103–105.

In this note the author obtains particular solutions of approximate equations of motion for plane and for axially symmetric gas flow. These solutions can be used in calculating the throat sections of nozzles.

Zaehringer, Alfred J., "A table of Soviet missiles," *The Journal of Space Flight,* Vol. 8, No. 5, May, 1956, pp. 1–4.

See Chapter 26.

# INDEX

A-4 (see V-2)
Abiants, V. Kh., 170
accelerations and overloads, 146-150
*Across the Space Frontier,* 257
Aerobee, 103
aerodynamic braking, 1, 76, 102
air regeneration, 43, 141-145
alcohol, 54
Ambartsumyan, V. A., 7, 329, 335
*American Journal of Mathematics,* 202
Ananov (Ananoff), Alexandre, 85
Andreev, V. G., 237
animal rocket experiments, 43, 44, 113,
    156-163
antioverload suit, 136
Associated Press, 6, 105
*Astronomicheskii Tsirkulyar,* 10, 289
*Astronomicheskii Zhurnal,* 10, 202, 289
atmosphere, structure of, 33, 83, 116-
    124, 282-285
atmospheric tests, 116-124, 282-287
atomic energy, 25, 56, 94, 191, 214-
    221, 222-225
atomic engines, 15, 214-221, 222-225
atomic fuel, 14, 31, 38

Bakhchivandzhi, G. Ya., 41
Balakhovskii, I. S., 134
Barabashev, N. P., 5, 335
Bardin, I. P., 5, 6, 9, 282
Bauman Institute of Technology, 15,
    192
Belousov, V. V., 12
biology of space flight, 42-44, 110, 127-
    133, 134-145, 146-155, 156-163
Blagonravov, A. A., 7, 8, 9, 12, 334
Blokhin, P. D., 237
Bogolyubov, N. N., 7, 334
Bolgarskii, A. V., 12
Bolkhovitinov, V. F., 7, 40, 335
*Bol'shaya Sovetskaya Entsiklopediya,*
    3, 13, 34
Borisov, V., 23
British Interplanetary Society, 104
*Bulletin for Visual Observers of Satel-
    lites,* 10
Bumper, 13, 103

California Institute of Technology, 15
Chebotarev, G. A., 17, 193

Chkalov Central Aeroclub, 4, 35, 82,
    85
circular velocity, 30, 59, 60
*Collier's* 175, 176, 177
Combustion Institute, 226
composite rocket, 30, 32, 55, 79
Congrès International des Fusées et
    Engins Guidés, 8, 124, 163
*Conquest of the Moon,* 206
cosmic boomerang, 193-196
cosmic rays, 43, 108, 109, 139-141, 284
cosmic velocity, 28, 96, 250
Crocco, G. A., 104, 105
CSAGI, 5, 6, 9, 287

Deacon, 104
Denisov, N. V., 237
Disney, Walt, 17, 115
Dobronravov, V. V., 4, 35, 36, 37, 38
dogs in rocket tests, 156-163
*Doklady Akademii Nauk SSSR,* 202,
    244
Doppler effect, 92, 101, 273, 296-300,
    307, 333
DOSAAF, 11, 318
Duboshkin, G. N., 335
Durant, F. C., 228
Dushkin, L. S., 40, 41

Egorov, V. A., 18, 197, 202
Ehricke, K. A., 106, 113
Einstein, A., 259, 263, 264, 274
Eötvös, Roland, 264
escape velocity, 223
Esnault-Pelterie, R., 12, 33, 97
*Etudes Sovietiques,* 163
exhaust velocity, 24, 29, 30, 31

Fedorov, V. P., 40
Fesenkov, V. G., 14, 49, 83, 202, 239
Florov, Yu. A., 335
fluorine, 14
Forrestal, J. V., 4
Fortikov, I. P., 1
Frank-Kamenetskii, D. A., 335
Friedrichs, K. O., 239

gasoline, 106
Gatland, K. W., 104
Germain, J., 227
*Gesellschaft für Weltraumforschung,*
    16, 173

378

Gil'zin, K. A., 12
Ginzburg, V. L., 15, 258, 335
GIRD, 1, 2
Goddard, R. H., 12, 33, 58, 97, 175

Hohmann, W., 12, 33
hydrazine, 105
hydrogen, 220-221

ICBM, Soviet, 230, 233-234
IGY, 4, 6, 9, 14, 105, 228, 237, 243, 258, 278, 280, 281, 282-287, 301, 303, 304, 311, 312, 324
International Astronautical Congress, 4, 105, 112-115, 330-331
International Astronautical Federation, 4, 5, 7, 95, 228, 334, 335
International Congress of Applied Mechanics, 227
Interplanetary Communications, 3, 28-34, 112; interdepartmental commission on, 3, 4, 7, 14, 82, 85, 95, 329, 333-335
ionosphere, 103, 108-110, 303-307
Isakov, P. K., 127, 155
*Izvestiya*, 16, 243, 245

Jaumotte, A., 227
*Journal of Applied Physics*, 244
*Journal of Space Flight*, 13, 232
*Journal of the British Interplanetary Society*, 202
Jupiter, 69, 75

Kapitsa, P. L., 7, 14, 110, 329, 334
Kaplan, Joseph, 106, 228
Karpenko, A. G., 14 ,16, 95, 240, 329, 335
Kasatkin, A. M., 12
Kazantsev, A. N., 11, 301
Keldysh, M. V., 202
kerosene, 1
Khaikin, S. E., 335
Khitrin, L. N., 226
Khlebtsevich, Yu. S., 4, 12, 15, 17, 35, 46, 178, 332
Khristianovich, S. A., 2, 239
Kibal'chich, N. I., 53, 78, 84
Kistiakowsky, G. B., 226, 227
Kölle, H. H., 16, 106, 115, 170, 173
*Komsomolskaya Pravda*, 10
Kondratyev, V. N., 226
Kondratyuk, Yu. V., 1, 24, 26, 33, 36, 53, 85, 97
Koski, W. S., 244

Krasilshchikova, E. A., 227
*Krasnaya Zvezda*, 6, 15, 16, 58, 239
*Krasnii Flot*, 16, 170, 172
Krotov, V. F., 15
Kryakutnoi, 36
*Kryl'ya Rodiny*, 15, 221
Kucherov, I., 15, 205
Kukarkin, B. V., 329
Kurnosova, L. V., 12

Lavrent'ev, M. A., 324
Lawden, D. F., 202
Lebedev, S. A., 335
*Lengird*, 1
Lenin, V. I., 24
Levin, B. Yu., 334
Lewis, Bernard, 226
Library of Congress, 2
Lucy, F. A., 244
Lyapunov, B. V., 12, 331, 332

Malkin, V. B., 134
*Man in Space*, 115
Markov, A. V., 335
Mars, 5, 15, 23, 32, 53, 56, 62, 66, 68, 69, 71, 72, 75, 79, 81, 90, 93, 94, 168, 169, 189-192, 268, 331
Martin, M., 201, 202
Masevich, A. G., 12
mass, gravitational, 263-264
mass, inertial, 263-264
Massachusetts Institute of Technology, 15, 227
mass ratio, 29-31, 96, 97, 251
Mercury, 14, 66, 71, 267-274
Merkulov, I. A., 2, 4, 35, 38, 54
Meshcherskii, I. V., 1
meteorites, danger from, 44, 45, 56; distribution of, 44-46, 285
Mighty Mouse, 13
Mikhailov, A. A., 10, 288
Minitrack II, 11
Mirtov, B. A., 8, 116
missiles, Soviet, 230-232
Montgolfier brothers, 36
moon, 5, 15, 26, 53, 56, 62, 63, 93, 167-169, 170-173, 174-177, 178-188, 331
moon rocket, 167-169, 170-173, 178-188, 193-196, 223
moon trajectories, 193-196, 197-202
Moscow Higher Technical College, 15
Moscow Military Air Academy, 2, 7
*Mosgird*, 1
*Moskovskaya Pravda*, 16, 240, 242
Mozhaiskii, A. F., 36

(Names in the Bibliography are not included in this Index)

# PUBLISHED RAND RESEARCH

PRINCETON UNIVERSITY PRESS, PRINCETON, NEW JERSEY

*Approximations for Digital Computers,* by Cecil Hastings, Jr., 1955
*International Communication and Political Opinion: A Guide to the Literature,*
  by Bruce Lannes Smith and Chitra M. Smith, 1956
*Dynamic Programming,* by Richard Bellman, 1957


COLUMBIA UNIVERSITY PRESS, NEW YORK

*Soviet National Income and Product, 1940-48,* by Abram Bergson and Hans
  Heymann, Jr., 1954
*Soviet National Income and Product in 1928,* by Oleg Hoeffding, 1954
*Labor Productivity in Soviet and American Industry,* by Walter Galenson, 1955


THE FREE PRESS, GLENCOE, ILLINOIS

*Psychosis and Civilization,* by Herbert Goldhamer and Andrew W. Marshall, 1949
*Soviet Military Doctrine,* by Raymond L. Garthoff, 1953
*A Study of Bolshevism,* by Nathan Leites, 1953
*Ritual of Liquidation: The Case of the Moscow Trials,* by Nathan Leites and
  Elsa Bernaut, 1954
*Two Studies in Soviet Controls: Communism and the Russian Peasant, and
  Moscow in Crisis,* by Herbert S. Dinerstein and Leon Gouré, 1955
*A Million Random Digits with 100,000 Normal Deviates,* by the RAND Corpora-
  tion, 1955


McGRAW-HILL BOOK COMPANY, NEW YORK

*The Operational Code of the Politburo,* by Nathan Leites, 1951
*Air War and Emotional Stress: Psychological Studies of Bombing and Civilian
  Defense,* by Irving L. Janis, 1951
*Soviet Attitudes Toward Authority: An Interdisciplinary Approach to Problems
  of Soviet Character,* by Margaret Mead, 1951
*Mobilizing Resources for War: The Economic Alternatives,* by Tibor Scitovsky,
  Edward Shaw, Lorie Tarshis, 1951
*The Organizational Weapon: A Study of Bolshevik Strategy and Tactics,* by
  Philip Selznick, 1952
*Introduction to the Theory of Games,* by J. C. C. McKinsey, 1952
*Weight-Strength Analysis of Aircraft Structures,* by F. R. Shanley, 1952
*The Compleat Strategyst: Being a Primer on the Theory of Games of Strategy,*
  by J. D. Williams, 1954
*Linear Programming and Economic Analysis,* by Robert Dorfman, Paul A.
Samuelson, and Robert M. Solow, 1958


ROW, PETERSON & COMPANY, EVANSTON, ILLINOIS

*German Rearmament and Atomic War: The Views of German Military and
  Political Leaders,* by Hans Speier, 1957
*West German Leadership and Foreign Policy,* edited by Hans Speier and W.
  Phillips Davison, 1957